Farm Management Pocketbook

by

JOHN NIX
with Paul Hill

TWENTY-EIGHTH EDITION

(1998)

SEPTEMBER 1997

Copies of this book may be obtained from Wye College Press,
Wye College, near Ashford, Kent, TN25 5AH.
(Tel. 01233-812401 ext. 285; Fax. 01233-813320)

PRICE £8.25
(12 to 49 copies: £7.75)
(50 to 199 copies: £7.50)
(200-499 copies: £7.25)
(Over 500 copies: £6.75)

ISBN 0 86266 033 5

FOREWORD TO THE FIRST EDITION

This booklet is intended for farmers, advisers, students and everyone else who, frequently or infrequently, find themselves hunting for data relating to farm management—whether it is for blunt pencil calculations on the back of an envelope or for feeding into a computer. The material contained is based upon the sort of information which the author finds himself frequently having to look up in his twin roles as adviser and teacher in farm management. There are several excellent handbooks already in existence, but this pocketbook endeavours to cover a wider field and thus to be substantially more comprehensive. It is intended that most of the data herein contained will have a national application, although there is inevitably some bias towards conditions in the south-eastern half of the country.

The development of farm planning techniques in recent years has outstripped the quality and quantity of data available. It is hoped that this booklet will go a little further in supplying the type of information required. It cannot, however, claim to be the ultimate in this respect. For example, there are many variations in labour requirements according to farm conditions and sizes and types of machine used and there are many more variations in sheep and beef systems than are dealt with here. More detailed data on these lines are gradually becoming available from various sources. It is hoped further to refine the material in this booklet and to keep it up to date in subsequent editions, as the information becomes available. As a help towards this end, any comments or criticisms will be gratefully received.

The author wishes to thank his many friends and colleagues who have given him so much time and help in compiling this information.

John Nix
October, 1966

First published October 1966

Twenty-eighth Edition   September 1997

FOREWORD TO THE TWENTY-EIGHTH EDITION

As always virtually all the figures in this edition have been revised and updated. Major overhauls have been carried out on several sections, such as flax (much expanded), mushrooms, angoras, turf and the metric conversion factors.

In the foreword to the 27th edition the following was said: "Of course the good times *may* roll on, but more likely they will not". This turned out to be a considerable understatement. No one could have foreseen what a transformation would occur within twelve months in the fortunes of the two major farming areas: cereals and milk. The £ strengthened beyond all comprehension, prices fell considerably (especially cereals – by around £30/tonne), and the consequent revaluations reduced support payments (though fortunately some were frozen). When outputs fall by a given amount (despite some assumed increases in yield) gross margins fall by a higher percentage (despite some reductions in variable costs, e.g. fertilizer and concentrate feed) and net profits disappear altogether for many – depending particularly on their levels of fixed costs.

It has been decided in this edition not to chase the prices down as they are dropping at the time of writing but to "hold the line" at a certain level which assumes that some recovery will occur over the next twelve months, assisted by the pound losing at least part of its present substantial overvaluation (as it seems) as this year progresses and into the next. Thus no £70 a tonne for feed wheat or 19p per litre of milk but £85 and 22p respectively. (Regarding cereals, however, it needs to be remembered that at the onset of the CAP, so-called MacSharry, reforms, in mid-1992, it was generally expected that the feed wheat price would fall to around £80/tonne by 1995, let alone 1997.)

Most of the figures are predicted forward one year, *i.e.* to 1998. *Thus the crops data relate to the 1998 harvest, i.e. the 1998/99 marketing year* (N.B. not just, in the case of product prices, those prevailing at or just after harvest time). *The livestock data relate either to the 1998 calendar year (e.g. for milk production) or to 1998/99 (e.g. for winter finished beef), as appropriate.* The estimates were made during the first half of the summer of 1997. In a few cases current (*i.e.* mid-1997) figures are given, where it seemed particularly difficult to try to forecast ahead. The year to which the figures relate is normally stated.

The figures for yields and prices assume a "normal", or average, season, based on trends, e.g. for potatoes, looking 18-24 months ahead to 1998/99, no one can predict what the *actual* average yield and price for that particular year will be. Similarly with pig production: no attempt is made to predict the *actual* position of the pig cycle during 1998 – only what the average trend figure is likely to be, in neither an "up" or "down" stage, given estimated changes in the relevant indices.

The data in this book should always be used with caution. *The figures should be adjusted as appropriate according to circumstances and price and cost differences.* As far as possible the assumptions in the tables are set out so as to enable this to be done fairly readily.

The principal author wishes to thank all those who assisted with this edition. In particular, and as for many years, Paul Hill has painstakingly revised many important sections. In addition this year Angela Edwards has thoroughly overhauled a number of enterprises.

John Nix
July, 1997

CONTENTS

I. GROSS MARGIN DATA

1. GENERAL NOTES

Definition. The Gross Margin of an enterprise is its enterprise output less its variable costs. Enterprise output includes the market value of production retained on the farm. The variable costs must (a) be specific to the enterprise and (b) vary in proportion to the size of the enterprise, i.e. number of hectares or head of stock. The main items of variable costs are: Crops: fertilizer, seed, sprays, casual labour and contract work specific to the crop. Non-Grazing Livestock: concentrate feed, vet. and med., marketing expenses. Grazing Livestock: as for non-grazing livestock, plus forage crop variable costs.

Points to Note about the concept are as follows:

1. The gross margin is in no sense a profit figure. The so-called "fixed costs" (rent, labour, machinery, general overheads—see pages 133-138) have to be covered by the total farm gross margin before arriving at a profit.

2. The gross margin of an enterprise will differ from season to season, partly because of yield and price differences affecting output and partly because variable costs may vary, e.g. the number and type of sprays required. Different soils and other natural factors, as well as level of management, will also cause differences between farms.

3. Items of variable cost may vary from farm to farm, e.g. some farmers use casual labour (a variable cost) to plant and pick their potatoes, others use only regular labour (a fixed cost); some farmers employ a contractor to combine their cereals (a variable cost), others employ their own equipment (a fixed cost); some employ a contractor to cart their sugar beet to the factory (a variable cost), others have their own lorry (a fixed cost). These differences must be borne in mind in making inter-farm comparisons.

4. Provided points 2 and 3 are borne in mind, comparison of gross margins (particularly averages over several seasons) with standards can be a useful check on technical efficiency.

5. The other main usefulness of gross margins lies in farm planning. This is not simply a matter of substituting high gross margin enterprises for low gross margin enterprises. The gross margin is only one relevant feature of an enterprise, although an important one. It says nothing about the call the enterprise makes on the basic farm resources—labour at different times of the year, machinery, buildings, working capital requirements, etc. All these factors and more have to be taken into account in the planning process.

1

6. This is not to argue that these other costs should be allocated. Complete allocation of many farm expenses is only possible on an arbitrary basis, since they are shared by two or more, possibly all, farm enterprises. Allocation can therefore be completely misleading when making planning decisions. The same is true even when regular labour and machinery are employed specifically on certain enterprises, if such costs are calculated on a per hectare or per head basis. This is because when enterprises are substituted, expanded, contracted or deleted the variable costs for each enterprise will vary roughly in proportion to the size of that enterprise, but other costs will not, except possibly for fuel and some repair costs. Most "fixed" costs may stay the same, others will change—but not smoothly in small amounts at a time. Either the same regular labour force will cope with a revised plan or a smaller or larger number of men will be needed. The same is true of tractors, other machines and buildings. Such cost changes must of course be taken into account, but allocating these costs on a per hectare or per head basis will not aid, and may positively confuse, planning decisions. The only point of making such calculations is for efficiency comparisons, e.g. labour costs per cow.

7. Allocating fixed costs at a flat rate (e.g. per hectare) for all enter-prises, deducting this from the gross margin and hence calculating a "net profit" from each enterprise can also be misleading. It ignores the whole problem of enterprise inter-relationships, differences between enterprises in total and seasonal requirements for labour, machinery and capital, and other factors such as different quality land on the same farm.

8. Changes in the scale of an enterprise may well affect its gross margin per unit, e.g. increasing the area of winter wheat from 30 per cent to 50 per cent on a farm will mean more wheat being taken after wheat, and a smaller proportion of the crop being drilled under the best conditions; hence yields will in all probability fall. Even if yields remain the same, variable costs (e.g. fertilizer use) will probably increase.

9. Gross margins used for planning future changes should also take account of possible changes in price, and the effect of changes in production techniques.

Low, Average and High Levels

The three performance and production levels given for most crop and livestock enterprises are meant for the most part to indicate differences in natural factors, soil productivity, and/or managerial skill, *given the level of variable cost inputs*. They refer, at each level, to *an average over several years* taking *trends* into account. The evidence on the effect of significantly higher or lower levels of variable inputs on gross margins is conflicting and highly uncertain, depending on many factors, including soil type, and will vary from season to season.

2. CASH CROPS

WINTER WHEAT

Production level				Low	Average	High
Yield: tonnes per ha (tons per acre)						
Feed				6·25 (2·5)	7·75 (3·1)	9·25 (3·7)
Milling				5·7 (2·25)	7·05 (2·8)	8·4 (3·35)
Price per tonne (Feed/Milling): £85/£93·50				£	£	£
Sale Value				530 (214)	660 (267)	785 (318)
Area Payment				255 (103)	255 (103)	255 (103)
OUTPUT:				785 (317)	915 (370)	1040 (421)
Variable Costs:						
Seed					50 (20)	
Fertilizer					80 (32·5)	
Sprays					125 (50·5)	
TOTAL VARIABLE COSTS					255 (103)	
GROSS MARGIN per ha (acre)				530 (214)	660 (267)	785 (318)

Notes

1. *Prices.* Market prices for cereals fell considerably in the 1996/97 marketing year, particularly compared with those in the previous marketing year. The average feed wheat price for the 1998 harvest crop is taken to be £85/tonne, rising from £80 at harvest to £95 in May/June 1999. The average milling price is taken to be £93·50/tonne after adjusting for a proportion of rejects.

   At 1st July 1997, with an ecu value of £0.720829 (16% below the mid-1996 peak), the November 1997 intervention price for eligible cereals (which excludes much feed wheat) was £86.64/tonne, increasing by 72p (1 ecu)/month to £90.96 in May 1998.

   Area Payments. The 1997 harvest crop payments for cereals were at the frozen ecu value of £0.803724. They were as follows, to the nearest £0.5/ha (£0.5/acre in brackets):-

England	Scotland (non LFA)	Scotland (LFA)	Wales (non LFA)	Wales (LFA)	N. Ireland (non LFA)	N. Ireland (LFA)
257 (104)	247·5 (100)	227·5 (92)	226 (91·5)	220·5 (89·5)	223 (92·5)	219·5 (89)

   The rounded figure for England is assumed for all (1998 harvest) cereal crops in this edition.

2. *Yields.* The overall average yield, for *all* winter wheat, is taken as 7·6 tonnes/ha (3·025 tons (60·5 cwt.)/acre).

3. *Feed v. Milling.* It is assumed that the yield of milling wheat *averages* 9% below that of feed wheat (the difference could be greater on high-yielding land and less on moderate quality land and also tends to be greater on second than on first wheats). The assumed milling premium of approximately £9/tonne is that needed to give the same gross margin for both, given the assumed difference in yield. Such survey data as exists indicates little difference in variable costs. Obviously different relative yields and premiums will give different gross margins: these can be readily calculated. The actual premium in any one season varies according to quality and scarcity. The best breadmaking wheat achieves substantially higher premiums. However, not all wheat grown for milling achieves a premium and more care is required. Currently around 20% of the UK wheat area is sown with milling varieties; the percentage has been falling in recent years.

4. *First v. Second (Feed) Wheats.* The evidence concerning the effect of different types and lengths of rotational breaks on subsequent cereal yields is variable. The table below (for *feed* wheat only, 1998 harvest) assumes a yield reduction of approximately 7·5% for second wheats compared with first and higher fertilizer and seed costs as shown; (the later the sowing date the less the yield gap tends to be). The same price and area payment is assumed as in the initial table. Only average and high levels are shown. Third wheats could yield 10-15% below second wheats; variable costs are likely to be similar.

Production level	Average		High	
Year (after break)	First	Second	First	Second
Yield: tonnes per ha (tons per acre)	8·25 (3·3)	7·65 (3·05)	9·75 (3·9)	9·00 (3·6)
	£	£	£	£
OUTPUT (inc. Area Payment) ...	955 (386)	905 (366)	1085 (439)	1020 (413)
VARIABLE COSTS	245 (99)	265 (107)	245 (99)	265 (107)
GROSS MARGIN per ha (acre) ...	710 (287)	640 (259)	840 (340)	755 (306)

5. *Straw* is not included above. Average yield is approx. 3·5 tonnes per hectare (range 2·5 to 5); value £10 to £25 per tonne according to region and season; variable costs (string) approx. £1·75 per tonne. In 1995, 70% of the area of wheat straw in England and Wales was baled and 30% ploughed in or cultivated. Standing straw (sold for baling): anything from no value to £75/ha (£30/acre), according to type of crop, season and area of the country/local demand.

6. *Seed and Fertilizer.* From survey data, updated. Seed includes part home-grown. Seed rates and fertilizer applications vary according to soil, season, variety, farm policy, etc.

7. *Sprays.* Amounts variable according to season, variety, policy, etc. Typical breakdown: herbicides 38%, fungicides 46%, insecticides 3%, growth regulators 8%, other 5%.

8. If a *Contractor* is employed, extra variable costs (£ per hectare) will be approximately as follows:

Spraying:	£11 (material included above)
Drilling:	£21
Combining:	£80 (excluding carting) £95 (including carting)
Drying:	£60 to £100 (according to yield and moisture content; transport one way is included; *this assumes that* ²/₃ of the crop needs to be dried in an average season).
Baling Straw:	£45 (including string).

9. *Fuel and Repairs* (per hectare): grain £85, straw £30.

10. *Specialized Equipment Prices:* see pages 115-117.

11. *Labour:* see page 96.

N.B.—Approximately 75% of home-grown wheat is used for feed, 20% for milling and 5% for seed.

SPRING WHEAT

Production level	Low	Average	High
Yield: tonnes per hectare (tons per acre) ...	4·6 (1·85)	5·8 (2·3)	7·0 (2·8)
	£	£	£
Price per tonne: £92			
Sale Value	425 (172)	535 (217)	645 (261)
Area Payment	255 (103)	255 (103)	255 (103)
OUTPUT	680 (275)	790 (320)	900 (364)
Variable Costs:			
Seed		65 (26·5)	
Fertilizer		55 (22)	
Sprays		85 (34·5)	
TOTAL VARIABLE COSTS		205 (83)	
GROSS MARGIN per ha (acre)	475 (192)	585 (237)	695 (281)

Notes

1. *Price:* In general, see Winter Wheat. A higher proportion of spring wheat is sold for milling compared with winter wheat. The average price taken above, for the 1998 harvest, (£92/tonne), assumes approximately two-thirds sold for milling, one-third for feed.

2. *Straw.* See Winter Wheat, page 4.

3. If a *Contractor is* employed, extra variable costs (£ per hectare) will be as shown for Winter Wheat above.

4. *Fuel and Repairs* (per hectare): grain £85, straw £28.

5. *Specialized Equipment Prices:* see pages 115-117.

6. *Labour:* see page 98.

N.B.—Normally only 1 or 2% of the UK wheat area is spring sown; the percentage is naturally higher following a particularly wet autumn.The percentage is even lower in Scotland (1% or less) than in England and Wales.

For the 1997/98 area payments in ECU/ha and cereal intervention levels in ECU/tonne see page 46.

WINTER BARLEY

Production level	Low	Average	High
Yield: tonnes per ha (tons per acre)			
Feed ...	5·1 (2·05)	6·35 (2·55)	7·6 (3·05)
Malting ...	4·3 (1·7)	5·35 (2·15)	6·4 (2·55)
Price per tonne (Feed/Malting): £80/£95	£	£	£
Sale Value (Feed and Malting) ...	410 (166)	510 (207)	610 (247)
Area Payment ...	255 (103)	255 (103)	255 (103)
OUTPUT (Feed and Malting) ...	665 (269)	765 (310)	865 (350)

Variable Costs:	Feed	Malting
Seed ...	50 (20)	55 (22)
Fertilizer ...	67·5 (27)	55 (22)
Sprays ...	97·5 (40)	105 (43)
TOTAL VARIABLE COSTS ...	215 (87)	215 (87)
GROSS MARGIN per ha (acre) ...	450 (182)	550 (223) 650 (263)

1. *Prices.* See Winter Wheat for CAP support details, but note intervention is available for feed barley. Prices are the assumed averages for the whole 1998/9 marketing year; prices are typically £5/tonne less at harvest time and £10 above by the end of the season. The feed price (£80/tonne) is taken as averaging £5/tonne below feed wheat. The malting price (£95/tonne) assumes a premium over feed of £15/tonne, which is what is required to equate the output and hence the gross margin for feed barley given the same total variable costs per hectare and the assumed yield difference. The *actual* premium obtained over feed barley will vary according to season and quality: for the best malting barleys the premium is usually at least £25, can be £50 plus and prices can exceed £160 a tonne. These higher prices for quality are normally available even at harvest time (when the differential over feed normally exceeds £15). However, premiums were very low for the 1997 harvest crop.
2. *Straw* not included. Average yield is approx. 2 ·75 tonnes per hectare, value £10 to £50 per tonne according to region and season, variable cost (string) approx. £1·05 per tonne. In 1995, 96% of the area both of winter barley straw and of spring barley straw in England and Wales was baled. Standing straw (sold for baling): anything from no value to £150/ha (£60/acre) according to crop, season and area of the country (local demand).
3. *Fertilizer.* Costs on continuous barley will be approximately £15 higher.
4. *Sprays.* Amounts variable according to season, variety, policy, etc. Typical breakdown: herbicides 39%, fungicides 44%, growth regulators 13%, other 4%.
5. If *Contractor* employed, extra variable costs as shown for Winter Wheat (p. 4, note 8).
6. *Fuel and Repairs* (per hectare): grain £85. straw £30.
7. *Specialized Equipment Prices:* see pages 115-117.   8. *Labour:* see pages 97-98.

SPRING BARLEY

Production level	Low	Average	High
Yield: tonnes per ha (tons per acre)			
Feed ...	4·3 (1·7)	5·4 (2·15)	6·5 (2·6)
Malting ...	3·65 (1·45)	4·55 (1·8)	5·5 (2·2)
Price per tonne (Feed/Malting): £80/£95	£	£	£
Sale Value (Feed and Malting) ...	345 (140)	430 (174)	520 (211)
Area Payment ...	255 (103)	255 (103)	255 (103)
OUTPUT (Feed and Malting) ...	600 (243)	685 (277)	775 (314)

Variable Costs:	Feed	Malting
Seed ...	55 (22·5)	60 (24·5)
Fertilizer ...	57·5 (23·5)	47·5 (19)
Sprays ...	62·5 (25)	67·5 (27·5)
TOTAL VARIABLE COSTS ...	175 (71)	175 (71)
GROSS MARGIN per ha (acre) ...	425 (172)	510 (206) 600 (243)

Notes: As for Winter Barley above.

The UK percentage of winter barley in 1993-96 has been between 56 and 59% each year. For England the percentage has been 72-76%, for England and Wales 70-73%, for Scotland and Northern Ireland around 20%. Naturally the proportion of spring barley increases following a wet autumn. The relative profitability of spring versus winter crops is improved under the present support system in that the flat rate area payments per hectare mean a higher payment *per tonne* for lower yielding crops.

N.B. Approximately 70% of winter barley is used for feed, 25% for malting and 5% for seed. The proportions for spring barley are approximately 45%, 50% and 5% respectively.

WINTER OATS

Production level	Low	Average	High
Yield: tonnes per ha (tons per acre)	5·25 (2·1)	6·75 (2·7)	8·25 (3·3)

Price per tonne (Feed/Milling): £82/£85

Sale Value	£	£	£
Feed ...	430 (174)	555 (225)	675 (273)
Milling	445 (180)	575 (233)	700 (283)
Area Payment	255 (103)	255 (103)	255 (103)

OUTPUT		Low	Average	High
	Feed	685 (277)	810 (328)	930 (376)
	Milling	700 (283)	830 (336)	955 (386)

Variable Costs:

Seed ...	47·5 (19)
Fertilizer	60 (24·5)
Sprays	67·5 (27·5)

TOTAL VARIABLE COSTS	175 (71)

GROSS MARGIN per ha (acre)

Feed ...	510 (206)	635 (257)	755 (305)
Milling	525 (212)	655 (265)	780 (315)

1. Prices. See Winter Wheat for CAP Support details. Prices are the assumed averages for the whole 1998/9 marketing year. Roughly half the UK oat crop goes for milling and half for feed.
2. Straw is not included above. Average yield is 3·5 tonnes per hectare; value £10 to £40 per tonne according to region and season; variable costs (string) approx. £1·05 per tonne. In 1995, 73% of the area of oat straw in England and Wales was baled.
3. If a *Contractor* is employed, extra variable costs will be as shown for Winter Wheat (p. 4, note 7).
4. *Fuel and Repairs* (per hectare): grain £75, straw £26.
5. *Labour:* see page 98

SPRING OATS

Production level	Low	Average	High
Yield. tonnes per ha (tons per acre)	4·50 (1·8)	5·75 (2·3)	7·00 (2·8)

Price per tonne (Feed/Milling): £82/£85

Sale Value	£	£	£
Feed ...	370 (150)	470 (190)	575 (233)
Milling	385 (156)	490 (198)	595 (241)
Area Payment	255 (103)	255 (103)	255 (103)

OUTPUT		Low	Average	High
	Feed ...	625 (253)	725 (294)	830 (336)
	Milling	640 (259)	745 (302)	850 (344)

Variable Costs:

Seed ...	57·5 (23·5)
Fertilizer	42·5 (17·5)
Sprays	55 (22)

TOTAL VARIABLE COSTS	155 (63)

GROSS MARGIN Per ha (acre)

Feed ...	470 (190)	570 (231)	675 (273)
Milling	485 (196)	590 (239)	695 (281)

Notes: As for winter oats above.

N.B.—The proportion of winter oats in Great Britain was 75% of the total oats area in 1995 and 80% in 1996; the proportion increases from north to south: it was thus 90% and 92% in England and Wales in 1995 and 1996 respectively but 26% and 34% in Scotland. Oats now account for only about 3·5% of the total UK cereals area (112,000 ha were grown in 1996). The risk of lodging and thus difficult harvesting remains a drawback.

OILSEED RAPE

Winter Rape

Production level	Low	Average	High
Yield: tonnes per ha (tons per acre)	2·25 (0·9)	3·00 (1·2)	3·75 (1·5)
	£	£	£
Sale Value (£150/tonne)	340 (138)	450 (182)	565 (229)
Area Payment	425 (172)	425 (172)	425 (172)
OUTPUT	765 (310)	875 (354)	990 (401)
Variable Costs:			
Seed		35 (14)	
Fertilizer		85 (34·5)	
Sprays		105 (42·5)	
TOTAL VARIABLE COSTS		225 (91)	
GROSS MARGIN per ha (acre)	540 (219)	650 (263)	765 (310)

Spring Rape

Production level	Low	Average	High
Yield: tonnes per ha (cwt. per acre)	1·5 (0·6)	2·1 (0·85)	2·7 (1·075)
	£	£	£
Sale Value (£150/tonne)	225 (91)	315 (128)	405 (164)
Area Payment	425 (172)	425 (172)	425 (172)
OUTPUT	650 (263)	740 (300)	830 (336)
Variable Costs:			
Seed		37·5 (15)	
Fertilizer		55 (22·5)	
Sprays		67·5 (27·5)	
TOTAL VARIABLE COSTS		160 (65)	
GROSS MARGIN per ha (acre)	490 (198)	580 (235)	670 (271)

1. *Prices/Area Payments. The price assumed for the 1998 crop, £150/tonne,* is the average for the whole of the 1998/9 marketing season, ranging from £140-145 at harvest to £155-160 at its peak. The *area payments* for the 1997 harvest crop, at a frozen ecu value of £0.803724, were as follows, assuming no deductions for excess production and high world prices, to the nearest £/ha (£0.5/acre in brackets):

England	Scotland (non LFA)	Scotland (LFA)	Wales	N. Ireland
455 (184)	509 (206)	419 (169·5)	464 (187·5)	431 (174·5)

The same, rounded, figure for England is used in the above tables with an *assumed deduction of 6·5%* through overshooting of the EU maximum guaranteed area plus possibly also of the regional arable base areas, although this is impossible to predict for a season ahead; cuts can also occur if prices are particularly high but high prices have not been assumed above.

2. Winter crops are mainly sown between 10th August and 10th September (before the end of August if possible). Spring-sown crops are best sown between late March and mid-April. Winter crops normally are harvested between late July and mid-August, most of the crops either being windrowed and combined from the swath or desiccated with diquat and direct combined. Spring-sown crops are harvested in the first half of September and a desiccant is less often used. Before the flat rate per hectare subsidy was introduced only about 4% of the crop was spring-sown; the proportion increased substantially afterwards, reaching 31% in 1994 (caused partly by wet late summer and autumn weather); it has fallen since, to 15% in the U.K. (excl. N. Ireland) in 1996 (only 11% in England). Inputs are lower, pigeons are less trouble and the late summer/autumn workload is eased; however, the later harvesting tends to clash with the winter wheat harvest, there is less time to prepare the ground for, and drill, the following winter cereal crop, and spring droughts are a potential hazard to establishment.

3. *Sprays.* Variable with season, etc. Typically: herbicides 72%, fungicides 21%, insecticides 2%, other 5%.

4. *Labour:* see page 104.

8

TURNIP RAPE

Spring-sown. 25,000 ha grown in 1994, two-thirds in Scotland, where it comprises two-thirds of the spring rape area. Average yields about 20% (0·4-0·5 tonne/ha) below spring swede rape, but substantially earlier to harvest, has fast early growth, giving good weed suppression; has good resistance to shedding. Savings in variable costs (seed, nitrogen and herbicides) and drying costs likely, but vulnerable to sclerotina and pollen beetle. Winter turnip rape now being tried: can be drilled up to ten days later than winter swede rape.

LINSEED

Production level					Low	Average	High
Yield: tonnes per ha (tons per acre):			...		1·0 (0·4)	1·5 (0·6)	2·0 (0·8)
					£	£	£
Sale Value (£130/tonne)	...	...	...		130 (53)	195 (79)	260 (106)
Area Payment...	...	...	...		495 (200)	495 (200)	495 (200)
OUTPUT	...	...	...	...	625 (253)	690 (279)	755 (306)
Variable Costs:							
Seed	...	...	...	...	...	60 (24·5)	
Fertilizer	...	...	...	...		32·5 (13)	
Sprays	...	...	...	...		67·5 (27·5)	
TOTAL VARIABLE COSTS		...	...	...		160 (65)	
GROSS MARGIN per ha (acre)			...	...	465 (188)	530 (214)	595 (241)

The *price* assumed, £130/tonne, is the average for the whole of the 1998/9 marketing season. Prices are very variable; they have varied from £110 to £165 in recent years.

The *area payments* for the 1997 crop, at a frozen ecu value of £0.803724, were as follows, to the nearest £0·5/ha (£0·5/acre in brackets):

England	**Scotland**	**Scotland**	**Wales**	**Wales**	**N. Ireland**	**N. Ireland**
	(non LFA)	(LFA)	(non LFA)	(LFA)	(non LFA)	(LFA)
497·5 (201·5)	478·5 (193·5)	440 (178)	436·5 (176·5)	426·5 (172·5)	441 (178·5)	425 (172)

The same, rounded down, figure for England is assumed in the above table for the 1998 harvest crop.

From 1,165 ha in 1984 the UK area increased to 150,000 ha (94% of the total EU area) in 1993. A considerable reduction has occurred since: to only 29,000 ha in 1996.

Drilling, mid-March to mid-April (best mid-March to end March). Susceptible to frost. Should not be grown more than 1 year in 5. Care needed re level of nitrogen use: too much (over 75 kg/ha) can cause severe lodging, delayed maturity and excessive weed growth—and hence difficult harvesting, poor quality and lower yields; it should be applied early.

Harvesting: normally not before September and can even be after mid-October in a late season. Does not shed. Moisture content most likely 12-16%: must be dried to 9% for storage.

Winter Linseed

Big surge in plantings for the 1997 harvest: 25 to 30,000 ha. Still too early to generalise re yield compared with spring crops: may average around one-third higher (i.e. 2.0 tonnes/ha (0·8 t/acre)). However, crop losses are a risk in a harsh winter, e.g. frost heave on lighter land; pigeons and rabbits can also be troublesome. Early sowing (late Sept./early Oct.) appears best, with higher seed rates; otherwise variable costs similar to spring. Earlier to harvest: mid-August the norm. Average gross margin (with same price, fertiliser and spray assumptions as for the spring crop): approx. £595/ha (£200/acre), *assuming no significant winter loss of crop*, but 1997 harvest crops were generally poor, some as low as 0·5 tonnes/ha..

Linola

Edible linseed: the oil contains more linoleic and less linolenic acid than conventional linseed, like sunflower oil. First grown on any scale in 1996 (1,600 ha). Spring-sown. Agronomy and yield similar to conventional linseed; good weed control essential. Price higher (based on oilseed rape price), same area payment. Harvest early-mid September.

FLAX
(Cut Flax for Industrial Fibre)

Production level	Low	Average	High
Seed			
Yield: tonnes per ha (tons per acre)	0·5 (0·2)	0·85 (0·34)	1.3 (0·52)
Price: £ per tonne [1]	130	130	130
Seed Output	65 (26)	110 (44)	170 (69)
Straw			
Yield: tonnes per ha (tons per acre)	rejected*	1·5 (0·6)	3·0 (1·2)
Price: £ per tonne [2]		20	20
Straw Output	0	30 (12)	60 (24)
Area Payment [3]	570 (231)	570 (231)	570 (231)
TOTAL OUTPUT	635 (257)	710 (287)	800 (324)
Variable Costs:			
Seed		115 (46·5)	
Fertilizer		30 (12)	
Sprays		70 (28·5)	
TOTAL VARIABLE COSTS		215 (87)	
GROSS MARGIN per ha (acre)	420 (170)	495 (200)	585 (237)

(1) As for linseed

(2) Can be higher depending on quality

(3) Non de-seeded crop £495

* From 1998 this may result in loss of area payment.

Notes

Flax is the same species as linseed, but the straw is longer. Over the last 3 or 4 years fibre flax has been reintroduced into the UK, not as the traditional, pulled, long fibre variety used for linen textiles but as a cut, combineable crop producing shorter fibres for industrial uses. New technology has been developed for processing the crop and new market outlets for the fibre established. It is a non-food industrial crop attracting EU aid. Natural fibres are biodegradable and renewable and therefore a "green" alternative to synthetic fibres and plastic produced from fossil fuels. The area grown in the UK expanded from 200 ha in 1992 to 22,000 ha in 1996.

Advantages to the farmer are that it can be grown on either IACS eligible or ineligible land, with no set-aside requirement (but it cannot be grown on set-aside land), there is a large area payment, it uses existing farm machinery and equipment and is a good cereal break crop.

The agronomy is similar to that of linseed but it is harvested earlier. It is spring-sown, suitable for most soil types although lighter soil is preferred. It is a low input crop but weed control is essential. It grows best in areas of high rainfall such as Wales and the South West. Potentially yields can be good but farmers are still learning; hence currently average yields are low and a significant proportion of straw has not been of an acceptable quality. From 1998 a minimum clean yield of straw will have to be produced in order to qualify for the area payment (that yield is still under discussion in the EU). A grower must otherwise demonstrate that the crop has been managed with good agricultural practice.

Currently short fibre flax can only be grown under contract with a merchant/processor, using a recognised fibre flax variety. The grower must make a sowing declaration, give notification of harvest, make a harvest declaration, use a minimum cutting height of 10 cm (4 in), and leave the stubble uncultivated for a minimum of 20 days. He receives the subsidy through the merchant or processor.

Although the crop is described as combineable, harvesting is not straightforward. There are several options: (i) swathing and combining: the swathed crop is left to partially rett, combined for the seed, retting is then completed and the straw baled; (ii) mowing: the crop is mown, retted, turning as necessary and then baled; a lower area payment is paid as the seed is not harvested; (iii) direct combining: this is possible but as the seed is mature while the plant is still green it can be difficult to process through the combine; (iv) desiccation and then combining: this is currently the preferred option. In both (iii) and (iv) the straw is left to rett in the field and baled when the process is complete.

Retting requires skill and judgement. It relies on the action of moisture, sun and soil bacteria and, depending on weather conditions, takes 10-21 days. The straw should be evenly spread over low stubble and turned if necessary. Weed growth in the stubble can be a problem. In well retted straw the plant is a dark dirty grey and the fibre silvery grey. There is no mould and no smell. Rubbing separates the fibres and the tensile strength should be good.

Flax straw must be treated as follows. After retting it should be made into large square bales using sisal twine; maximum moisture content 16%; maximum weed content 5%; no contamination with plastic, wood or stone, storage must be weatherproof; all straw must be sampled before movement. The price paid for straw will reflect quality. The fibre content of a reasonable crop is 20-30%.

Researcher: Angela Edwards.

INDUSTRIAL OILSEED RAPE

Rape for non-food uses may be grown on set-aside land, provided a direct contract with a first *processor* (or collector) is obtained and signed before the crop is sown. The contract must contain specific items of information. The non-food product must be worth more than the total value of any food by-products. Only approved varieties may be grown, or high erucic rapeseed.

The full set-aside area payment is paid but no other EU payments can be claimed. If the rules concerning contracts are broken both the set-aside payment and area payments for other crops could be forfeited, and a further penalty imposed.

The first processor or collector has to lodge a security equal to 120% of the set-aside payments on the fields concerned; this is returned provided an equivalent quantity of raw material has been processed into the final end product in the contract. Area aid is only paid after delivery of the crop to the collector and the weight is declared to the Regional Service Centre.

Two types of industrial rape are grown: high erucic acid (HEAR) and, mainly, double low, which is primarily spring-sown. The former usually has a lower yield, reckoned to be around 10% for winter-sown and up to 20% for spring sown; the price is consequently higher; possibly up to £155 for the 1997 crop.

The following are estimated gross margins for double low industrial rape for the 1997 harvest, given a price of £125/tonne and slightly lower variable costs (lower seed cost). The set-aside payments are a rounded figure for England, as given on page 44.

	Winter-sown		Spring-sown	
Production level	Average	High	Average	High
Yield (tonnes per ha (tons per acre)) ...	3·00 (1·2)	3·75 (1·5)	2·1 (0·85)	2·7 (1·075)
	£	£	£	£
Sale Value (at £125/tonne) ...	375 (151)	470 (190)	265 (107)	340 (137)
Set-aside Payment	325 (132)	325 (132)	325 (132)	325 (132)
OUTPUT	700 (283)	795 (322)	590 (239)	665 (269)
VARIABLE COSTS	215 (87)	215 (87)	150 (61)	150 (61)
GROSS MARGIN per ha (acre)	485 (196)	580 (235)	440 (178)	515 (208)

Mainly because the set-aside payment is well below the area payment for non-industrial rape the gross margins are naturally lower. However, the additional gross margin compared with set-aside should cover any additional fixed costs incurred on most farms, unless substantial fixed cost savings can be made by adhering to fallow set-aside; also, it is widely believed that subsequent crops benefit more from following oilseed rape than from following a (virtual) fallow.

INDUSTRIAL LINSEED

Similar rules apply to those for industrial rape.

Production level	Average	High
Yield (tonnes per ha (cwt. per acre)) ...	1·5 (0·6)	2·0 (0·8)

	£	£
Sale Value (at £120/tonne)	180 (73)	240 (97)
Set-aside Payment	325 (132)	325 (132)
OUTPUT	505 (205)	565 (229)
VARIABLE COSTS*	140 (57)	140 (57)
GROSS MARGIN per ha (acre)	365 (148)	425 (172)

*Seed £20/ha less than non-industrial linseed.

The price varies a little depending on the details of the contract, which must be signed before the crop is sown. Some contracts include seed supplied at a special price as well as the purchase price.

Acknowledgement. Tony Hardwick (consultant agronomist) gave considerable advice on industrial rape and linseed but the financial data is the author's responsibility.

FIELD BEANS

Winter Beans

Production level	Low	Average	High
Yield: tonnes per ha (tons per acre) ...	2·8 (1·1)	3·4 (1·35)	4·0 (1·6)

	£	£	£
Sale Value (£105/tonne)	295 (119)	355 (144)	420 (170)
Area Payment	370 (150)	370 (150)	370 (150)
OUTPUT	665 (269)	725 (294)	790 (320)
Variable Costs: (3)			
Seed		60 (24·5)	
Fertilizer		15 (6)	
Sprays		75 (30·5)	
TOTAL VARIABLE COSTS		150 (61)	
GROSS MARGIN per ha (acre)	515 (208)	575 (233)	640 (259)

Notes

1. *Price.* The (1998/99) price assumed is £105 per tonne. Prior to the 1995 harvest field bean prices were usually just below those for feed wheat; however, in 1995/96 they were generally more than £10/tonne higher and in 1996/97 at least £20/tonne higher. Tannin-free varieties usually fetch about £8 a tonne more but yield some 5% less. Beans for human consumption normally fetch a premium of around £12/tonne.

   The *area payments* for the 1997 crop, at a frozen ecu value of £0·803724, were as follows, to the nearest £0·5/ha (£0·5/acre in brackets):

England	**Scotland** (non LFA)	**Scotland** (LFA)	**Wales** (non LFA)	**Wales** (LFA)	**N. Ireland** (non LFA)	**N. Ireland** (LFA)
371·5 (150·5)	357·5 (145)	328·5 (133)	326 (132)	318·5 (129)	329·5 (133·5)	317·5 (128·5)

   The same figure for England, rounded down, is used in the above table, for the 1998 crop.

2. *Physical input.* Seed: 225 kg per hectare; average cost is approximately £10 less if own seed is sown in alternate years. Fertilizer: 200 kg of no (or low) nitrogen compound where applied, but some crops receive no fertilizer.

3. *Labour:* see page 104.

Spring Beans

Production level	Low	Average	High
Yield: tonnes per ha (tons per acre)	2·6 (1·05)	3·2 (1·25)	3·8 (1·5)
	£	£	£
Sale Value (£105/tonne)	275 (111)	335 (136)	400 (162)
Area Payment	370 (150)	370 (150)	370 (150)
OUTPUT	645 (261)	705 (286)	770 (312)
Variable Costs:			
Seed		65 (26·5)	
Fertilizer		15 (6)	
Sprays		65 (26·5)	
TOTAL VARIABLE COSTS		145 (59)	
GROSS MARGIN per ha (acre)	500 (202)	560 (227)	625 (253)

Notes

1. *Price.* The (1998/99) price assumed is £105 per tonne (see above). Spring beans contain more protein than winter beans (except for tannin-free varieties), but large-scale compounders appear to make no distinction between them. For area payments see above.

Winter versus Spring Beans. It used to be assumed that the yield of winter beans was about 0·5 tonnes per hectare above spring beans *provided* a full crop was obtained, that is, where there was no exceptional damage from frost and birds and, in particular, where there was no severe attack of chocolate spot. Thus, whether the average yield over a period of years was higher or lower than spring beans depended mainly upon the incidence of attacks of chocolate spot, which can write off the crop completely. In drier parts of the Eastern Counties this may be only one year in six or eight but in south-eastern counties the frequency may be substantially higher. NIAB data have shown an average 8% yield advantage for winter over spring beans.

Other points in favour of spring beans are that: cold, wet seedbeds and winter kill can lead to poor establishment of winter beans; the yield difference between autumn- and spring-sown crops is less than for other crops, especially cereals; there is a longer "near-optimal" period during which they can be sown; and there have been substantial genetic improvements in recent years for spring beans but little for winter beans. However, spring beans are vulnerable to droughts in spring and early summer, especially on light land.

The relative area of winter and spring beans is largely determined by the autumn rainfall and recent comparative yields. In 1993 the UK area of spring beans well exceeded that of winter; in 1994 they were roughly equal; in 1996 the area of winter beans more than doubled that of spring.

DRIED PEAS

Production level	Low	Average	High
Yield: tonnes per ha (tons per acre)	3·0 (1·2)	3·8 (1·5)	4·6 (1·85)
	£	£	£
Sale Value (£105/tonne)	315 (127)	400 (162)	485 (196)
Area Payment	370 (150)	370 (150)	370 (150)
OUTPUT *(feed)*	685 (277)	770 (312)	855 (346)
Variable Costs:			
Seed		100 (40·5)	
Fertilizer		15 (6)	
Sprays		100 (40·5)	
TOTAL VARIABLE COSTS		215 (87)	
GROSS MARGIN per ha (acre)	470 (190)	555 (225)	640 (259)

Notes

1. Dried peas are combine harvested and include peas (especially marrowfats) for human consumption (after processing) and protein peas, for animal feed. About 75% of the crop goes for feed compounding.

2. *Price.* The (1998/99) price assumed above (which is for feed peas) is £105 per tonne. Prices for the 1995 and 1996 harvest crops were very high, similar to those for field beans most of the year. Feed peas sold on the open market are subject to wide price variations, particularly

as poor samples can fetch very low prices. The price for peas for processing (*e.g.*, marrowfats for canning) for *human consumption* obtain a premium of generally £20 to £50/tonne according to quality (size and colour) and the percentage of wastage, but marrowfat yields are generally 5 to 10% lower than feed varieties; most peas for human consumption are grown on contract. The premium for peas for the pigeon trade is usually around £10/tonne.

The *area payments* are as for field beans (page 11).

3. *Physical Inputs.* Seed: 200 to 250 kg. Fertilizer: 250 kg of no nitrogen compound where applied, but some crops receive no fertilizer.

4. *Harvesting* (normally in late July-early August) can be a difficult operation. Most crops are direct combined, although there is a high risk of loss and poor quality, as well as heavy wear and tear on the combine. Drying and handling the crop can be very difficult, much care being needed. Sometimes the crop is desiccated before direct combining, using diquat, to even out maturity and kill green weeds.

5. *Winter Peas:* increasing interest, with new, more frost-resistant, French varieties. Nearly 5,000 ha sown in UK for the 1997 harvest. Earlier to harvest (by 10 to 14 days) and potentially advantageous on droughty soils, but at risk in a severe winter, and disease, weeds and pigeons more of a problem than with spring-sown crops. Average yields may just exceed those of spring crops.

6. *Labour:* see page 103.

7. *Peas versus Beans* (for feed). *On average,* yields of peas are slightly above those for beans nationally. Peas are normally spring-sown (winter peas are beginning to be tried) and spring beans are easier to manage than peas. Peas are unsuited to heavier soils and are more vulnerable if the weather is wet during flowering and harvest. They are more sensitive to soil compaction and waterlogging. Their yields are thus more variable than for beans. Their seed costs are also much higher. On the other hand, peas (especially for human consumption) normally fetch higher prices (though this was not true of feed peas from the 1995 and 1996 harvests) and are usually easier to sell, given reasonable quality; they are also less sensitive to drought. They are normally ready to harvest well before spring beans. The UK area of beans used to be nearly double that of peas, but since 1995 the area of beans has fallen sharply, following poor yields, whereas that of peas has remained stable.

VINING PEAS

Production level (1)	Low £	Average £	High £
OUTPUT (2), (3)	900 (365)	1080 (435)	1250 (505)
Variable Costs:			
Seed (4)		135 (55)	
Fertilizer (5)		15 (6)	
Sprays (6)		60 (24)	
TOTAL VARIABLE COSTS		210 (85)	
GROSS MARGIN per ha (per acre)	690 (280)	870 (350)	1040 (420)

Notes

1. The categories "low", "average" and "high" are related to the actual growers of vining peas, not to farmers and farm land in general. As the factories will normally only place contracts with the better growers the "average" figure above virtually refers to "premium" farmers on good land. If all farmers had the opportunity of producing this crop the average output would probably be no higher than the "low" figure above.

2. The average sale value equals 4·5 tonnes/ha (1·8 tons/acre) @ £240 per tonne (1998 estimate). This is an average over the whole crop where it goes for freezing. Where the peas are for canning yields are likely to be heavier and prices lower. The opposite is true for *petits pois:* the yield is around 20% lower and the price 15% or so higher.

3. The above price excludes payment for harvesting (approx. £67·50 per tonne) and transport (approx. £25 per tonne). The average price assumed including these two items is therefore approx. £335 per tonne. Some firms work on a delivered factory price basis. Harvesters cost £240,000-£275,000 (capacity 500 ha).

4. *Seed:* this is a "subsidised" price in the sense that the grower pays below the market price for seed but receives a lower price for his product than he otherwise would.

5. *Fertilizer:* many growers use no fertilizer; it is more often used on light land.

6. *Sprays:* both herbicide and aphicides. There are large seasonal variations according to weather conditions and the need for midge control.

7. *Labour:* see page 103.

8. Around 40,000 ha are grown in the UK annually.

Note:

For full details (yields, prices, variable costs) of *actual* average past Cash Crop Gross Margins in different parts of the country, see the following annual reports:

Report on Farming in The Eastern Counties of England: University of Cambridge, Agricultural Economics Unit, Department of Land Economy.

An Economic Review of Farming in the North West: University of Manchester, Farm Business Unit, School of Economic Studies.

Farm Management Handbook: University of Exeter, Agricultural Economics Unit.

(Full addresses on page 213).

MAINCROP POTATOES

Production level	... ...	Low	Average	High
Yield: tonnes per ha (tons per acre)	...	32 (12·75)	42 (16·75)	52 (20·75)
		£	£	£
OUTPUT		2405 (970)	3155 (1275)	3905 (1580)
Variable Costs:				
Seed			550 (222)	
Fertilizer			210 (85)	
Sprays			420 (170)	
Casual Labour for harvesting				
and grading (3)			340 (137)	
Sundries (levy, sacks, etc.)	...	300 (121)	350 (141)	400 (161)
TOTAL VARIABLE COSTS		1820 (735)	1870 (755)	1920 (775)
GROSS MARGIN per hectare (acre)		585 (235)	1285 (520)	1985 (805)

Notes

1. *Prices.* The price assumed above is £80 per tonne for ware and £15 for chats (assumed to be 7½ per cent), which is £75 per tonne for the whole crop. The *actual price* in any one season will depend mainly on the national average yield. The five-year *average* GB price between 1990/91 and 1994/95 was £91 per tonne (£103 at 1997 price levels) but varied from £56 to £157 per tonne (£64 to £170 at 1997 price levels). The Potato Board, together with its regulatory powers, ceased to exist from June 1997. The average price for the 1994 crop was exceptionally above the level assumed above and the 1995 crop prices were also well above average. 1996 crop prices were much lower and 1997 crop prices look certain to be low also.
    The average seasonal monthly price indices over the same period (with each annual price = 100) are as follows: July 106, Aug. 85, Sept. 86, Oct. 87, Nov. 87, Dec. 93, Jan. 101, Feb. 109, Mar. 118, April 132, May 137, June 151. The variation between years is considerable, particularly at the beginning and end of the season.

2. *Physical Inputs.* Seed: 80% planted with certified seed: 2·8 tonnes per hectare at £215 per tonne (the price varies widely from season to season); 20% with once-grown seed: 2·4 tonnes per hectare at £140 per tonne. Sprays: herbicide, blight control, and haulm destruction.

15

3. *Casual Labour.* The figure in the table above is for assistance during harvesting (£90/ha; machine harvesting is assumed) and for grading/riddling (£250/ha); it is assumed that half the labour for the latter is supplied by casuals, half by regulars. Other jobs for which casual labour may be employed are:

Planting:	£105 per hectare
Picking by hand:	£495 per hectare
Grading/Riddling (all):	£495 per hectare (£11·80 per tonne).

4. *Contract mechanical harvesting:* £265/hectare (excl. carting, etc.). Other contract work see pages 119-120.
5. *British Potato Council levy:* £35/ha (£14/acre) for growers, 20p a tonne for first buyers.
6. *Sacks.* Approx. £6·75 per tonne.
7. *Chitting.* Additional annual cost of chitting is approximately £43·50 per tonne of seed, or £120 per hectare, including depreciation and interest on the chitting house.
8. *Fuel and Repairs (per hectare):* £165.
9. *Specialised Equipment Prices:* see page 117.
10. *Potato Store Costs:* see page 151.
11. *Labour:* see page 100.

In 1995, the percentages of the total potato area in Great Britain planted in maincrop, second early and first early varieties respectively were 62·4, 28·0 and 9·6; in England and Wales: 60·8, 29·0 and 10·2; in Scotland: 69·5, 23·2 and 7·3. Approximately 17·5% of the total GB potato area is in Scotland.

EARLY POTATOES

Production level	Low	Average	High
Yield: tonnes per ha (tons per acre): ...	19·0 (7·6)	25·0 (10)	31·0 (12·3)
	£	£	£
OUTPUT	2500 (1010)	3500 (1415)	4500 (1820)
Variable Costs:			
Seed		800 (322)	
Fertilizer		170 (69)	
Sprays		200 (81)	
Casual labour		165 (69)	
Sundries		200 (81)	
TOTAL VARIABLE COSTS		1535 (620)	
GROSS MARGIN per ha (acre)	965 (390)	1965 (795)	2965 (1200)

Notes

1. *Prices and Yields.* The price assumed above is £140 per tonne. However, yields increase and prices fall as the season progresses. Thus both depend on the date of lifting, e.g. late May to early June, 7 to 12 tonnes per hectare; July, 20 to 30 tonnes per hectare. Prices in late May to mid June are typically three times those in July; the very earliest crops (early May) can even fetch more than £1,000 per tonne, but the price could be down to £500 by mid May and to £250 or even £200 by the end of May. Thus the average output of £3500 given above could also be obtained from 10 tonnes at £350 per tonne, 15 at £233, 20 at £175 or 30 at £117.
2. *Casual labour* for planting: £105 per hectare.
3. *Chitting.* See Maincrop Potatoes.
4. *Fuel and Repairs (£ per hectare):* £135.
5. *Labour:* see page 101.

SECOND EARLY POTATOES

Output (average): 40 tonnes/ha (16 tons/acre) @ £70/tonne = £2800 (1135) (lifting July to early September).

Variable Costs: Seed £550 (222), fertilizer £200 (81), sprays £275 (112), casual labour £300 (122), miscellaneous £325 (133); total £1650 (670).

Gross Margin: £1150 (465).

Labour: see page 101.

SUGAR BEET

Production level	Low	Average	High
Yield: tonnes per ha (tons per acre)* ...	35 (14)	49 (20)	62 (25)

	£	£	£
OUTPUT	1290 (522)	1810 (733)	2290 (927)

Variable Costs:			
Seed		115 (46)	
Fertilizer		125 (51)	
Sprays		165 (67)	
Transport (Contract)	135 (55)	185 (75)	235 (95)
TOTAL VARIABLE COSTS	540 (219)	590 (239)	640 (259)
GROSS MARGIN per ha (acre)	750 (303)	1220 (494)	1650 (668)

*"*Adjusted tonnes*" *at standard 16% sugar content (MAFF)*

Notes

1. *Prices.* The above table assumes a price, for the 1998 crop, of £33 per tonne, for roots of 16 per cent sugar content (i.e. the S.C. at which yields are adjusted by MAFF); this assumes that 90% of the crop is paid for at an A and B contract price of £35/tonne (£38·15 at 17% S.C.) and 10% is C beet at £15/tonne; (the C beet price has varied in recent years from less than £10 to over £25). Transport allowance and early and late delivery bonuses are additional; these are taken to be £3·70 and £0·50/tonne respectively at 17% S.C.; they are scaled down for 16% S.C. in the table, making £36·90/tonne overall.

   The price is varied by 0·9 per cent (1 per cent below 15 per cent sugar content) of the contract price for each 0·1 per cent difference in sugar content.

   In addition, early and late delivery allowances are paid as follows (all dates approximate only). Early delivery: 18% is added to the basic price if crops are delivered on Sept. 15th; this reduces by one per percentage point per day till Oct. 10th, when just the basic price is paid. Late delivery: 26th Dec.-7th Jan.: 0·8% of U K minimum price; thereafter, the rate rises by 0·2% per day.

2. *Effect of Harvesting Date.* As the season progresses, changes occur in the crop before lifting, approximately as follows, on average:

	early Sept. to early Oct.	early Oct. to early Nov.	early Nov. to early Dec.	early Dec. to early Jan.
Yield (tonnes of washed beet per hectare) ...	up 3·75	up 1·9	up 1·25	up 1·25
Sugar Content (%) ...	up 1%	up ¼%	down ¼%	down ¾%
Yield of Sugar (kg per hectare)	up 1000	up 375	up 190	down 60

3. *Contract* Contract mechanical harvesting costs approx. £145 per hectare excluding carting or £190 per hectare including carting.

4. *Transport.* Contract haulage charges vary widely according to distance from the factory. The figure assumed above is £3·35 per tonne of unwashed beet including cleaner-loader hire (dirt and top tare assumed at 14%).

5. *Fuel and Repairs* (per hectare): £150.

6. *Specialized Equipment Prices:* see page 117.

7. *Labour:* see page 102.

HERBAGE SEEDS

					Italian Ryegrass		Early Perennial Ryegrass	
					Average	High	Average	High
Yield (tonnes/ha)	...	...			1·1	1·5	1·2	1·6
Price per 50 kg (£)	...	...			37·50		37·50	
Aid per 50 kg (£)	...	...			8·50		10·50	
OUTPUT	...	...	...	...	1010	1380	1150	1535
Variable Costs:								
Seed	...	...	...	...	90		75	
Fertilizer	...	...	...		70		70	
Sprays	...	...	...	...	75		75	
Cleaning, etc.	...	...	...		145	195	155	205
TOTAL VARIABLE COSTS	...	...			380	430	375	425
GROSS MARGIN per ha	...	...			630	950	775	1110
GROSS MARGIN per acre	...	...			255	385	315	450

					Intermediate Perennial Ryegrass		Late Perennial Ryegrass	
					Average	High	Average	High
Yield (tonnes/ha)	...	...			1·2	1·6	1·15	1·5
Price per 50 kg (£)	...	...			40		47·50	
Aid per 50 kg (£)	...	...			10·50		14·00	
OUTPUT					1210	1615	1415	1845
Variable Costs:								
Seed	...	...	...	...	70		70	
Fertilizer	...	...	...		70		70	
Sprays	...	...	...	...	75		75	
Cleaning, etc.	...	...	...		155	205	150	195
TOTAL VARIABLE COSTS	...	...			370	420	365	410
GROSS MARGIN per ha	...	...			840	1195	1050	1435
GROSS MARGIN per acre	...	...			340	485	425	580

	Hybrid Ryegrass		Kent Wild White Clover & Kent Indig. Perennial Ryegrass	
	Average	High	Average	High
Yield (tonnes/ha)	1·2	1·6	·08(C); 0·5(R)	·11(C); 0·7(R)
Price per 50 kg (£)		37·50	300(C); 40(R)	
Aid per 50 kg (£)		8·50	30·20(C); 14·00(R)	
OUTPUT	1105	1470	1070	1480
Variable Costs:				
Seed		70		40
Fertilizer		70		35
Sprays		75		40
Cleaning, etc.	155	205	100	130
TOTAL VARIABLE COSTS	370	420	215	245
GROSS MARGIN per ha	735	1050	855	1235
GROSS MARGIN per acre	295	425	345	500

Notes

1. The following were the number of hectares entered for certified seed production for the main grasses and clovers in the UK for the 1997 harvest:

Italian Ryegrass	1,099	Timothy	32
Early Perennial Ryegrass ...	1,054	Red Fescue	314
Intermediate Perennial Ryegrass	3,658	Tall Fescue	25
Late Perennial Ryegrass ...	3,526	Meadow Fescue	13
Amenity Perennial Ryegrass	737	Sheeps Fescue	13
Hybrid Ryegrass	662	White Clover	96
Westerwold Ryegrass... ...	42	Red Clover	24
Cocksfoot	138	Vetch	190

The ryegrasses total 10,778 ha (26,632 acres)
All herbage seeds total 11,623 ha (28,720 acres)

2. Average yields are approximate 5-year (1992-96) averages for cleaned seed. The crop is very risky, i.e. yields are highly variable, depending especially on the weather at, and precise timeliness of, harvesting. A considerable amount of skill is necessary to attain the "high" levels. Most grasses give their highest yield in their first harvest year, assuming good establishment.

3. Prices in the table are estimated prices for certified seed. The actual prices received in any one year are very uncertain. Prices in 1996 and 1997 were the highest for some years. Diploid prices are above tetraploid prices, but yields of diploid are usually lower. The subsidy levels are approximate levels for 1997/98.

4. No allowance has been made above for by-products. Some crops produce 4 to 5 tonnes of threshed hay, which is, however, of low feeding value. This could be worth £200 or more per hectare. Some grasses, especially spring-sown ryegrass, also provide substantial quantities of autumn and winter grazing. Clovers can be either grazed or cut for hay or silage and do not have to be "shut up" until mid or late May, or, in some cases and seasons, even early June. More grazing (until end of May) and better quality threshed hay is provided with a combination of ryegrass and white clover than with the specialist herbage seed grasses.

5. If the seed crop is to be undersown, specialist growers often reduce the seed rate for the cover crop by up to half and restrict nitrogen dressing: the cereal yield may thus be reduced by up to 0·6 tonnes per hectare. If this is not done the grass seed yield is usually lower in the first year compared with direct drilling, except for ryegrass.

6. *Labour:* see page 105.

Acknowledgement: The basic data for this crop have been provided by D. I. White, Head of Fodder and Oilseeds Section, NIAB, but the price, variable costs and gross margin assumptions and calculations are solely the author's responsibility.

RYE

Production level	Low	Average	High
Yield: tonnes per ha (tons per acre):	4·6 (1·85)	5·8 (2·3)	7·0 (2·8)
	£	£	£
Sale Value (£100/tonne)	460 (186)	580 (235)	700 (283)
Area Payment	255 (103)	255 (103)	255 (103)
OUTPUT: (Contract price)	715 (289)	835 (338)	955 (386)
Variable Costs:			
Seed		65 (26·5)	
Fertilizer		70 (28·5)	
Sprays		100 (40)	
TOTAL VARIABLE COSTS		235 (95)	
GROSS MARGIN per ha (acre):	480 (194)	600 (243)	720 (291)

Largely grown on light, infertile, sandy or stony soils, where yields are poor for other cereals. Yields would clearly be higher on better soils, but then rye has difficulty in competing with wheat and barley; it could never do so on good wheat land. The average yield in England and Wales in the three years 1994 to 1996 has been 5·8 tonnes/ha (MAFF).

Close to 8,000 ha have been grown in the UK in recent years, mainly in the south, south-east and East Anglia. Rye crispbread is the biggest outlet, Ryvita alone using nearly 30,000 tonnes a year. It is also milled into flour, used in mixed-grain bread and muesli. Increasing concern with dieting means that demand is increasing. About two-thirds of UK requirements are imported, mainly from Canada (which produces the highest quality), Denmark, Germany and Spain.

The price assumed above (£100 a tonne) is an estimated 1998 price at harvest for crispbread. Typically, £3 is added for delivery in October or November and £6 if grown within, say, 80 miles of the processing plant; deductions are made for low quality, particularly if it is only of feed grade (between feed wheat and feed barley price). Only about 15% of the crop is grown for the free market, which is risky. The area payment is as estimated for England (see page 3).

Rye, which is autumn-sown, is drought tolerant and very hardy, can withstand low temperatures and starts growing early in the spring. It has all-round resistance to wheat and barley diseases, e.g. eyespot, and suffers less from take-all than wheat—hence it is a possible replacement for third or fourth wheat. Its vigour keeps weeds down. Its herbicide, fungicide and fertilizer requirements are lower than for other cereals. Harvested earlier than winter wheat (useful for following with oilseed rape).

Drawbacks: it sprouts in a wet harvest: must thus harvest early, at relatively high moisture content. It grows very tall and lodges easily: hence high levels of nitrogen are not possible; but growth regulators help. Its heavy straw crop means very slow combining (takes about twice as long per hectare as wheat and barley), and difficult straw incorporation. New hybrid varieties, with shorter, stiffer straw, are being developed; these would improve the comparative profitability of rye on better soils.

Drilling: 2nd and 3rd weeks September.

Harvesting: by mid-August (at relatively high moisture content, then dry to 14-15%).

TRITICALE

Production level	Low	Average	High
Yield: tonnes per ha (tons per acre):	4·75 (1·9)	6·0 (2·4)	7·25 (2·9)
	£	£	£
Sale Value (£82·50/tonne)	390 (158)	495 (200)	600 (243)
Area Payment	255 (103)	255 (103)	255 (103)
OUTPUT	645 (261)	750 (303)	855 (346)
Variable Costs:			
Seed		65 (26·5)	
Fertilizer		75 (30)	
Sprays		65 (26·5)	
TOTAL VARIABLE COSTS		205 (83)	
GROSS MARGIN per ha (acre)	440 (178)	545 (220)	650 (263)

A "man-made" cross between rye and hard wheat. Combines the hardiness of rye and the marketability of feed wheat. The main use is in pig and poultry rations: it contains a superior quality of protein. The UK area was down to around 6,100 ha in 1997. In Germany the triticale area has risen tenfold since 1986 to about 280,000 ha and the area in France now exceeds 200,000 ha.

Price is between feed wheat and feed barley and the average throughout the 1998/9 season is taken to be £82·50 per tonne. The area payment is as estimated for England (see page 3).

Its main scope to date has been on light land, especially thin, drought-prone, poorish, marginal cereal-growing soils, where it frequently outyields wheat or barley, especially the former, and it has lower input requirements. Its yields tend to be more consistent on such soil than those of barley. It tends to do well compared with second and subsequent wheats owing to its resistance to drought and fungal diseases. Given that it is mainly grown on poorer soils the average yield in England and Wales of 6·0 tonnes/ha in the three years 1994 to 1996 (MAFF) is commendable.

Lower levels of fungicide are needed because of its good disease resistance, except for ergot, but including take-all (making it a possible replacement for a third or fourth wheat, as indicated above). It is a tall crop, which helps to suppress weeds, but it is susceptible to lodging; growth regulators are beneficial.

The crop is best drilled early (September) on very light, drought-prone soils; otherwise October is satisfactory.

Harvesting is at approximately the same time as wheat. There is more straw, which slows combining, and incorporation is very difficult; this is less of a problem on poor soils as there is less straw.

NAKED OATS

Production level	Low	Average	High
Yield: tonnes per ha (tons per acre): ...	3·5 (1·4)	4·75 (1·9)	6·0 (2·4)
	£	£	£
Sale Value (£130/tonne)	525 (213)	715 (290)	900 (364)
Area Payment	255 (103)	255 (103)	255 (103)
OUTPUT	780 (316)	970 (393)	1155 (467)
Variable Costs:			
Seed		57·5 (23)	
Fertilizer		60 (24·5)	
Sprays		77·5 (31·5)	
TOTAL VARIABLE COSTS		195 (79)	
GROSS MARGIN per ha (acre)	585 (237)	775 (314)	960 (388)

Naked oats have a higher protein, energy and oil content than "traditional" oats, but the fibre content is lower—as the husk falls off during harvesting. Because of the high oil content it can go rancid if stored too moist, hence contracts require a maximum moisture content of 14% and 12% is recommended for long-term storage. The crop needs priority treatment at harvest.

Between 6,000 and 8,000 ha are grown in the UK at present and the area is steadily increasing. The traditional markets such as for racehorses and dog foods are increasing and the bird food market has been developed, but at least half the crop is now sold for human consumption: for health foods, fancy breads and breakfast cereals.

The (1998/9) price assumed is £130 per tonne. Contracts offering premiums between 30% and 75% above the average feed wheat/feed barley price, according to husk content, are available. One company offered a single fixed premium for 1997 of 50% and a no screenings clause. The area payment is as estimated for England (see page 3).

About 85% of the crop is winter sown. NIAB suggests that yields average 20 to 25% less than conventional oats, but survey data over several years is as yet unavailable. Like other oats, the variable inputs are lower than for wheat or barley and the crop provides a break in the take-all cycle.

Naked barley, suitable for roasting, flaking or milling as pearl barley, is getting increasingly in the news. It is available on buy-back contracts with a £30/tonne premium over feed grains. Both winter and spring varieties are available. The crop is grown like normal barley, but yields are expected to be some 15% lower.

DURUM WHEAT

Production level	Low	Average	High
Yield: tonnes per ha (tons per acre): ...	2 ·75 (1·1)	3·75 (1·5)	5·00 (2·0)
	£	£	£
Sale Value (£125/tonne)	315 (128)	470 (190)	625 (253)
Area Payment	255 (103)	255 (103)	255 (103)
OUTPUT	570 (231)	725 (293)	880 (356)
Variable Costs:			
Seed		85 (34·5)	
Fertilizer		80 (32·5)	
Sprays		80 (32)	
TOTAL VARIABLE COSTS		245 (99)	
GROSS MARGIN per ha (acre)	325 (132)	480 (194)	635 (257)

N.B. Extra drying costs estimated at £8 per tonne.

A Mediterranean crop. Used for pasta, semolina (if high quality) and breakfast cereals. Must be grown under contract. The UK demand is relatively small (60,000 tonnes a year); UK consumption per head is approx. 4% that of Italy and 10% that of France. 11,000 ha (27,000 acres) were grown in UK in 1984, but poor results reduced this to approx. 2,000 ha by 1992 and now only a few hundred hectares are grown; hence no recent data on yields etc. are available. Imports are mainly from France, Spain and Greece.

Yields well above the average given above were often quoted, but the 5-year average yield in Cambridge University's Farm Business Survey in 1988-92 was only 3·55 tonnes/ha, despite averaging 4·83 in the 1992 harvest. Possibly it has been mainly grown on dry, poorish soils.

The (1998 harvest) *price* assumed is £125 per tonne. Contract prices vary according to quality. Growers in Mediterranean type areas get a higher area payment to compensate for the lower yield compared with other wheat. The area payment is as estimated for England (see page 3).

As with milling wheat, there is a risk of rejection if contaminated with excess foreign seeds, especially self-set cereals from previous crop; thus safer as first cereal crop. A poor price is obtained (no EU subsidy) if quality is too poor for pasta and thus has to go for feed.

The crop is likely to be grown only in the driest parts of the east/south east, where it can best compete with second and third wheats. It is now mainly (approx. 90%) sown in the spring (March) compared with in the autumn (October) less than 10 years ago. The crop is very sensitive to stress and frost-kill in severe winters; the spring-sown crop is more reliable, and cheaper to grow. The crop has a higher disease resistance than other wheats, except for eyespot and ergot.

Harvest: spring crop usually mid-August. Critical operation: need to harvest as soon as reaches 20% moisture content, or at most 18%: crop very prone to sprouting and quality for semolina reduced if harvest delayed. Must be dried (slowly) to 15%: easier and quicker to dry than normal wheat. The straw is of poorer quality than wheat straw.

MINORITY CROPS

The following crops have limited possibilities at present, if indeed they can be grown successfully at all, but such factors as the breeding of new varieties could alter the position in the future. Some can be grown, but there is a very limited market, e.g., borage.

Borage

Indigenous to Britain: both grown wild and cultivated for centuries. Grown for use as a dietary food supplement. The oil has a high gamma linolenic acid (GLA) content—more than twice as much as evening primrose. Demand slumped after 1986 owing to over-production of GLA from non-contract crops of evening primrose in other countries. The current area is around 800 ha, grown in Suffolk, Essex and Yorkshire.

Compared with evening primrose it has the advantages of spring-sowing (about mid-March), bigger seeds, faster growth, and earlier harvesting (August). Its aggressive growth gives good weed control with a high plant density. It prefers low rainfall. There are no known pests and diseases, except for powdery mildew. It is combinable, after swathing. Harvesting can be difficult. Seed shedding at maturity is a serious problem.

Yields: from virtually nothing to 0·625 tonnes/ha (5 cwt./acre); average 0·35 (2·8).

Price: £2,200 a tonne. Output at average yield, £770/ha (310/acre).

Variable costs (approx.) (£ per ha (acre)): seed 170 (68); fertilizer 55 (22); sprays 25 (10); total £250 (100).

Gross margin: £520/ha (210/acre).

Evening Primrose

The seed oil is a good source of essential fatty acids, especially gamma-linolenic acid, which has medicinal properties for many serious diseases and disorders. Brand-named evening primrose oil capsules are widely available in chemists and health food shops.

Grown only in small areas, mainly 2 to 5 ha. About 1,000 ha (2,500 acres) now grown in UK; contract necessary. Wide range of soils suitable, but not acid, high pH, or fen. Good drainage and firm seedbed necessary.

Some growers (especially if on sands) sow in March/April for harvesting early/mid-October, but most sow in late July-early August for harvesting in late September/October the following year—but winter kill is possible. Germination and establishment very difficult (the seeds are tiny), shallow drilling (½″) and seedbed consolidation important. Weed control a major problem until established. No significant pest or disease problems known at present. Relatively little fertilizer needed—lush vegetative growth unwanted.

Uneven ripening and pod setting a further problem. Harvesting is difficult. Crop has to be desiccated (perhaps twice) before combining, which needs to be slow to avoid shattering the pods; seeds must be dried quickly, to 10-12%.

Yields: 0·15 to 0·75 tonnes/ha (1·25 to 6 cwt./acre): 0·4 (3·2) a good crop. A high-risk crop best grown on contract.

Price: approx. £1,800 a tonne; 0·35 tonne (2·4 cwt.) = £630/ha (255/acre).

Variable costs (approx.) (£ per ha (acre)): seed 25 (10), fertiliser 55 (22), sprays 95 (37); desiccant 65 (27); cleaning 60 (24); total £300 (120).

Gross margin at 0·35 tonnes/ha therefore approx. £330 (135).

Hemp (Cannabis)

Now approved for growing in UK for industrial purposes, under licence obtained from the Home Office. For use in textiles and building materials. Drilled in late April/early May the crop grows 3 to 3·5m (10 to 12 feet) tall. Approx. 1,600 ha were grown under licence in 1996. Average yields have been around 5 tonnes ha (2t/acre). The target average yield is 7·5 t/ha (3t/acre). The price is approximately £55/tonne delivered. There is an EU subsidy of approx. £575/ha. Variable costs/ha are, approx.: seed £145, fertiliser £90, (sprays nil), contract swathing and baling £150, haulage to factory £50 (£10/tonne). It may be grown on set-aside land but then without the EU subsidy, only the set-aside payment. Around 6,000 ha are grown in France, the EU's top producer.

Lupins

Some 1,300 ha were grown in the UK in 1985, but the results were so poor that year that only 260 ha grown in 1986 and little has been grown in the country since. The area in France has also fallen substantially. Has a high protein content (50% more than peas and beans), making it a good substitute for soya beans in livestock feed compounds, and it is easy to mill. But it has a high fibre content, variable protein ratings and an unbalanced amino acid profile. Some 30,000 tonnes of lupin produce is currently imported per year from Australia.

It is a leguminous, light land crop. Mainly white-flowered varieties grown at present. It is spring-sown (mid-March/early April), nitrogen fixing, has erect growth, is resistant to lodging and shattering, and unmodified cereal machinery is suitable. But it is difficult to grow: it needs careful seedbed preparation and free-draining fertile soil; botrytis lowers yields, especially in a wet year: there is no certain control at present, late-germinating weeds can cause problems; fairly susceptible to frost damage; possibly uneven ripening; harvested late. To produce a mature crop its heat requirements are even higher than for grain maize: thus many crops have been combined at very high moisture contents or have even failed to mature. Work on a new type of lupin, winter-sown and semi-topless, promising earlier maturity and higher yields, is underway at Rothamsted. There are many farm trials currently in the UK. 2,000 ha of sweet white lupins were grown in north Germany in 1994.

Might average 2 tonnes per ha (0·8 tons per acre) in a good year, though up to 5 tonnes/ha claimed in trials of latest varieties of white lupins. Price about £130 a tonne. Area payment approximately £385/ha in England in 1996. Variable costs per ha (approx.): seed £50, fert. £15 sprays £85; total £150.

Maize for Grain

Little scope with present varieties because, as with Sunflowers, our climate is not warm enough. Did reasonably well in good springs and summers for a while, in Southern England, over ten years ago, but results were very poor in late springs and cool summers and harvesting between mid-October and mid-December is grim in a wet autumn/early winter, and drying very costly. Possibly 200 ha are being grown annually in the UK. Do well to average 4 tonnes/ha (the average is about double this in France); price for the 1997 crop could be £115-120 a tonne; area payment (England) £257/ha (£104/acre). Seed (125), fertilizer (65) and sprays (30); total approx. £220/ha (£90/acre); drying £100/ha (£40/acre). Forage maize (p. 78) has been much more successful.

Navy Beans

Produced for baked beans. About 80,000 tonnes a year imported from North America, at £450/tonne in 1996. Limited chance of commercial production in the UK in the foreseeable future (*i e.*, with present varieties) because of insufficient cold tolerance. Current production is on a trial basis, in the south (Chichester Plain, Romney Marsh and S.E. Essex), supported by supermarkets keen to provide British baked beans; 25 ha grown in total in 1996. New cold and disease resistant varieties required. Its chances are better than for soya beans. Sown early to mid-May. Late to harvest (Sept./Oct.). Target yield 2·5 tonnes/ha, but the average is likely to be well below this (1·6 in some 1995 trials). At present the crop receives no EU area aid. Output (say 1·7 tonnes/ha (13·5 cwt/acre) at £450/tonne) £765/ha. Variable costs around £225 (seed 75, fertilizer 60, sprays 90). Gross margin then £540/ha (£220/acre).

Soya Beans

Mainly grown in the USA. In Europe, mainly in the Po Valley (the area of this crop is growing rapidly in Italy) and Southern France (40,000 ha). Very little chance of successful commercial production in the UK, as the crop is unlikely to mature in our climate. Sown mid-May. Yield approx. 1·7 tonnes/ha (13·5 cwt./acre); price approx. £160/tonne; eligible for oilseeds area payment (approx. £425/ha); variable costs £175/ha. Average EC yield (80% in Italy) 3·0 tonnes/ha (1·2 tons/acre).

Sunflowers

Continues to be of considerable interest but because of late harvests and low yields only some 200 ha are currently grown in the UK, producing 350-400 tonnes a year. 200,000 tonnes of sunflower seed are imported each year for oil production.

Average yield around 1·7 tonnes/ha (13·5 cwt./acre). Even in France the average yield is only 55-60% of that of oilseed rape. Price: approx £180/tonne, plus approx. £425/ha area aid (same as oilseed rape). Output = £730. Variable costs approx. £235 per ha (seed 115, fertilizer 55, sprays 65). Gross margin £495/ha (£200/acre). Drying costs are high: approx. £50/ha.

Sown in April or early May, when soil temperature exceeds 5°C. Wide range of soils suitable.

Problems: the crop needs a warm climate: in Southern England a "fair" crop might be grown 3 years in 5; susceptible to botrytis, especially in a wet August/September, difficult to control; sclerotina also a major problem in France; birds too can be damaging (thus at least 4 ha (10 acres) need to be grown in one piece); post-emergence weed control is difficult. Harvesting is late in England (late September/early October at best); a dry autumn is needed. Dried to 10% for safe storage.

Others

Other crops that have been in the news" in recent years as possible new crops for the future (or present crops capable of substantial development) include the following: chickpeas and lentils, fenugreek, meadowfoam, cuphea, peppermint, poppies (for cooking oils, not opium), quinoa, buckwheat and sunwheat (a new early maturing short type of sunflower). At present there are no reliable data for these crops on average yield expectations and little on prices or variable costs, when grown on a commercial scale in this country. A number of them are either for the health food market or are sources of oil for industry as replacements for whale oil and light mineral oil. Research continues on many of them.

HOPS

1. Output data

Average Yield per ha, 1992-96: 30·3 zentners (50 kg).

Average Price (per zentner): 1992, £167; 1993, £178; 1994, £204; 1995, £211;1996, £206 (contract), £165 (spot).

Main varieties (80% of total area):

	ha 1996	av. yield 1992-96 (z. per ha)	av. £ per zentner (contract prices) 1995	1996
Target	1,095	32·6	145	104
Goldings	450	28·9	257	282
Northdown	323	31·2	237	254
Challenger	309	31·9	231	242
Fuggles	305	27·2	239	255

Total area of hops (ha): 1984: 5,091; 1994: 3,136; 1995: 3,094; 1996: 3,112.

EC income aid for 1995 (£ per ha): aromatic £370; bitter, £347; other and experimental, £248. An increased rate, raised from 450 to 480 ecu/ha, was announced in August 1997, to be paid immediately after harvest.

2. Variable Costs per mature hectare (materials only)

	£
Fertilizers and Manure	185
Washes and Powders	1000
Herbicides	135
String	195
Pockets/Bales	65
Drying Fuel	195
Total	1775

3. Average Direct Labour Costs per mature hectare

	£
Growing	765
Picking	700
Drying	185
Total	1650

N.B. The above costs are the author's approximations for 1998 based on a limited sample for the 1994-96 crops.

A new hop garden (erecting the poles, wiring and planting) could cost in the order of £13,750 to £16,000 per hectare (£5,565 to £6,475 per acre).

Acknowledgement: T. W. Smith, Grower Liaison Manager, English Hop Products Limited.

VINEYARDS

In September 1994 there were 436 active vineyards in the UK, covering 1,035 ha (2,555 acres). Of these, 419 (1,016 ha) were in England, with the South-east predominating. 148 of these vineyards have wineries. Production in 1994 was 1·9 million litres: 90·5% white wine, 9·5% red.

Under EU regulations there is a ban on new plantings of vines for producing wine once annual production exceeds 2·5 million litres, but 'quality' wine is exempt. This means that no new areas of the hardy and popular hybrid grape varieties may be planted. A Quality Wine Scheme for England and Wales was introduced in 1991. English wines have to bear the same excise duty and VAT as imported wines, which is not the case in any other EU country. UK wine supplies only 0·3% of the home market. English wine growers, particularly in Kent and East Sussex, have been badly hit, since the introduction of the Single European Market in early 1993, by British people being allowed now to bring virtually unlimited amounts of wine into the country duty-free.

Vineyards need south facing land, less than 100 m. (330 ft.) above sea level, well drained and sheltered, in (at most) the southern half of England and Wales. High level management and marketing are essential, as is expert advice. Good scope for sales to visiting groups farm shops, local restaurants and hotels. A few big producers dominate the national market.

Investment capital of £12,000 to £15,000 per ha (£4,850-£6,075 per acre) typically required. No production for 3 years; full production possibly not until the 6th. Yield and quality highly variable from year to year. At least 5 ha (12 acres) now needed for commercial viability, but many who can afford it produce small areas purely out of interest or personal pleasure. A vinery adds well over £60,000 to initial costs, even for a small unit. Selling to a winery elsewhere entails additional transport costs.

There are two main systems:

Intensive (Double Guyot): 3,450 vines/ha (1,400/acre).
   Establishment costs per ha(acre) (over 2 years): approx. £17,000 (£6,900) inc. materials £11,500 (£4,650) and labour £2,700 (£1,100). (The common system in France and Germany).

Extensive (Geneva Double Curtain): 1,500 vines/ha (465/acre).
   Establishment costs per ha(acre) (over 3 years): approx. £10,500 (£4,250) inc. materials £5,750 (£2,325) and labour £2,300 (£930). (More common system in Britain).

Subsequent annual costs per ha (acre) of growing and harvesting are approximately:

	Intensive System £	Extensive System £
Growing: Materials	1,250 (500)	1,250 (500)
Labour	1,150 (465)	725 (295)
Harvesting	120 (50)	110 (45)

Yield: 5 tonnes/ha (2 tons/acre). 1 tonne of grapes = approximately 1,000 bottles of wine. At least £3·50 a bottle estimated to be needed to break even in an average sized, average cost, commercial unit.

Source: Largely from The Diversification Guide (RASE), including costs adapted from ADAS data.

For further information: English Vineyards Association, 38 West Park, London SE9 4RH (tel. 0181-857 0452).

FRUIT

Established crops: per hectare (per acre in brackets)

Note: The *wide range* of yields, prices and costs, both from farm to farm and season to season, has to be stressed. Thus these figures (which are deliberately rounded) can only be considered to be broad guidelines, i.e. yields and prices in any particular year may differ markedly. Similarly, labour requirements, both regular and casual, vary considerably. *Prices* are net of marketing, handling and transport and assume sales in the open market unless otherwise stated and exclude pick-your-own crops. *Yields* **refer to** *marketed* **yields only, of established crops.** The figures relate to *average* levels; "high" outputs may be about 50 per cent above those shown; naturally the top producers will achieve still better results, especially in good years.

	Dessert Apples	Culinary Apples	Pears	Plums
Yield: tonnes/ha (tons/acre)	16 (6·4)	22 (8·8)	11 (4·4)	8 (3·2)
Net Price (£/tonne)	400	240	450	1500
	£	£	£	£
OUTPUT	6400 (2590)	5275 (2135)	4950 (2000)	12000 (4855)
Variable Costs: [1]				
Fertilizer	50 (20)	50 (20)	50 (20)	50 (20)
Sprays	450 (182)	450 (182)	350 (141)	375 (152)
Packaging	675 (273)	725 (294)	475 (192)	1150 (466)
Casual Labour (picking)	975 (395)	825 (334)	675 (272)	1425 (577)
TOTAL VARIABLE COSTS[1]	2150 (870)	2050 (830)	1550 (625)	3000 (1215)
GROSS MARGIN	4250 (1720)	3225 (1305)	3400 (1375)	9000 (3640)
Regular Labour (hours) ...	185 (75)	185 (75)	185 (75)	135 (55)

	Strawberries	Raspberries	Blackcurrants
Yield: tonnes/ha (tons/acre)	9 (3·6)	5·75 (2·3)	7 (2·8)
Net Price (£/tonne)	1700	2200	625
	£	£	£
OUTPUT...	15300 (6190)	12650 (5120)	4375 (1770)
Variable Costs: [1]			
Fertilizer	50 (20)	75 (30)	100 (40)
Sprays	600 (243)	350 (142)	350 (142)
Packaging	2700 (1095)	1725 (700)	—
Casual Labour... ...	3500 (1415)	3450 (1395)	300 (122)
Other	450 (182)	475 (193)	275 (111)
TOTAL VARIABLE COSTS [1] ...	7300 (2955)	6075 (2460)	1025 (415)
GROSS MARGIN	8000 (3235)	6575 (2660)	3350 (1355)
Regular Labour (hours) ...	200 (80)	300 (120)	125 (50)

(1) Excluding establishment, storage and transport.

Sources: In particular, for yields and prices, the annual "Economic Results from Horticulture", by Alan Renwick, Agricultural Economics Unit, Department of Land Economy, University of Cambridge. Supplemented by updated data based on periodic small-scale surveys, mainly in Kent.

FRUIT ESTABLISHMENT

It is important to appreciate that the figures on page 28 refer only to established crops. In previous years establishment costs have to be borne, with no (or, later, low) returns.

Apples and Pears. Trees, stake, etc., approx. £4·50/tree. Total establishment costs £3,250-£16,000/ha depending especially on planting density, which varies from 750 to 3,500/ha.

First picking: apples—commonly year 3, 30% of full crop.
pears—commonly year 4, 20% of full crop.
Full picking: apples—generally year 6 to 9; pears—year 7 to 12.

Orchard duration: traditional, apples 20 years, pears 30 years plus; denser bed systems 15 years.

Strawberries. Costs in establishment year approx. £4,500/ha for traditional system, £10,500/ha for intensive systems; 60% of the cost is for plants. 35% pick in year 1 in intensive systems, none in traditional systems, full pick in year 2, generally 3 years cropping.

Raspberries. Establishment costs approx. £2,750/ha, including wirework. 50% pick in year 2, full pick in year 3; 10 years cropping.

Blackcurrants. Establishment costs approx. £5,500/ha using bushes, £2,750/ha using cuttings. Takes 1½ years to establish from 1 year old bushes (i.e. planting Nov. 1995 gives first crop in July 1997), 2½ years from cuttings. Approx. one-third of full crop in first picking year, 75% in second, peak in third, levelling out at slightly lower yield thereafter; 8 or 9 years cropping.

Researcher: Angela Edwards (who assisted further with revising the established fruit and vegetables data). Acknowledgements: Farm Advisory Services Team Ltd. and SmithKline Beecham. Figures updated by author.

FIELD-SCALE VEGETABLES

Per hectare (per acre in brackets)

Note: The same comments regarding variability apply as to fruit (page 28). The same main source has been used, for most of the crops, plus the annual "Report on Farming", from the same department. The "other" variable cost figures are intended only as a general indication of their level; survey data on many of these crops is rarely available and, when it is, particularly variable between farms and seasons.

	Carrots	Dry Bulb Onions	Dwarf Beans (for Processing)
Yield: tonnes/ha (tons/acre)	22·5 (10)	35 (14)	7 (2·8)
Price (£/tonne)	85	85	175
	£	£	£
Output	1915 (775)	2975 (1205)	1225 (495)
Variable Costs: [1]			
Seed	325 (131)	300 (121)	275 (112)
Fertilizer	125 (50)	110 (44)	100 (40)
Sprays	350 (142)	375 (151)	125 (51)
Other*	525 (212)	590 (239)	275 (112)
Total Variable Costs [1] ...	1325 (535)	1375 (555)	775 (315)
Gross Margin	590 (240)	1600 (650)	450 (180)
Regular Labour (hours) ...	50-150	40-60	N.A.

		Brussels Sprouts	Cabbage	Spring Greens
Yield: tonnes/ha (tons/acre)		13 (5·2)	36 (14·3)	20 (8)
Price (£/tonne)		310	140	220
		£	£	£
OUTPUT		4025 (1630)	5050 (2045)	4400 (1780)
Variable Costs: [1]				
Seeds/Plants		500 (202)	575 (232)	350 (141)
Fertilizer		120 (49)	170 (70)	170 (70)
Sprays		280 (114)	230 (93)	280 (114)
Other*		775 (315)	1875 (760)	2375 (960)
TOTAL VARIABLE COSTS [1]		1675 (680)	2850 (1155)	3175 (1285)
GROSS MARGIN		2350 (950)	2200 (890)	1225 (495)
Regular Labour (hours)		75 (30)	75 (30)	60 (24)

* Other = Casual Labour, Packaging, etc.

	Cauliflower	Broccoli	Calabrese	Sweetcorn
Yield: tonnes/ha (tons/acre)	17 (6·8)	15 (6)	8·5 (3·4)	N.A.
Price (£/tonne)	240	240	700	N.A.
	£	£	£	£
OUTPUT	4075 (1640)	3600 (1455)	5950 (2410)	2500 (1010)
Variable Costs: [1]				
Seed/Plants	700 (283)	675 (273)	700 (283)	240 (97)
Fertilizer	170 (69)	150 (61)	150 (61)	110 (45)
Sprays	180 (73)	175 (71)	275 (111)	110 (45)
Other*	1625 (660)	1200 (485)	1875 (760)	465 (188)
TOTAL VARIABLE COSTS ...	2675 (1085)	2200 (890)	3000 (1215)	925 (375)
GROSS MARGIN	1400 (565)	1400 (565)	2950 (1195)	1575 (635)

	Lettuce (Outdoor)	Parsnips	Leeks	Rhubarb
Yield: tonnes/ha (tons/acre)	30 (12)	25 (10)	22 (8·75)	37·5 (15)
Price (£/tonne)	450	210	475	600
OUTPUT	13500 (5465)	5250 (2125)	10450 (4230)	22500 (9100)
Variable Costs:				
Seed/Plants	1150 (465)	125 (50)	625 (253)	135 (55)
Fertilizer	175 (70)	100 (40)	150 (60)	85 (34)
Sprays	325 (130)	375 (150)	450 (182)	75 (30)
Other*	5950 (2410)	1700 (690)	6225 (2520)	N/A
TOTAL VARIABLE COSTS ...	7600 (3075)	2300 (930)	7450 (3015)	N/A
GROSS MARGIN	5900 (2390)	2950 (1195)	3000 (1215)	N/A

* Other = Casual Labour, Packaging, etc.

HORTICULTURE—WHOLE FARM DATA

Comparative whole farm data is less generally available for horticultural holdings than for various types of farm in different regions of the country (see sources of reports listed on page 133). Data from across a wide area of England is presented below. Because the results vary so much from year to year two-year averages are presented: for 1993/94 and 1994/95. The data are collected by eight College/University centres: Askham Bryan, Cambridge, Exeter, Manchester, Newcastle, Nottingham, Reading and Wye.

All financial figures are *per hectare*. The averages cover a wide range.

Type of Holding	Specialist Glass		Specialist Fruit	Market Gardens
	Mainly edible crops	Flowers & nursery stock		
No. of Farms in Sample	49	46	45	49
Average Size (ha (acres))	1·82 (4·5)	0·99 (2·5)	61 (151)	20 (49)
	£	£	£	
Gross Output...	209,545	372,660	5,440	29,085
Less:				
Bought Seed and Plants ...	14,995	60,390	160	6,785
Market Charges	14,695	13,845	775	660
Packing Materials	12,710	23,405	470	1,605
Net Output	167,145	275,020	4,035	20,035
Other Costs:				
Labour (inc. Unpaid Manual)	64,105	126,810	2,135	9,430
Glasshouse Fuel	24,180	21,030	15	280
Manures	7,720	14,975	45	795
Sprays and Fumigants ...	3,010	4,690	325	655
Horticultural Sundries ...	6,880	15,460	240	1,235
Power and Machinery ...	22,220	25,305	730	2,270
Land Rent, Glass Deprecn.	16,975	22,975	265	960
Other Fixed Costs	15,520	29,490	495	2,140
Total Other Costs	160,610	260,735	4,250	17,765
Management and Inv. Inc. ...	6,535	14,285	−215	2,270
Grower and Spouse Labour(+)	25,120	33,865	405	1,725
Net Income	31,655	48,150	190	3,995
Tenant's Valuation	158,705	252,365	4,270	21,980

Source: Horticultural Business Data, compiled by R. L. Vaughan and R. T. Crane, Department of Agricultural and Food Economics, The University of Reading, 1996.

MUSHROOMS
(Completely revised, 1997)

						Per sq. metre bed area per year 100kg £	Per tonne of compost 180kg £
Yield ...	...	...	...	...	...	100kg	180kg
Value (£1·45/kg net)	...	...	...	...		145·0	261·0
Spent compost	...	...	...	...	...	1·0	2·0
TOTAL OUTPUT	...	...	...	...	...	146·0	263·0
Variable Costs:							
Spawn ...	...	...	...	...	...	4·3	8·0
Compost (raw materials)		...	...	...		7·5	14·0
Casing (peat and lime)		...	...	...		7·0	13·0
Heating and electricity		...	...	...		10·0	18·5
Packaging (10p/kg) ...		...	...	...		10·0	18·0
Sundries (disinfectant, etc.)	...		...	...		2·5	4·6
TOTAL VARIABLE COSTS	...	...	...	...		41·3	76·1
GROSS MARGIN	...	...	...	...		104·7	186·9

Notes:

1. Length of cropping period determines:
   (i) number of crops grown per year;
   (ii) volume (and cost) of compost, casing and spawn used per unit area;
   (iii) the weight of mushrooms produced per tonne of compost.

   Assumptions: 5 crops/year; 180 kg mushrooms/tonne compost spawned; 108 kg compost/m^2/crop (22 lb/ft^2/crop).

2. *Price:* £1·45 kg net. The average annual wholesale price 1986-1996 rose from £1,370 to £1,700/tonne, most of the improvement taking place since 1993. UK annual production peaked at 113,000 tonnes in 1990, falling to around 105,000 tonnes in 1997. There is a marked trend for more of the crop to be sold direct to retail concerns and processors and less through wholesale markets and agents. The return to the grower is therefore improving.

3. *Labour:* Total £45-55/m^2/year: 30% composting and growing, 70% picking and packing. This figure is reduced if compost is purchased (see below).

4. *Capital investment:* Composting machinery £30-40,000. Typical building (50m^2 per tier of trays) £10-12,000 including heating/cooling system. Trays £15-20 per sq. metre, life 5-10 years (depending on handling). Buildings for composting, peak heating, spawn running; packhouse and coolstore may also be required, depending on the system.

5. Above figures based on tray/movable shelf system (approx. 42% of UK crop) using home made compost; other systems include mechanised shelf (34% of crop), bags and block. Phase I compost can be purchased at £25/tonne plus delivery, Phase II (pasteurised plus spawn) at £85-90, Phase III (spawn run) at £120-125/tonne. Currently around 66% of the crop is grown from Phase I compost, 21% from Phase II and 13% from Phase III, with Phase III share increasing. Yields may be higher if Phase II or III compost is used; variable costs will be greater but fixed costs, both labour and buildings, will be lower.

6. Note: mushroom growing is not recommended as a casual enterprise. It is a highly specialised business requiring production and marketing expertise.

Researcher: Angela Edwards.

ORGANIC FARMING

The UK area of organic farming is estimated to be approximately 50,000 ha (125,000 acres), (approx. 860 farmers), slowly expanding. About 0·5% of UK farms are registered organic, compared with approximately 1% in the EU as a whole and a high of 8% in Austria. There are more than 55,000 organic farms in the EU, totalling more than 1,250,000 ha of organic land. The UK market is estimated to be worth around £200 million, increasing by some 25% annually (MAFF); 70% is imported.

The benefits to the nation claimed are as follows:
  (i) lower yields = less surpluses = less national and EU expenditure on storage and disposal;
 (ii) environmental benefits of non-use of inorganic fertilizers and agrochemical sprays;
(iii) reduction in use of fossil energy;
 (iv) increasing concern over health means a rising demand and thus an expanding market.
  (v) a saving in imported produce.

Against these points critics argue that:
  (i) it is unproven that inorganic fertilizers and (tested and approved) agro-chemicals harm the environment;
 (ii) it is unproven that organically produced foods are more nutritious, healthier or tastier;
(iii) there is insufficient land available to feed the present population adequately if all farming were organic;
 (iv) if organic production became widespread in the UK compared with other countries our competitive position in terms of production costs per tonne would become increasingly eroded.

The economics to the farmer (though this is of secondary interest to many organic farmers) depend *primarily* upon:
  (i) relative yield compared with conventional farming;
 (ii) the price premium compared with conventional farming.

However, there are also the wider whole farm effects to be considered, *e.g.,* unless the farm already has a substantial percentage of its area down to leys this will probably have to be increased in order to maintain yields and this extra grass has to be utilised profitably—which is far from easy, and the extra capital requirements could be heavy.

Furthermore, there is a two year "conversion period" to undergo before full price premiums can be claimed; (though note the aid scheme, next page). Also, quality (in the sense of appearance) can be badly affected by pests and diseases.

In order to illustrate the gross margin contrast with conventional farming just one crop will be taken: *Winter Wheat.* The estimates are for the 1998 harvest crop, with national average yields. The price for organic wheat in the table is "artificial", in that it is simply the price required to give the same gross margin as conventionally grown wheat, given all the other assumptions as regards relative yields and variable costs.

| | | Conventional | | Organic |
		Feed	Milling	(Milling)
Yield: tonnes/ha (tons/acre)	...	7·75 (3·1)	7·05 (2·8)	4·5 (1·8)
		£	£	£
Price per tonne		85	93·50	112
Area Payment	...	255 (103)	255 (103)	255 (103)
Output per ha (acre)	...	915 (370)	915 (370)	760 (307)
Seed	...	50 (20)	50 (20)	60 (24)
Fertilizer/Manures ...	...	80 (32·5)	80 (32·5)	40 (16)
Sprays	...	125 (50·5)	125 (50·5)	—
TOTAL VARIABLE COSTS ...	...	255 (103)	255 (103)	100 (40)
GROSS MARGIN per ha (acre)	...	660 (267)	660 (267)	660 (267)

Notes on above comparison:

Thus, on the assumptions given, including that £40/ha of inorganic manures are applied, the break-even price for organic wheat in 1998/9 will be approximately £112/tonne, i.e. a premium over the estimated price for conventional feed wheat of £27 (32%) and (more appropriately) conventional milling wheat of £18·50 (20%). Although future cereal prices are full of uncertainty it seems certain that such premiums will be readily achieved, given the likely supply and demand position. Organic wheat prices for recognised breadmaking quality have been much higher than these levels; they are expected to be £150-£160/tonne in 1997/98. Hence the gross margin of organic wheat should comfortably exceed that of conventional wheat, given the relative yields assumed above: 58% of feed wheat and 64% of milling wheat conventionally grown. However, the rotational aspect referred to above has very much to be borne in mind, as has the cost of the conversion period, though the land to be converted can be included in the set-aside area.

As regards relative cultivation costs, in one ADAS monitored study these were reported to be 15 per cent higher on the organically grown wheat (approximately £17·50 more per ha (£7 per acre) at present costs). However no spraying is required. Survey data have indicated overall labour requirements to be 10-30% higher than on conventional farms, with machinery costs generally similar.

As already stated, *the big questions are the relative yields and the price difference.* Future price premiums will depend on how much the consumption of organic produce increases compared with increases in supply.

An *Organic Aid Scheme* for England to encourage new organic producers (but providing nothing for existing producers), with extra help for the conversion period, was introduced in 1994. Participants must register their proposed land for conversion with one of the organic sector bodies or with the United Kingdom Register of Organic Food Standards and provide a conversion plan. There is a minimum eligible size of 1 ha; there is no maximum eligible size but aid will not be paid beyond 300 ha. The rates of aid (£/ha) are:

Year:	1	2	3	4	5
Non-LFA	70	70	50	35	25
LFA	14	14	10	7	5

with an additional £30/ha for the first 5 ha.

For considerable further details on organic farming, including gross margin data on many enterprises, see "1995/6 Organic Farm Management Handbook", by Nic Lampkin and Mark Measures, available from the Department of Agricultural Sciences, University of Wales, Aberystwyth, Dyfed, SY23 3DD (Tel. 01970 622248), or from the Elm Farm Research Centre (address below). Prices for individual copies £10 including postage.

See also "Organic Farming as a Business in Great Britain" (1992) by M. C. Murphy, Agricultural Economics Unit, University of Cambridge, 19 Silver Street, Cambridge, CB3 9EL. (Tel. 01223 337147). Price £15.

Addresses:

United Kingdom Register of Organic Food Standards (UKROFS), c/o MAFF, Room 320C, Nobel House, 17 Smith Square, London SW1P 3JR; (Tel. 0171-238 5915).

Organic Farmers and Growers Limited, 50 High Street, Soham, Cambs. CB7 5HU (Tel. 01353 720250).

The Soil Association Organic Marketing Company, 86 Colston Street, Bristol BS1 5BB; (Tel. 01179 290661).

Elm Farm Research Centre, Hamstead Marshall, nr. Newbury, Berks. RG15 0HR; (Tel. 01488 658298).

Bio-Dynamic Agricultural Association, Woodman Lane, Clent, Stourbridge, West Midlands DY9 9PX; (Tel. 01562 884933).

TURF

(Completely revised, 1997)

Currently turf producers report no rapid expansion of the market but feel that the outlook is good. The main movement within the turf sector is the continued growth in market share of "seed sown" turf or "turfgrass", produced by specialist companies, at the expense of traditional pasture turf. This is due both to the difficulty of finding good pasture to cut for turf and progress in turfgrass production. Special seed mixtures and cultivation techniques can now produce a range of types of turf which can be closely matched to particular sites or uses. It is estimated that there are 4,000-5,000 ha (10,000-12,000 acres) of turfgrass grown in the UK. The business is moving away from mainstream farming, although several turfgrass companies were set up by farmers.

Farms and farmers may be involved however in the following ways:

1. **Selling existing pasture turf to a turf company**

   This is the main, traditional option. The approach may be by the farmer to the company or vice-versa. Minimum 5-6 year ley/pasture generally needed for spring or autumn lifting, 8-10 year grass better for summer cutting.

   Important features: good root structure, number and type of weeds, level, well-drained, stone-free land; good access; timing (farmer wants lifting completed in time to drill next crop).

   Payment varies between £750-1500/hectare (£300-600/acre), but mainly £900-1200/ha (£360-480/acre). Usually initial payment plus further payments as turf is lifted. There may be a penalty clause if lifting delays prevent subsequent timely drilling. Lifting can take from two months to even a year. It can be done at any time of year except when there is snow on the ground. The turf company usually sprays against broadleaved weeds, fertilizes and mows before lifting; the farmer may do these tasks, for payment. He may graze the land, for a rent, if lifting is delayed.

   Apparently the effect on the land is not detrimental; some say there are benefits (removal of accumulated pests, etc. in the top inch of grass, roots and topsoil).

2. **Farmer cutting, lifting and selling pasture turf himself**

   Not usual. The turf must be treated, as in option 1. A small turf cutting machine can be hired for about £50 a day. This slices off the turf which must then be cut into lengths and picked up by hand. Two or three workers are required. It is slow going even in good conditions. The wastage figure is commonly 10 to 20% of the area, perhaps more.

   Turf has a short life once cut and stacked—3 days in summer, 7 days in winter, preferably less. Thus transport and outlets must be well organized: probably to a very local market; may soon be over-supplied.

3. **Renting land to a turf company for production of special turf**

   Turf companies rent land for turfgrass production in addition to using their own land. As before, well-drained, stone-free land with good access is required. Typically the land is rented on a per crop basis and one or two crops grown. A turf crop usually takes 15 to 18 months from preparation to harvest but autumn sown crops may be harvested within 9 months. Rent levels depend on the quality of the land and the profitability of competing agricultural enterprises. Currently rents are £850-1200/ha/crop (£350-500/acre) or approximately £550-800/ha/yr (£220-325/acre/yr).

4. **Specialist turf production**

   On their own land turf producers can grow turf continuously, taking a crop every 18 months to two years on average. On rented land (as in option 3), they take one or two crops and move on. Usually they produce a quick growing type of turf which sells quickly on rented land and cultivate more specialist and slower growing turf on their own land. A high level of agronomic expertise and considerable investment in machinery are needed and labour requirements are heavy. As the business is very competitive a high degree of marketing expertise is essential. While the bulk of the trade goes into general landscaping or garden centres there is an increase in the number of contracts where the quality and type of turf is specified. It is estimated that a turf farm would need to be 60 hectares (150 acres) or more in size to be viable – in order to justify the machinery necessary and to produce a succession of turf for the market. It is very unlikely that a farmer will grow turfgrass either for a company or "on spec".

Costs and Returns

Variable Costs plus Rent per crop

Domestic/general contract turfgrass

	£/ha (acre)
Seed	250-450 (100-180)
Fertilizer	125-250 (50-100)
Herbicide	25-100 (10-40)
Fungicide	0-100 (0-40)
Rent (for 18 months) ...	850-1,100 (350-450)
Total	1,250-2,000 (510-810)

It may be necessary to irrigate and on occasions use netting to grow the grass through for certain sites.

Labour

Special seed bed preparation (including subsoiling and stone burying), regular mowing (twice a week May/June), picking up clippings, harvesting (2 men on harvester plus one loading lorry) between 0·2-0·4 ha/day (0·5-1·0 acre).

Total costs of order of £4,000-6,000/ha (£1,500-2,400/acre), approx. 45-67p/sq.m. (35-55p/sq.yd.)

The cost of *specialist machinery* for turf production can be up to £150,000.

Value of Turf (on the field)

	per sq. metre	per sq. yd.	per ha*	per acre*
Pasture turf	45-50p	38-43p	£4,050-4,500	£1,650-1,875
Hardwearing, domestic general contract	80-90p	68-77p	£7,200-8,000	£3,000-3,300
Football, hockey, prestige landscape	100-110p	85-94p	£9,000-10,000	£3,700-4,100
High quality/specialist**	150-200p	125-170p	£13,500-18,000	£5,450-7,400

* assuming 90% recovery, but some producers work on 85%.

** for some contracts the price may be higher.

Delivery charges average 30p/sq.m. Delivered turf is subject to VAT.

N.B. On tenanted land landlord's permission is necessary to cut pasture turf.

Reference. Sports Turf Research Institute, Bingley, West Yorkshire, BD16 1AU. (Tel. 01274 565131).

Researcher: Angela Edwards.

GOLF

Golf is said to be the fastest growing sport in the world. In the five years 1989-93 388 golf courses were constructed in Britain, at a total cost of £1·5 billion. They covered an area the size of Greater Manchester. However, the bubble burst: in 1995, it was calculated that 88% of golf courses built since 1989 were "at financial risk"; 14 were in receivership, with many more predicted to be following. Large consortia were seeking to buy courses for as little as half the cost to the original developer. (Golf Research Group).

Between 40 and 60 ha (100 and 150 acres) are needed for an 18-hole course, which takes between 1 and 2 years to construct. A nine-hole par 3 course needs only 4 to 6 ha (10-15 acres), a driving range 4 ha (10 acres) and a pitch and putt course 1½ ha (4 acres).

Four important requirements are: location close to a centre of substantial population, a good distance from other similar courses, good road access, and an attractive, free-draining site. Obtaining planning permission can be difficult.

Development options; the farmer has five:

  (i)   To sell land with planning permission. Could have twice the agricultural value, possibly much more, if near London and with hotel consent.

 (ii)   To let land to a developer/operator. Assuming the latter pays for constructing the course, a long lease will be required. This can either be at a premium with a nominal rent or an annual rental, of two to five times the agricultural value, with reviews.

(iii)   To form a joint company with a developer/operator. This obviously means the farmer shares the success, or loss. The land would be all or part of the farmer's equity. A well constructed agreement is essential.

 (iv)   To develop the course and let the completed development to an operator. This is not recommended: too low a return on the land value and investment.

  (v)   To develop and operate the course himself. Also not recommended: the farmer needs good knowledge of golf and exceptional management ability.

Construction methods and costs; there are three alternatives:

  (i)   Contract. Expensive. Approximate costs (excl. the land):
        18-hole course (approx. 40 ha (100 acres)): £600,000-£900,000, according to drainage and earthmoving; includes greenkeeper's building and equipment.
        9-hole course (approx. 20 ha (50 acres)): £350,000-500,000.
        9-hole par 3 course (approx. 3·25 ha (8 acres)): £120,000.
        Driving range: £50,000.
        Covered driving range: £120,000.
        Clubhouse (approx. 600m²) and car parking: £600,000.
        The total cost for an 18-hole course could thus be £1¼–£1½ million, but anything between £2–£4 million can, and has, been spent.

 (ii)   Direct labour. A golf architect is required. Costs may be reduced by about a third.

(iii)   Own (farm) labour. Possible, but very risky, in terms of ultimate quality and cost.

Returns. A well-run 18-hole golf course may given an annual profit of £100,000 plus, but it is more typically £50,000-£75,000 and often less, giving a poor return on capital. It is, however, a long-term investment with capital growth potential. Houses close by, or a hotel, beneficial. A high risk element.

FORESTRY

(Estimated for 1998)

A. Establishment Costs (before grant)

1. Unit cost of operations

Year/s	Operation	Estimated Cost (£)	
1.	**Trees for planting**		
	(i) Bare rooted:		
	Conifers	80-150 per 1,000	
	Broadleaves	200-280 per 1,000	
	(ii) Rooted in small peat blocks:		
	Conifers	140-180 per 1,000	
	Broadleaves	240-280 per 1,000	
1.	**Tree Protection**		
	(i) Fencing (materials and erection)		
	Rabbit	1·50-2·50 per metre	
	Stock	2·00-2·75 per metre	
	Deer	3·50-6·00 per metre	
	Split post and rail	5·50-6·50 per metre	
	(ii) Tree guards/shelters		
	Plastic spiral (600-750 mm)	18-22 per 100	
	Plastic tubes (1200 mm) ...	70-80 per 100	
	Stakes	30 per 100	
1.	**Planting at approx. 2 m spacing**		
	Conifers	130-160 per ha	
	Broadleaves*	450-650 per ha	
2-3.	**Replacing dead trees****		
	Operation	30-40 per ha	
	Plant supply	35-45 per ha	

	Costs specific to location	*Upland*	*Lowland*
1.	Ground Preparation (ploughing) ...	90-110/ha	40-60/ha
1.	Drainage	40-60/ha	—
1.	Fertilizing	90-150/ha	—
1.4	Weeding per operation***		
	Hand weeding	—	180-200/ha weeded
	Herbicide	70-80/ha weeded	70-90/ha weeded

* Includes cost of erecting guards/shelters.
** Replacing dead trees (beating up) may be necessary, once in the second year and again in the third year. Costs depend on number of trees.
*** Up to 2 weeding operations may be necessary in each of the first 4 years in extreme situations. Costs are inclusive of materials.

Access roads may need to be constructed and can typically cost between £6,000 and £22,000 per kilometre (£9,600 to £35,000 per mile) depending on availability of roadstone and the number of culverts and bridges required.

2. Total Establishment Costs up to Year 3.

(i) *Conifer—Lowland Sites*

On a fairly typical lowland site, requiring little or no clearing or draining, the approximate cost before grant of establishing a conifer plantation would be in the range £1,200-£1,800 per hectare. Up to 8 separate weeding operations may be required.

(ii) *Conifer—Upland Sites*

Establishing a similar conifer plantation on an upland site could cost £1,100 to £1,500 per hectare. Normally some form of site preparation and drainage is required but only one weeding operation may be necessary. Overall costs tend to be £100-£200 per ha less than on lowland sites.

(iii) *Hardwoods*

Costs of establishing hardwood plantations could be in the range £1,600-£2,400 per ha. Site conditions normally mean that hardwoods being grown for timber production are restricted to lowland sites.

(iv) *Farm Woodlands*

Establishment costs for farm woodlands may be lower than those indicated for hardwoods in (iii) above if lower planting densities are used. Initial establishment costs in the first year of the order of £1,600 per ha for woods under 3 ha and £1,500 per ha for woods of 3 to 10 ha would be typical.

(v) *Size Factor*

Savings in fencing and other economies of scale may reduce average costs per ha by 10 to 20% where large plantations are being established; conversely costs for small woods may easily be 25% higher per ha established.

(vi) *Method of Establishment*

A range of organisations and individuals undertake forestry contracting work and competitive tendering can help to control costs.

B. *Maintenance Costs*

Once trees have been established they will normally require some maintenance and management work each year. For trees being grown primarily for timber production on a large scale, operations required may include ride maintenance, fence maintenance, pest control, fire protection, management fee and insurance charges. Costs will normally fall within the range £15-£50 per ha per annum depending upon the size of the plantation and the complexity of management. One or more fertilizing operations may be needed in the first 20 years in the life of a tree depending on the quality of the site. Estimated cost £90-£150 per ha, depending on elements applied. For trees being grown for sporting and amenity purposes, annual maintenance costs are likely to be less and may range up to about £10 per ha.

A brashing operation which involves removing branches up to two metres may be required for access reasons as the crop matures. Opening up inspection racks over 5-10% of the crop may cost £30-£50 per ha. Brashing 40-50% of the crop could cost £150-£300 per ha.

C. *Production*

Production is usually measured in terms of cubic metres (m^3) of marketable timber per hectare and will vary according to the quality of the site, species planted and thinning policy. Sites in lowland Britain planted to conifers typically produce an average of 12 to 18 m^3 of timber per ha per year over the rotation as a whole and would accordingly be assessed as falling in yield classes 12 to 18. Under traditional management systems thinning begins 18 to 25 years after planting and is repeated at intervals of approximately 3 to 5 years until the wood is clearfelled at between 40 and 60 years. Approximately 40-45% of total production will be from thinnings. Broadleaves typically produce an average of between 4 and 8 m^3 of timber per hectare per year and fall in yield classes 4 to 8.

Prior to a thinning sale the trees normally have to be marked and measured at an estimated cost of £30-£50 per ha depending on species, crop density and age. The cost can range from £200-£400 per ha, or about £1 per m^3, for a clearfelling sale.

D. Prices

Prices for standing timber are extremely variable, depending on tree size and quality, ease of extraction from site, geographical location (nearness to end user), quantity being sold, world market prices and effectiveness of marketing method used.

Conifers

Average prices paid for standing coniferous timber sold from Forest Enterprise areas in the year to 31st March, 1997, were:

Harvesting stage	Average tree size (m³)		England	Price (£ per m³) Wales	Scotland
1st Thinning	Up to 0·074	...	8·98	7·85	3·59
	0·075-0·124	...	11·98	7·09	4·96
Subsequent	0·125-0·174	...	14·74	9·79	10·49
Thinnings	0·175-0·224	...	17·16	15·79	13·72
	0·225-0·274	...	16·18	11·70	13·52
	0·275-0·424	...	20·92	15·32	15·24
	0·425-0·499	...	20·98	20·25	16·60
Clearfellings	0·500-0·599	...	24·62	19·90	17·42
	0·600-0·699	...	26·22	18·45	20·19
	0·700-0·799	...	28·12	18·26	19·87
	0·800-0·899	...	25·50	24·45	19·84
	0·900-0·999	...	27·43	26·33	28·02
	1·000 and over	...	34·10	26·08	19·93

Hardwoods

The hardwood trade is very complex. Merchants normally assess and value all but the smaller trees on a stem by stem basis. Actual prices fetched can show considerable variation depending on species, size, form, quality and marketing expertise of the seller. Felling usually takes place in the winter months.

Some indicative prices for hardwoods are given below, but it is important to note that actual prices fetched can vary quite widely. Wood quality is particularly important in determining prices.

Harvesting stage	Tree size Range (m³)	Price range £ per m³	Possible use
First thinnings	<0·13	1-12	Firewood, board products and pulp wood. Poles for refineries and turnery.
Subsequent thinnings...	0·13-0·3	5- 20	Smaller sizes and lower
	0·3 -0·6	8- 22	quality material may go
	0·6 -1·0	10- 40	for fencing or for use in the mining industry. Trees
Clearfellings	1·0 -2·0	15- 80	over 30 cm in diameter and of better quality may
	2+	25-150	go for planking, furniture or joinery. High quality material may go for veneers and can fetch between £150 and £300/m³ depending on species and specifications.

Prices for Oak, Ash, Sycamore, Cherry and Elm tend to be significantly higher than for Beech, which seldom exceeds about £45/m³ standing even for stands containing significant volumes of first quality planking.

E. Timber Marketing

Nationwide electronic sales of timber by auction and tender are now available for all types and quantities of timber. This method offers full exposure to the trade and should realise the correct market value. (Beacon Forestry, Edinburgh).

F. Market Value of Established Plantations and Woods

The value of woods depends on many factors, such as location, access, species, age and soil type. The following table gives an indication of the range of current (1997) market values of commercial woodlands of different ages, based on recent market sales.

Market Value of Commercial Sitka spruce Woodlands

Age of Commercial Woods and Plantations					Price Range for crop and land £/ha	£/acre
0-5 years	...	...	...	...	250-1000	(100- 400)
6-10 years	...	...	...	...	750-1375	(300- 550)
11-15 years	...	...	...	...	1000-1875	(400- 750)
16-20 years	...	...	...	...	1500-2750	(600-1100)
21-25 years	...	...	...	...	1500-3500	(600-1400)

From years 20 to 25 onwards prices of commercial woods will also be increasingly influenced by the quantity of merchantable timber they contain. Depending on the time of clearfelling, the timber may be worth between £3,750 to £10,000 per hectare (£1,500 to £4,000 per acre).

Woods with high amenity can often command a premium over prices fetched for commercial woodlands.

The value of woods containing mature hardwoods will depend on the quality and value of the timber they contain.

G. Grants

(a) Woodland Grant Scheme (WGS)

The WGS is administered by the Forestry Authority (part of the Forestry Commission). Revised terms were announced in July 1994, as follows:

Establishment grants are determined by the type of wood (conifer or broadleaved) and whether new planting or restocking is being undertaken. Levels of payment in £ per hectare are as follows:

New planting: conifers   £700 (for any size of wood)
         broadleaves   £1350 for woods less than 10 hectares
              £1050 for woods 10 hectares or more

Payment is 70% after planting and 30% in year 5, but the plantation must be maintained to a standard acceptable to the Forestry Authority for 10 years after planting. A stocking density of 2250 trees per hectare is required unless the woods are native woodlands or small (3 ha or less) amenity woodlands.

Restocking (including natural regeneration):
         conifers   £325
         broadleaves   £525
         Payment is 100% after planting (or once establishment has been achieved through natural regeneration). A stocking density of 2250 trees per hectare is required for conifers and 1100 for broadleaves. In certain woodlands a discretionary payment of up to 50% of the agreed costs of work to encourage natural regeneration may also be made.

New planting of short rotation coppice:

               Set-aside land   £400

               Non set-aside land £600

A *'better land supplement'* of £600 per hectare for new woodland (excluding short rotation coppice) plantings on arable or improved grassland. A *community woodland supplement'* of £950 per hectare is available to encourage the creation of new woodlands close to towns and cities which will be of value for informal public recreation. The new woodlands must be within 5 miles of the edge of a town or city and be where there are few other woodlands that can be used by the local community for recreation. To be eligible for this supplement there must be free access to the woods for the public and appropriate car parking facilities must be close at hand.

Management grants, of £35 per hectare per year, are available for any age of woodland which has special environmental potential requiring additional management input and/or where public access to woodlands will be created, enhanced or maintained.

Woodland Improvement Grants are available on a discretionary basis , based on 50% of the agreed costs of capital payments for work in existing woodlands which will enhance their value for conservation, landscape or recreation.

Livestock Exclusion Annual Premia of £80 per hectare per year for up to 10 years are available for certain types of woodland in Less Favoured Areas where protection or regeneration is a high priority.

Under a three-year pilot scheme a *"location supplement"* of £600 per hectare is available if planting either conifers or broadleaves in one of the 13 Community Forests in Britain. No more than 10 hectares per landholding will qualify for the supplement.

(b) *Farm Woodland Premium Scheme (FWPS)*

This scheme was introduced in April 1992 as a successor to the Farm Woodland Scheme. It is administered by The Forestry Authority and offers annual payments to compensate farmers for loss of income from farming where woodlands are established on agricultural land. To qualify for entry to the FWPS the proposed woods must attract establishment grants under the Woodland Grant Scheme (WGS).

The magnitude of annual payments depends on the type of land and its location:

	Annual Payment (£ per ha)		
	Arable Land	Other Improved Land	Unimproved Land
Outside Less Favoured Areas (LFAs)	300	260	Ineligible
Disadvantaged Areas of LFAs	230	200	60
Severely Disadvantaged Areas of LFAs	160	140	60

For the above purposes arable land is land eligible for Arable Area Payments. To qualify as improved grassland outside the LFAs (Less Favoured Areas) over half the sward must comprise, either singly or in mixture, ryegrass, cocksfoot, timothy or white clover. Within the LFAs, to qualify as improved grassland, over one third must comprise the above species *or* alternatively the land must have been"improved" by management practices such as liming and top-dressing provided there is no significant presence of sensitive plants indicative of native unimproved grassland.

Arable land and improved grassland will be eligible for the better land supplement under the WGS.

Unimproved land is land other than arable or improved grassland which has been in agricultural use for at least three years prior to the date of the application for the FWPS. Only unimproved land which is in LFAs can be entered in the FWPS.

Annual payments continue for 15 years for woodland containing more than 50 per cent by area of broadleaved trees and 10 years for woodland containing less than 50 per cent broadleaved trees or fast growing broadleaves that will be felled in less than 30 years (e.g. poplars). Woodlands planted for the purpose of agroforestry, Christmas trees or coppicing are not eligible for annual payments under the FWPS (unless coppicing is for conservation purposes, in which case prior approval will be required).

There is a minimum area requirement of 1 hectare to enter the FWPS but no restriction on the minimum size of individual woods created, providing WGS criteria are met. Not more than 200 hectares of an agricultural business can be entered into the FWPS (and not more than 40 hectares of unimproved land in the LFAs).

H. Woodland and Set-aside

Farm woodland planted under the Woodland Grant Scheme and the Farm Woodland Premium Scheme on arable land meeting the eligibility requirements for arable area payments will count towards a farmer's set-aside obligations. Farmers will receive the Woodland Grant and Farm Woodland Premium Scheme payments, not set-aside payments. The exception is short-rotation coppice planted on set-aside land, which is not eligible for entry into the Farm Woodland Premium Scheme and will receive set-aside payments.

I. Taxation

Income from commercial woodlands is no longer subject to tax, and tax relief cannot be claimed for the cost of establishing new woodlands.

In general Woodland Grant Scheme grants are tax free but annual payments under the Farm Woodland Premium Scheme and Livestock Exclusion Annual Premia are regarded as compensation for agricultural income forgone and are liable to income tax.

The sale of timber does not attract Capital Gains Tax, although the disposal of the underlying land may give rise to an assessment.

Woodlands which are managed commercially or which are ancillary to a farming business may be eligible for either Business Property Relief or Agricultural Relief for Inheritance Tax purposes.

Acknowledgement. The above estimates are based in part on information supplied by John Clegg & Co.

A Note on Short-Rotation Coppicing

The area of short-rotation coppicing for bio-fuels in Britain rose from 90 ha in 1993 to 230 ha in 1994, but could increase to over 5,000 ha in the next few years, particularly concerning a recent decision to allow the crop to be grown on set-aside land.

There is, inevitably, little or no hard evidence as yet on the costs and returns involved. Most estimates of establishment costs range from £1,200 to £1,800/ ha, with cuttings the major cost (10,000/ha at 8p to 10p); rabbit fencing and contract planting are other large items. Variable costs per annum could be £100/ ha for weeding and fertilizer.

On returns and harvesting costs, one estimate is for 42 dry tonnes/ha every three years, giving a return of £560/ha/year; costs of harvesting, chipping, transport etc., are put at £20/tonne, or £280/ha/year; (John Seed, Border Biofuels). Contracts were offered in 1996 with index-linked payments of £20 per dry tonne, free of costs, with harvests predicted at 12 dry tonnes a year.

SET-ASIDE

A. THE "CAP REFORM SCHEME"

(i) *The Provisions*

The set-aside scheme must be complied with in order to obtain the area payments introduced under the 1992 CAP Reform programme to compensate for reduced market price support.

Payments to the nearest £0·5/ha (£0·5/acre in brackets)for 1997 were as follows, based on a frozen ecu value of £0·803724 (and excluding any penalties for overshooting area limits):

England	Scotland non LFA	Scotland LFA	Wales non LFA	Wales LFA	N. Ireland non LFA	N. Ireland LFA
326 (132)	313·5 (127)	288 (116·5)	286 (115·5)	279·5 (113)	289 (117)	278·5 (112·5)

A simplified scheme with no set-aside commitment is available for those claiming payments on a standardised area that would produce 92 tonnes of grain at average grain yields for the area; this is approximately 15·5 ha (38·3 acres) in England. However, only the cereals aid rate per ha is then paid, even on land used to grow oilseeds or protein crops. To claim the higher aid rates for these crops it is necessary to join the general scheme and set aside land. Those growing more than the (approx.) 15·5 ha may opt out of set-aside and claim the cereal aid rate on just the 15·5 ha, but over 20 ha (50 acres) or so the penalty of doing so in terms of the area payments forgone is prohibitive, particularly since the set-aside percentage requirements have been reduced.

To be eligible for set-aside the land must meet certain eligibility requirements: it must have been cultivated with a view to harvest or have been in a set-aside scheme the previous year, and it must have been farmed by the claimant for at least two years (with certain exemptions).

A number of different set-aside options are available:

1. *Obligatory set-aside*

    Prior to 1996 there was a choice between the following:

    (i)   Rotational set-aside: different land must be set aside each year over a six-year rotation.

          A shorter interval than six years is possible if no other land is eligible, e.g. if the size of holding is altered.

    (ii)   Flexible set-aside, with three different options:

          (a) non-rotational set-aside,

          (b) some rotational, some non-rotational,

          (c) rotational, in any way the farmer chooses.

    The required set-aside percentages were higher for flexible than for rotational set-aside. However in 1996 the distinction between the two was abolished and there is now complete flexibility of choice. The percentage was set at 10% in 1996 and 5% in 1997 and 1998. These percentages are percentages of the total area of claimed land plus the set-aside area. The eligible crops consist primarily of cereals, oilseed rape (with specified requirements), linseed, field beans, dried peas and maize. These crops are eligible for aid whether grown for grain, seed or fodder—except in the latter case for any crop(s) grown on land counting towards the forage area under the beef regime (stocking rate restriction).

2. *Voluntary set-aside*

    This is open to all those receiving area aid under the main scheme. However, there is a limit: the extra set-aside area, together with the obligatory set-aside area, must not exceed the total cropped area on which area aid is claimed, plus any penalty set-aside (see 5 below).

3. *Additional Voluntary set-aside*
Where land was set-aside under the *old 5-year scheme,* the limit described above for voluntary set-aside may be exceeded right up to 100%, but it has to remain in set-aside for a further five years. However, the set-aside payment is reduced on that area which exceeds the cropped area: this is at 70% of the full rate, i.e. approx. in England (in 1997).

4. *Guaranteed set-aside*
Where the farmer undertakes that the same plots will be set aside for five years the prevailing set-aside payment (in ECUs/hectare) will not be reduced for five years, though it may be increased. This only applies up to the percentage limit for non-rotational set-aside or on any ex-5 year scheme set-aside land. If any of the latter exceeds the cropped area on which arable area payments are claimed the lower additional voluntary set-aside rate is paid. One may opt out of the agreement to enter a scheme under a forestry or agri-environment action programme, or if compulsorily purchased; a penalty is imposed if withdrawn for other reasons. Only land down to short rotation coppice or entered into the Countryside Access Scheme (see page 45) is now eligible for new guaranteed set-aside agreements.

5. *Penalty set-aside*
This is imposed if a regional base area for eligible crops is exceeded; it receives no set-aside payment. Maize and oilseeds each have separate base areas.

Transfers of part or all of ones set-aside obligation are allowed, either to another farm within 20km (12 miles) or to a farmer with eligible land in a category designated for transfers on environmental grounds. The basic set-aside obligation was increased by 3% but this was reduced to a 1% increase in 1996/7, with no increases for transfers on environmental grounds.

Land normally ineligible for area payments or set-aside are permanent grass, permanent crops (e.g. top fruit), woodland or a non-agricultural use. However, for woodland planted under grant schemes (including short-rotation coppice) see page 42 (G).

Whether it is better to choose rotational or non-rotational set-aside depends on how variable in quality the land is (the more it varies the more this is likely to favour non-rotational) and how much the rotational benefits are valued (possible increases in yield, opportunities for grass weed control, good entry for oilseed rape). Non-rotational entails easier management and probably lower costs and provides greater scope for environmental benefits.

A range of non-food crops may be grown on set-aside land (e.g. industrial rape and linseed (see page 10)), under contract, including a few perennial crops such as short rotation coppice. Otherwise no cash crop must be planted, nor must any livestock or non-agricultural animals be grazed upon it. Indeed no lucrative non-agricultural activity is allowed, unless it could equally well be carried out if there were a standing crop; certain small-scale local and/or charitable events may be given permission.

The minimum size of each set-aside block must be 0·3 ha, with a minimum width of 20 metres; given these requirements, field margins may be set aside. The land must be kept in good agricultural condition.

The rotational set-aside period is from 15th January to 31st August, but from 15th July producers may sow crops for harvest the next year. From 1st September to 14th January producers may not sell any green cover remaining on the land, whether for grazing, hay or silage, but they may harvest these crops for their own use or graze their own animals on it during this period. No crop may be sown to harvest or graze before 15th January, e.g. stubble turnips.

Rules (1997). A *cover crop* must be established on set-aside land by 15th December, unless a harvest crop is still in the ground after 1st October; natural regeneration is permitted, legumes are not; cover crops must not contain more than 5% clover. *Cutting is* allowed at any time but it is not advised between April and mid-July; if a non-selective herbicide is used cutting is banned between 15th April and 30th June and cultivation banned before 1st July (except for registered organic farmers (1st May)).

45

Cover remaining on 15th July had to be cut short by 15th August (exemptions granted if birds are still nesting), or destroyed with herbicide by 31st August; however, the latter rule was relaxed in 1996: 25% of each set-aside field may now be left uncut, for up to three years, to provide a more varied habitat for wildlife. Non-residual *herbicides* are allowed to be used in England and Wales (but not Scotland, in 1997, between 15th April and 1st July) provided that green cover is not destroyed before 15th April (unless it is to be replaced); spot applications or selective (but not non-selective) herbicides are allowed before that date as long as most cover is left intact; there are no restrictions on herbicide use after 15th April. *Cultivations* (including ploughing) are allowed after 1st May only to control weeds, although these are not advised before the end of June (all operations are discouraged during the April and May nesting season); cultivations are allowed from 15th July for crops to follow set-aside for harvesting the following year (after 15th January). *Fertilizer and manure* applications are not allowed unless the manure or slurry is generated on the same farm and applied to establish cover; liming is allowed.

(ii) *Gains and Losses*

On the land that has to be set aside the farmer will lose the crop gross margins forgone less the set-aside payment and fuel and repair costs saved (approx. £85/ha, £35/acre); contractors' charges, where used e.g. for harvesting, will also be saved. There will also be some saving in interest on working capital. Adding to the (likely) net loss will be the cost of cover crops, if sown, cutting, etc.

With rotational set-aside there should be some yield benefit. There should also be some timeliness benefit if the same labour and machinery is available as before. Both are difficult to estimate financially.

On some larger farms at least it has been possible to cut fixed costs, primarily regular labour and machinery depreciation/leasing—possibly by enough to compensate. But for many smaller and medium-sized farms this is impossible. However, some savings in casual labour and overtime, and, given time, machinery depreciation, should be possible on many farms.

Any net loss may also have been reduced by crop substitutions: primarily higher for lower gross margin crops. However, unless the farmer had been slack in his choice of crops in the past this possibility was limited and could have led to rotational losses, e.g. if more second and third wheats were grown, but it should at least have been possible to put a higher percentage of the land into first wheats.

Inevitably the possibilities and balance of gains and losses are different on every farm.

(iii) *The Countryside Access Scheme*

This voluntary scheme, launched in autumn 1994, offers farmers additional payments on top of the set-aside payments for providing new opportunities for public access to suitable farmland for walking and other forms of quiet recreation. The scheme is intended to provide for permissive access and does not aim to create new permanent rights of way. Only particularly suited land is targeted, e.g. if it provides access to vantage points, attractive landscape or links existing access ways. Any land entered into this scheme has to be entered into guaranteed set-aside. Farmers entering land into the scheme must continue to manage the land in accordance with set-aside rules and, in addition, observe a range of other conditions regarding maintenance of easy access, etc.

The annual supplementary payments are based on 10m wide access strips along field margins and/or on whole or part fields. Payments are £90/ha (i.e. £90/km) for access strips and £45/ha for whole or part fields.

A NOTE ON DIVERSIFICATION

In recent years a whole host of "new" enterprises have attracted farmers' attention, largely in attempts to maintain their total incomes, when those from farming, especially in real terms, were falling substantially. This development has been strongly encouraged by the government.

New enterprises must not be undertaken lightly: most require a substantial amount of capital; many need skills (both in production and marketing) which take time, or a particular type of personality, to acquire; the market may be limited; hence there is often a considerable level of risk attached. Nevertheless, there are many ventures to be seen where entrepreneurial skills have achieved notable success.

Some of these "diversification enterprises" have been included above and there are more in the next section. There are many others. Some are as follows:

Christmas Trees	Barn Conversions
Herbs	Horses*:
Crayfish	Livery
Llamas	Riding School
Ostriches	Trekking
Quails	Tourism:
Rabbits	Bed and Breakfast
Snails	Caravans
Wild Boar	Holiday Cottages
Adventure Games	"Added Value" enterprises.
Clay Pigeon Shooting	Yoghurt, ice cream, etc.

Update on these, and other, enterprises are published periodically in the monthly "Farm Development Review" (MCB University Press Limited, Bradford).

* Horses. See the Equine Business Guide, Warwickshire College.

A 1994 series of "Success Within" guides are available free from MAFF Publications (tel. 01645 556000) on: Farm Diversification, Farm-based Tourist Accommodation, Sporting Enterprises on Farms, Marketing Diversified Enterprises.

Area Payments for 1997/98 in ECU/ha

	England	Scotland (non LFA)	Scotland (LFA)	Wales (non LFA)	Wales (LFA)	Northern Ireland (non LFA)	Northern Ireland (LFA)
Cereals	320·06	308·11	283·11	280·94	274·42	283·65	273·33
Oilseeds	565·75	633·72	521·67	576·78	576·78	536·36	536·36
Linseed	619·04	595·92	547·57	543·37	530·76	548·62	528·65
Proteins	462·31	445·04	408·93	405·79	396·37	409·72	394·80
Set-aside*	405·41	390·27	358·60	355·85	347·59	359·29	346·21

*Voluntary set-aside over 50% is 70·175% of the above set-aside figures.

Note. The above figures are subject to cuts if regional base areas are exceeded. The oilseeds payments are also subject to cuts if the total EU base area is exceeded and if world prices are above a prescribed level.

Cereal Intervention levels in ECUs/tonne, 1997/98

Basic July	119·19	January	122·19	April	125·19
November	120·19	February	123·19	May	126·19
December	121·19	March	124·19		

3. GRAZING LIVESTOCK
DAIRY COWS

Holstein Friesians (per Cow)

Performance level (yield (1))	Low	Average	High	Very High
Milk Yield per Cow (litres) (2)	5000	5600	6300	7000
	£	£	£	£
Milk Value per Cow (3)	1100	1232	1386	1540
Plus Value of Calves (4)	90	90	90	90
Plus Value of Cull Cows (5)	95	95	95	95
Less Cost or Market Value of Replacements (6, 7)	180	180	180	180
Output	1105	1237	1391	1545
Concentrate Costs (8)	178	215	261	309
Miscellaneous Variable Costs (10)	115	120	125	130

Gross Margin before deducting Forage
Variable Costs (inc. Bought Fodder)* ... 812 902 1005 1106
(Margin of Milk Value over Concentrates (9) ... 922 1017 1125 1231)

*No deduction has been made for annual value of leased or purchased milk quota, which will vary considerably between farms.

Gross Margins per Cow and per Hectare (Acre) at 4 different stocking rates (11) are:

Performance level	Low	Average	High	Very High
1. At 1·75 cows per forage hectare (low):				
(0·57 forage hectares (1·4 acres) per cow)				
Forage Variable Costs per Cow (11)	65	65	65	65
Gross Margin per Cow	747	837	940	1041
Gross Margin per Forage Hectare	1305	1465	1645	1820
Gross Margin per Forage Acre	528	593	666	737
2. At 2 cows per forage hectare (average):				
(0·5 forage hectares (1·25 acres) per cow)				
Forage Variable Costs per Cow (11)	**80**	**80**	**80**	**80**
Gross Margin per Cow	**732**	**822**	**925**	**1026**
Gross Margin per Forage Hectare	**1465**	**1645**	**1850**	**2050**
Gross Margin per Forage Acre	**593**	**666**	**749**	**830**
3. At 2·25 cows per forage hectare (high):				
(0·45 forage hectares (1·1 acres) per cow)				
Forage Variable Costs per Cow (11)	95	95	95	95
Gross Margin per Cow	717	807	910	1011
Gross Margin per Forage Hectare	1615	1815	2045	2275
Gross Margin per Forage Acre	654	735	828	921
4. At 2·5 cows per forage hectare (very high):				
(0·4 forage hectares (1 acre) per cow)				
Forage Variable Costs per Cow (11)	110	110	110	110
Gross Margin per Cow	702	792	895	996
Gross Margin per Forage Hectare	1755	1980	2235	2490
Gross Margin per Forage Acre	710	801	904	1008

1. Performance level refers primarily to milk yield, although increases in this are usually (though not *necessarily*) associated with higher gross margins. Some increase in concentrate feeding (kg/litre) has been assumed as yield rises: see further note 8, page 50.

2. *Yield* The yield referred to is litres produced during a year divided by the average number of cows and calved heifers in the herd. The average given (5,600 litres) is an estimated national figure for sizeable commercial herds of black and white cows. Note the average yield for *costed herds* (e.g. Genus Milkminder, Dalgety) is likely to be close to 6,500 litres in 1998, i.e. even higher than the Pocketbook "high" level.

3. *Milk Price.* This is assumed (as an average for the 1998 calendar year) to be 22p per litre, after deducting transport costs. It incorporates all adjustments: for milk composition, hygiene and seasonality. Prices have fallen markedly since mid-1996; some are predicting a fall greater than the 3p assumed (compared with the 1995/6 peak year) by 1998. Variable transport charges according to amount collected have cut prices for many smaller producers further.

The average price received by individual producers depends on seasonality of production and compositional quality. Receipts (£) per cow are changed as follows by each 0·25p per litre difference in price at each performance level:

Low	Average	High	Very High
±12·5	±14	±15·75	±17·5

Seasonality Price Adjustments (Milk Marque and most of the major dairy companies, p per litre):

	April	May	June	July	Aug.	Sept.	Oct.	Nov.-Mar.
1997/8	−2·0	−3·0	−1·5	+3·5	+3·0	+0·5	0	0

There is a level delivery option: no seasonal adjustments if supplies in a calendar month are within 10% of an agreed daily volume.

Compositional Quality Payments
Constituent values vary widely between buyers. Milk Marque's were, in July 1997:
Butterfat: 2·28p per litre per 1 per cent.
Protein: 3·84p per litre per 1 per cent.

Breeds and average milk composition by breed are as follows (England and Wales, MMB recorded herds, 2-year averages, 1993/4 and 1994/5):

	% Cows 1988/9	Butterfat %	Protein %
Holstein Friesians ...	94·1	4·03	3·21
Ayrshire	1·9	4·04	3·27
Jersey	1·7	5·57	3·81
Guernsey	1·4	4·81	3·50
All Breeds		4·06	3·22

Within Breed Quality Variation. For Friesians only, the upper and lower deciles in the 1986/87 Milkminder (MMB) sample were as follows:

Upper: Butterfat 4·11%; Protein 3·32%.
Lower: Butterfat 3·75%; Protein 3·17%.

The difference in milk value between these two levels is approx. 1·4p per litre (6·5% of the average price).

Hygiene Price Adjustments (Milk Marque, from 1st April 1997, p per litre):
Note: these adjustments vary widely between the different dairy companies.

A. *Bactoscan (bacteria measure)*

Band	Bactoscan Reading	Price Adjustment
A+	0- 50,000	+0·2
A	51-100,000	nil
B	101-500,000	−0·5
C	Over 500,000	−6 or −10

B. Somatic Cell Count (Mastitis)

Band	Count	Price Adjustment
1+	0-150,000	+2
1	151-250,000	nil
2	251-400,000	−0·5
3	401-500,000	−6 or −10

C. *Antibiotics.* The price of all milk in a consignment that fails an antibiotics test is lp/litre. A bonus of 0·2p pl is awarded for consistent top quality.

Organic milk: 29p-30p litre in mid-1997.

4. *Value of Calves.* Average annual value per cow of purebred (mainly) and beef cross heifer and bull calves of all qualities, at 10-20 days old, allowing for mortality and average calving index of 385 days.

5. *Value of Cull Cows.* £420, allowing for casualties; 22·5% per annum replacement rate.

6. *Cost of Replacements.* £800 per down-calving heifer (purchase price or market value (mainly home-reared)); 22·5% per annum replacement rate.

7. *Herd Depreciation:* thus averages (approx.) £85 per cow per year, *i.e.,* 22·5 per cent of £380 *(i.e., £800-£420).*

   Net Replacement Value = £5 per cow per year, *i.e.,* value of calves (£90) less herd depreciation (£85).

   Bull. AI is assumed in the tables; bull depreciation would be approx. £325 a year (£2,500 purchase price less £875 cull value, 5-year herd life); tight calving pattern: 60 cows per bull, well spread calving pattern: 100; 10 to 20 tonnes silage, 0·75 tonnes concentrates a year.

8. *Concentrate Costs.*

Amounts: Performance level :	Low	Average	High	Very High
kg/litre :	·25	·27	·29	·31
tonnes/cow :	1·25	1·51	1·83	2·17

Price: taken (for 1998) as £142·50 per tonne, which is an average of home-mixed rations at £132·50 and purchased compounds at £152·50 (delivered) of varying nutritive value, averaged throughout the year.

A difference of £10 per tonne has the following approximate effect on margin over concentrates and gross margin per cow (£), on the assumptions made regarding the quantity fed at each performance level:

Low	Average	High	Very High
±£13	±£16	±£19	±£22

Seasonality. Typically, specialist spring calving herds (60% or more calvings between January and May), compared with autumn calving herds (60% or more calvings between August and December), use 0·9 kg per litre/0·6 tonnes (£96) per cow per year less concentrates. See further note 12 below.

Typical Monthly Variation in Concentrate Feeding (kg per litre)

		Winter					Summer	
		Average	Premium				Average	Premium
October	...	0·32	0·24	April ...	...		0·25	0·16
November	...	0·34	0·25	May ...	...		0·15	0·08
December	...	0·34	0·25	June ...	...		0·15	0·09
January	...	0·34	0·25	July ...	...		0·19	0·12
February	...	0·33	0·25	August	...		0·24	0·16
March	...	0·31	0·24	September	...		0·28	0·19

Average winter: 0·33   Average summer: 0·21
Premium winter: 0·25   Premium summer: 0·13

Average whole year: 0·27
Premium whole year: 0·19

The actual distribution on any individual farm will obviously vary according to such factors as seasonality of calving, level of milk yield, grazing productivity during the summer, and the quantity and quality of bulk feeds in the winter. The March figure in particular will be affected by type of soil and seasonal rainfall.

Yield with no concentrates and good quality silage: approx. 4000 litres (autumn calvers; 4,500 claimed in New Zealand).

9. *Margin over Concentrates and Concentrates per litre*

   The emphasis in the initial tables should be laid on the differences between the margin of milk value over concentrates per cow; the same large variation can occur with widely differing combinations of milk yield and quantity of concentrates fed.

   In the following table, at each yield level figures are given for (a) *margin of milk value over concentrates* per cow (£) and (b) *concentrates per litre* (kg) at five levels of concentrate feeding.

Yield level Milk Yield per cow (litres)	Low 5,000		Average 5,600		High 6,300		Very High 7,000	
	(a)	(b)	(a)	(b)	(a)	(b)	(a)	(b)
	£	kg	£	kg	£	kg	£	kg
0·75 tonne (£107) concs. per cow	993	·15	1125	·13	—	—	—	—
1·00 tonne (£142) concs. per cow	958	·20	1090	·18	1244	·16	—	—
1·50 tonne (£214) concs. per cow	886	·30	1018	·27	1172	·24	1326	·21
2·00 tonne (£285) concs. per cow	815	·40	947	·36	1101	·32	1255	·29
2·50 tonne (£356) concs. per cow	—	—	—	—	1030	·40	1184	·36

On the same assumptions re the other items of output and variable costs as in the tables on page 48 a very high *margin over concentrates of £1,300 per cow* (in 1998) would give the following results (£):

Stocking rate	Average	High	Very High
Gross Margin per Cow	1095	1080	1065
Gross Margin per Forage Hectare	2190	2430	2665
Gross Margin per Forage Acre	885	985	1080

This level of margin over concentrates (£1,300) can be achieved by a range of combinations of yield and concentrate feeding. With the price of milk (22p/l) and concentrates (£142·50/ tonne) assumed the following are examples: 7,000 litres, 1·68 tonnes/cow, ·24 kg/l; 7,500, 2·46, ·33; 8,000, 3·23, ·40.

10. *Miscellaneous Variable Costs (average)*

	£
Bedding*	12
Vet. and Med.	42
A.I. and Recording Fees	29
Consumable dairy stores, etc. ...	37
Total	120

* *Straw* can vary from 0·4 to 1·5 tonne per cow and from £10 to £30 per tonne (or even more in some areas in exceptional years).

11. *Stocking Rate and Forage Costs.* **The stocking rates given assume that nearly all requirements of bulk foods—for both winter and summer—are obtained from the forage area**, i.e. little is bought in. On average about 55 per cent of the forage area (or production) is grazed and 45 per cent conserved. It will be observed that as the stocking density increases, gross margin *per cow* falls, but gross margin *per hectare* rises.

   The levels of nitrogen are assumed to be as follows: 1·75 cows per forage hectare, 160 kg (128 units/acre), 2·0, 220 (176); 2·25, 275 (220); 2·5, 360 (288). An increase in potash application is also assumed. Seed costs clearly depend on the percentage of permanent pasture, if any, the length of leys, etc. **The following forage costs per hectare (fertilizer, seed and sprays) have been assumed:** 1·75 cows per forage hectare, £95 (£38/acre); 2·0, £130 (53); 2·25, £170 (69); 2·5, £212·50 (86).

   A small amount of purchased bulk fodder is assumed, increasing with the stocking rate as follows (per cow): low £10, average £15, high £20, very high £25.

An increase in stocking density can be obtained not only by intensifying grassland production, as above, but also by buying in winter bulk fodder (assuming the same level of concentrate feeding in both cases). This will cause the gross margin *per cow* to fall still further, but will usually result in a higher gross margin *per hectare* than where all forage is conserved on the farm—at any given level of grassland management.

In the table below four examples are given: two policies at two different stocking rates. (A) and (B) assume the land is used for grazing only, i.e. all winter bulk fodder is purchased. (C) and (D) assume the land provides grazing and half the winter bulk fodder, the other half being bought in. (A) and (C) assume a stocking rate equivalent to 2 cows per hectare where the land provides both grazing and all the winter bulk fodder, which is an average level of stocking. (B) and (D) assume the equivalent of 2·5 cows per hectare where all bulk food is provided both summer and winter, which is a very high level of stocking. It is assumed that the full winter fodder requirement is 2 tonnes of hay (or other equivalent foods), costing £130 per cow if it is all purchased. (Prices vary widely according to the season and part of the country.) Forage variable costs per hectare (acre) are £130 (53) and £212·50 (86) at the average and high levels of stocking respectively.

| | | Margin of Milk Value over Concentrates | | | |
		Low	Average	High	Very High
		Gross Margin per Forage Hectare (Acre)			
		£	£	£	£
(A)	All winter fodder purchased; average stocking rate... ...	2350 (950)	2675 (1085)	3050 (1235)	3420 (1385)
(B)	All winter fodder purchased; very high stocking rate ...	2890 (1170)	3395 (1375)	3750 (1520)	4225 (1710)
(C)	½ winter fodder purchased; average stocking rate... ...	1800 (730)	2030 (820)	2295 (930)	2555 (1035)
(D)	½ winter fodder purchased; very high stocking rate ...	2200 (890)	2490 (1005)	2820 (1140)	3145 (1275)

It must obviously not be forgotten that "fixed" costs per hectare, e.g. labour and depreciation on buildings, can increase considerably if an increase in stocking density is achieved by keeping more cows, at least when cow numbers outstrip the capacity of existing buildings and labour. Furthermore, husbandry problems such as poaching will multiply, unless zero-grazing is practised—with its further additions to fixed costs and management difficulties.

12. *Seasonality.* Price and concentrate feeding differences according to the seasonality of production have already been outlined in notes 3 and 8.

Typically, autumn calving herds tend to average 6 or 7% (300-400 litres) above spring calving herds but feed 80% (0·6-0·7 tonnes) more concentrates cow/year; spring calving herds should normally only be feeding about 0·15 kg/litre (for the whole year). The average milk price would be expected to be higher for autumn calving herds, but the difference is less than might be supposed and has been reduced in recent years with better prices being paid for summer milk.

13. *Quota.* For many years the price of unused quota averaged around 35p/litre and leasing 5p to 5·5p, with levels in Scotland significantly higher. However, values have been much higher since late 1993; in mid 1994 they were mainly in the 40p-50p and 7p-8p ranges respectively for average butterfat levels. In late 1994/early 1995 they rose to a peak of 80p and 20p respectively, falling by mid 1995 to around 60p-65p and 12p; in mid-1996 they were around 65p-70p and 14p-16p and in mid-1997 45-50p and 9·5-11p.

14. *Labour:* see page 111.   15. *Building Costs:* see pages 148-9 and 151-2.

Channel Island Breeds

Performance level (yield)	Low	Average	High	Very High
Milk Yield per Cow (litres)	3625	4075	4575	5075
	£	£	£	
Milk Value per Cow	979	1100	1235	1370
Concentrate Costs per Cow	171	208	250	297
Margin of Milk Value over Concentrates per Cow	808	892	985	1073
Herd Depreciation less Value of Calves	20	20	20	20
Miscellaneous Variable Costs	115	120	125	130
GROSS MARGIN per Cow before deducting Forage Variable Costs	673	752	840	923
Forage Variable Costs/Bought Fodder	66	66	66	66
GROSS MARGIN per Cow	607	686	774	857
GROSS MARGIN per Forage Hectare (2·35 cows per hectare: 0·425 hectares/cow)	1425	1610	1820	2015
GROSS MARGIN per Forage Acre (1·05 acres/cow)	577	652	737	815

Notes

1. *Yield.* Average of Jerseys and Guernseys. See Note 2 for Holstein Friesians (page 49). Guernseys average some 250 litres more than Jerseys (i.e. approx. 3875 for Jerseys, 4125 for Guernseys) but the latter achieve a higher average price of around 3p per litre. Note that the average for Channel Island *costed herds* should not be compared with the average national (Pocketbook) figure for Holstein Friesians; costed herd yield averages are some 15% higher than national averages; (i.e. it is likely to be close to 4,700 litres for CI costed herds in 1998).

2. *Milk Price.* This has been assumed to be 27p per litre (average of Jerseys and Guernseys), i.e. 5p above Holstein Friesian milk; (28·5p Jersey milk, 25·5p Guernsey).

3. *Concentrate Costs.*

Amounts: Performance level:	Low	Average	High	Very High
kg/litre :	·315	·34	·365	·39
tonnes/cow :	1·14	1·39	1·67	1·98

Price: taken (for 1998) as £150 per tonne.

The following table shows for each production level (a) the margin of milk value over concentrates per cow (£) and (b) concentrates per litre (kg) at three levels of concentrate feeding.

Performance level	Low		Average		High		Very High	
Milk Yield per cow (litres)	3625		4075		4575		5075	
	(a)	(b)	(a)	(b)	(a)	(b)	(a)	(b)
	£	kg	£	kg	£	kg	£	kg
0·75 tonnes (£112) concs. per cow	867	·21	1088	·18	—	—	—	—
1·25 tonnes (£187) concs. per cow	792	·34	913	·31	1048	·27	1183	·25
1·75 tonnes (£262) concs. per cow	717	·48	838	·43	973	·38	1108	·34
2·25 tonnes (£337) concs. per cow	—	—	—	—	898	·49	1033	·44

4. *Net Annual Replacement Value.* (i.e. Value of Calves less Herd Depreciation) were calculated as follows:

	£ per cow in herd
Cost of replacements: 22·5 per cent of herd per year @ £450 ...	101
LESS Value of culls: 22·5 per cent of herd per year @ £235 (allowing for casualties)*	53
Herd Depreciation	48
Annual Value of Calves**	28
Net Annual Replacement Cost	20

* Cull cow prices for Guernseys are about £65 higher than for Jerseys.

** Allowing for calving index of 390 days and calf mortality; mixture of pure bred calves and beef crosses. Guernsey calves, especially crosses, fetch more than Jersey calves, averaging perhaps £10 more per head—but a lot more for some Guernsey beef crosses. (Calf Processing Scheme (in its mid-1997 form) is assumed to have finished by 1998; average value could be some £30 higher if it remains).

5. *Miscellaneous Variable Costs.* See Note 10 for Holstein Friesians (page 51).

6. *Stocking Rate.* See, in general, Note 11 for Holstein Friesians (page 51). The effect of varying the stocking rate on gross margin per forage hectare is as follows:

		GM/Cow before deducting Forage V.Cs.				
	Forage	Low	Average	High	Very High	Forage V.Cs.
Cows per	Hectares	£673	£752	£840	£923	per Cow
Forage	(Acres)					(inc. Bought
Hectare	per Cow	Gross Margin per Forage Ha (Acre) (£)				Fodder) £
2·1	0·48 (1·18)	1300 (526)	1470 (595)	1655 (670)	1825 (739)	53
2·4	**0·42 (1·03)**	**1455 (589)**	**1645 (666)**	**1860 (753)**	**2055 (832)**	**66**
2·7	0·37 (0·92)	1605 (650)	1815 (735)	2055 (832)	2280 (923)	79
3·0	0·33 (0·82)	1745 (706)	1985 (803)	2245 (909)	2495 (1010)	91

A small amount of purchased bulk fodder is assumed, increasing with the stocking rate as follows (per cow): low £8, average £12, high £16, very high £20.

At the average stocking rate given above for combined Channel Island breeds (2·4 cows per forage ha) the average figure for Jerseys would be approximately 2·55 and that for Guernseys 2·25.

Other Breeds (including Ayrshires)

Performance level (yield)	Low	Average	High	Very High
Milk Yield per Cow (litres)	4450	5000	5600	6250
	£	£	£	
Milk Value per Cow	1001	1125	1260	1406
Concentrate Costs per Cow	158	192	231	276
Margin of Milk Value over Concentrates				
per Cow	843	933	1029	1130
Herd Depreciation less Value of Calves ...	23	23	23	23
Miscellaneous Variable Costs	115	120	125	130
GROSS MARGIN per Cow before deducting				
Forage Variable Costs	705	790	881	977
Forage Variable Costs/Bought Fodder ...	76	76	76	76
GROSS MARGIN per Cow	629	714	805	901
GROSS MARGIN per Forage Hectare (2·1				
cows per hectare: 0·475 hectares/cow) ...	1320	1500	1690	1890
GROSS MARGIN per Forage Acre (1·175				
acres/cow)	535	607	684	765

Notes
1. *Yield.* See Note 2 for Holstein Friesians (page 49).
2. *Milk Price.* See in general, note 3 for Holstein Friesians (page 49). The price assumed in the above table is 22·5p per litre. The compositional quality of milk from Ayrshires is higher than for the black and white breeds.
3. *Concentrate Costs.* See notes 8 and 9 for Holstein Friesians (pages 50-51). In the above table, the levels of feeding per kg (and tonnes per cow) are as follows: low ·25 (1·11 tonne), average ·27 (1·35), high ·29 (1·62), very high ·31 (1·94); price £142·50 per tonne.

   The following table shows, for each production level, (a) the margin of milk value over concentrates (£) and (b) concentrates per litre (kg) at three levels of concentrate feeding.

Performance level	Low		Average		High		Very High	
Milk Yield per Cow (litres) ...	4450		5000		5600		6250	
	(a)	(b)	(a)	(b)	(a)	(b)	(a)	(b)
	£	kg	£	kg	£	kg	£	kg
0·75 tonnes (£107) concs. per cow	894	·17	1018	·15	—	—	—	—
1·00 tonnes (£142) concs. per cow	859	·22	983	·20	1118	·18	1264	·16
1·50 tonnes (£214) concs. per cow	787	·34	911	·30	1046	·27	1192	·24
2·00 tonnes (£285) concs. per cow	—	—	840	·40	975	·36	1121	·32
2·50 tonnes (£356) concs. per cow	—	—	—	—	—	—	1050	·40

4. *Net Annual Replacement Value.* (i.e. Value of Calves less Herd Depreciation) were calculated as follows (for Ayrshires):

	£ per cow in herd
Cost of replacements: 22·5 per cent of herd per year @ £625 ...	141
LESS Value of culls: 22·5 per cent of herd per year @ £325 (allowing for casualties)	73
Herd Depreciation	68
Annual Value of Calves*	45
Net Annual Replacement Cost**	23

* Allowing for calving index of 385 days and calf mortality; mixture of pure bred calves and beef crosses.
** Higher cull and calf prices should be obtained for Shorthorns.

5. *Miscellaneous Variable Costs.* See Note 10 for Holstein Friesians (page 51).
6. *Stocking Rate.* See, in general, Note 11 for Holstein Friesians (page 51). The (average) stocking rate of 2·1 cows per forage hectare given above relates to Ayrshires (and compares with 2·0 for Holstein Friesians); Shorthorns would have as high a requirement as Holstein Friesians.

DAIRY FOLLOWERS *(per Heifer reared)*

A. Holstein Friesians

Performance Level	Low £	Average £	High £
Value of heifer (allowing for culls) (1)	750	750	750
LESS Value of calf (allowing for mortality)	85	85	85
OUTPUT	665	665	665
Variable Costs:			
Concentrate Costs (2)	155	135	115
Miscellaneous Variable Costs (3)	65	65	65
TOTAL VARIABLE COSTS (excluding Forage)	220	200	180
GROSS MARGIN per Heifer, before deducting Forage Variable Costs	445	465	485
Forage Variable Costs (fert. and seed)	55	65	75
GROSS MARGIN per Heifer	390	400	410
Forage Hectares (Acres) per Heifer reared (4)	0·95 (2·3)	0·725 (1·8)	0·575 (1·4)
GROSS MARGIN per Forage Hectare (5)	410	550	715
GROSS MARGIN per Forage Acre	166	223	290

B. Channel Island Breeds

Performance Level	Low £	Average £	High £
Value of heifer (allowing for culls) (1)	425	425	425
LESS Value of calf (allowing for mortality)	25	25	25
OUTPUT	400	400	400
Variable Costs:			
Concentrate Costs (2)	130	115	100
Miscellaneous Variable Costs (3)	60	60	60
TOTAL VARIABLE COSTS (excluding Forage)	190	175	160
GROSS MARGIN per Heifer, before deducting Forage Variable Costs	210	225	240
Forage Variable Costs (fert. and seed)	45	50	55
GROSS MARGIN per Heifer	165	175	185
Forage Hectares (Acres) per Heifer reared (4)	0·75 (1·85)	0·575 (1·4)	0·45 (1·1)
GROSS MARGIN per Forage Hectare (5)	215	305	410
GROSS MARGIN per Forage Acre	87	123	166

N.B. On average, Channel Island heifers calve about three months younger than Holstein Friesians.

C. Ayrshires

Performance Level	Low £	Average £	High £
Value of heifer (allowing for culls) (1) ...	585	585	585
LESS Value of calf (allowing for mortality) ...	40	40	40
OUTPUT	545	545	545
Variable Costs:			
Concentrates (2)...	145	125	110
Miscellaneous Variable Costs (3) ...	65	65	65
TOTAL VARIABLE COSTS (excluding Forage)	210	190	175
GROSS MARGIN per Heifer, before			
deducting Forage Variable Costs ...	335	345	370
Forage Variable Costs (fert. and seed) ...	55	60	65
GROSS MARTIN per Heifer	280	285	305
Forage Hectares (Acres) per Heifer			
reared (4)	0·9 (2·2)	0·7 (1·75)	0·55 (1·35)
GROSS MARGIN per Forage Hectare (5) ...	310	405	555
GROSS MARGIN per Forage Acre	125	164	225

Notes

1. The heifer values are based on the purchase price of down-calving heifers, allowing for culls. Most heifers are home-reared. If heifers are reared for sale, the price of whole batches are likely to be lower than the values given in the tables, by perhaps 10 or 15 per cent. On the other hand the purchaser will often take the batch a few months before the average expected calving date, thus reducing feed and area requirements for the rearer.

2. The lower levels of concentrate costs are the combined result of more economical feeding and a lower average calving age. (Other things being equal, however, including the overall level of management, a lower calving age requires higher levels of feeding.)

3. Miscellaneous variable costs exclude straw. Straw requirements average approx. 1 tonne per heifer reared, but are variable, depending on time of year and age when calved, as well as system of housing and extent of outwintering. Vet. and med. approx. £32·50 per heifer reared.

4. The lower levels of area per heifer reared are the combined result of a higher stocking density and a lower average calving age.

   With an average calving age of 2 years 4 months, a "replacement unit" (i.e. calf + yearling + heifer) equals about 1·25 livestock units. The three stocking rates given above are equivalent to approximately 0·67, 0·58 and 0·5 forage hectares (1·65,1·45,1·25 acres) respectively per Holstein Friesian cow. The low figure assumes an average calving age of 2 years 6 months (1·4 livestock units) and the high figure one of 2 years 2 months (1·15 livestock units).

5. Much higher gross margin figures per hectare can be combined by intensive grazing methods, particularly if combined with winter feeding systems which involve little dependence on home-produced hay or silage (cf. Note 11, last three paragraphs, page 52).

6. *Contract Rearing:* see page 73.

7. *Labour:* see page 112.

Self-Contained Dairy Herd: Cows and Followers

At average annual replacement rates (22·5 per cent of the milking herd), just over one-quarter of a replacement unit is required for each cow in the herd, i.e. roughly one calf, yearling and heifer for every four cows (including calved heifers)—with a few extra calves reared to allow for culling. At average stocking rates for both this means approximately 1 hectare devoted to followers for every 3 hectares for cows. Since surplus youngstock are often reared and frequently the stocking rate is less intensive the ratio is often 1: 2·5 or even 1·2 in practice. 1: 3·5 is about the minimum where all replacement heifers are reared, unless their winter feeding is based largely on straw and purchased supplements, or unless there is a combination of long average herd life and early calving, i.e. at 2 years old or just over.

Gross Margin per Forage Hectare (Acre) (£) for the Whole Herd (i.e., Cows and Followers Combined); (at four levels of performance, including four commensurate levels of stocking rate, for the dairy cows; and three levels of performance, including different stocking rates, for the followers) are as follows, *assuming a 3:1 land use ratio* (dairy cow area: followers area); (Holstein Friesians only):

		G.M. per Forage Hectare (Acre)			
		Dairy Cows			
		£	£	£	£
		Low	Average	High	Very High
		1305 (528)	1645 (666)	2045 (828)	2490 (1008)
G.M. per Forage	Low	410 (166)	1080 (437)	1335 (540)	1635 (662) 1970 (797)
Hectare (Acre),	Average	550 (223)	1115 (451)	**1370 (554)**	1670 (676) 2005 (811)
Followers	High	715 (290)	1155 (467)	1415 (573)	1715 (694) 2045 (828)

As an example, the above table indicates that at the average level of performance and stocking rate for both cows and followers, the whole dairy gross margin per hectare (acre) figure falls to £1370 (554) compared with £1645 (666) for the dairy cows alone, a reduction of 17 per cent. If more than the assumed (minimum) number of dairy followers are kept and the ratio is 2:1 the whole forage area figure (on the assumption again of average performance) falls to £1280 (518), which is a reduction of 22 per cent compared with cows only. However, the requirements per hectare for labour, machinery and buildings are of course less for heifer rearing than for dairy cows. The higher the value of replacement dairy heifers and cows the less the discrepancy between the gross margins of dairy cows alone and the self-contained herd.

Note that *for a combined, self-contained enterprise budget for the dairy herd and followers* there are the following differences:

Fewer calves for sale (as the required number of heifer calves are retained).

No replacement heifers/cows are purchased. (Thus high prices for replacement heifers reduces the gross margin of the milking herd and raises that of the dairy followers, but they have no effect on the gross margin of the combined, fully self-contained dairy herd breeding all its own replacements (assuming no surplus stock are reared)).

Value of any culled or surplus heifers are included.

Variable costs of replacements are added to those for the cows (on the basis of approximately one in-calf heifer entering the herd each year for every four cows (which allows for mortality and culling)).

BEEF

Finished Cattle Prices

In the early summer of 1997 (at the time of preparing this section) finished cattle prices have fallen to only 90-95p/kg/lw, even lower than in the 12 months following the onset of the BSE crisis in March 1996, during which the price was around 95p in autumn 1996 and nearly 110p in midwinter 1996/97. (The yearly average in the few years "pre-BSE" had been around 120p.)

A limited improvement is assumed for 1998, but still only to levels about 15p below pre-BSE levels.

Any additional payments that are purely to compensate the effects of BSE (and are therefore presumably temporary) are excluded from the financial data in this section.

The prices assumed in the subsequent tables relate either to the *1998 calendar year or 1998/99* as appropriate (e.g. the latter is used for winter finished beef). They assume a spring (March/April) peak of 105p and an autumn (October) trough of 100p.

Suckler Cow Premium: £117·36 per head. See page 72 for full details. Suckler cow *"quotas"* (premium rights) are tradeable; typical values in autumn 1996 — lowland: £110-120/cow to buy, £30-35 to lease; LFAs: £95-105 to buy, £20-25 to lease.

Beef Special Premium: £88·04 per head. See page 72 for full details. Because the extent of any future *overshooting* cannot be forecast, *no reductions have been allowed for this in the tables below.*

Extensification Premium: £29·16 per head if stocking rate below 1·4 livestock units/ha; increased to £42·12 if below 1·0 LU/ha. Applies to both the above premiums. See page 72 for full details.

Calf prices

Highly variable. It is the balance between three (or four) factors: calf (or store) prices, finished cattle prices and feeding stuff prices (and in some cases stocking rate), that will mainly determine the levels of the gross margin and profit for the different beef systems included in the following pages. Small differences in each factor can cause large differences in the margins. The values assumed below relate to *all qualities,* in *all* markets, *at 7 to 10 days old:*

	Bulls	Heifers
Friesians...	85	85
Hereford × Friesians	110	80
Limousin × Friesians	140	105
Simmental × Friesians	160	110
Charolais × Friesians	170	115

Note. Results from the Meat and Livestock Commission's Beefplan recording and costing service have been widely used in estimating many of the figures in this section.

Early Weaning—Bucket Rearing (per calf)

	3 months	6 months
Value of Calf	190	285
Less Calf (1)	88	88
Output	102	197
Variable Costs:		
Milk Substitute and Concentrates (2)	45	90
Miscellaneous Variable Costs (3)	15	25
Hay (4)	—	6
Total Variable Costs	60	121
Gross Margin per Calf reared	42	76

Notes

1. £85 per calf (Friesian bull calves, 1 week old, average of all qualities except the poorest); 4 per cent mortality assumed, mainly in first 3 weeks.

2. Milk substitute: 14 kg @ £1250/tonne = £17·50. Calf concentrates: to 3 months, 165 kg @ £160/tonne = £26·50; to 6 months, additional 300kg @ £150/tonne = £45. Calves fed less well, i.e. with lower concentrate costs, will fetch proportionally lower market prices, probably resulting in a lower gross margin.

3. Misc. Variable Costs include vet. and med.: 8 (3 months), 11·5 (6 months); and bedding: 3·5 (3 months), 8 (6 months).

4. Hay: 7 kg to 3 months, 200 kg to 6 months. Variable costs assume made on farm; double the cost if purchased.

5. Weights: at start, 50 kg; at 3 months, 115 kg; at 6 months, 200 kg.

Contract rearing charge (both 0 to 3 months and 0 to 6 months): £11 per week. Direct labour cost: approx. £17 per head to 3 months, £30 per head to 6 months.

Labour requirements (all beef systems): see page 112.

59

BEEF

Single Suckling (per cow): Lowland

System	Spring Calving		Autumn Calving	
Performance Level (1)	Average	High	Average	High
	£	£	£	£
Value of Calf (2)	272	299	338	368
Calf Sales/Valn. per Cow (3) ...	245	275	304	339
Headage Payment (4)	117	117	117	117
LESS COW and Bull Depreciation and Calf Purchases (5)... ...	47	46	53	52
OUTPUT	315	346	368	404
Variable Costs:				
Concentrate Costs (cow and calf)	23	21	42	40
Miscellaneous Variable Costs (6)	42	42	46	46
TOTAL VARIABLE COSTS (excluding forage)	65	63	88	86
GROSS MARGIN per cow, before deducting Forage Variable Costs	250	283	280	318
Forage Variable Costs	37	35	44	42
Purchased Bulk Feed	24	19	18	14
GROSS MARGIN per Cow	189	229	218	262
Cows per ha (7)	2·0	2·4	1·7	2·0
Forage Ha (Acres) per Cow ...	·5	·42	·59	·5
	(1·24)	(1·04)	(1·45)	(1·24)
GROSS MARGIN per Forage Hectare	380	550	370	525
GROSS MARGIN per Forage Acre ...	153	222	150	212

Notes

1. Performance level relates to variations in two factors: weaner calf weight and stocking rate. "High" refers to the average levels likely to be achieved by the better fifty per cent of producers. It is clearly possible to set still higher "targets".

2. Weight of calves (kg) at sale/transfer: spring calving: average 265 (at approx. 7 months old), high 285 (slightly older); autumn calving: average 330 (at approx. 11 months old), high 350 (same age). Price (per live kg): average 102·50p, high 105p.

3. Calves reared per 100 cows mated: average 90, high 92.

4. Headage payments: see page 72. Numbers are assumed to be within available quota. At the stocking rates assumed the stocking density limit (2 LU/ha) is exceeded for spring calving herds and the payments would be scaled down accordingly; however, the limit may not be exceeded when *all* the grazing livestock on the farm are considered and this is what is assumed in the table. The stocking rates assumed for both spring and autumn calving herds are too high for the extensification premium to be paid. No allowance has been made for any overshooting of regional reference herd limits.

5. Assumptions. Herd life: spring calving, 6 years; autumn calving, 5 years. Purchase price £650, average cull value £450. Calves purchased: average, 4 per 100 cows mated, premium 3, at £115. Bull: purchase price £2,500, cull value £750.

6. Vet. and med. £22; bedding: spring calving £12, autumn £16; miscellaneous £8. Where yarded in winter, straw requirements average 0·5-0·75 tonne per cow for spring calvers and around 0·75 tonne for autumn calvers.

7. The higher stocking density implies better use of grassland. Higher stocking rates can also be achieved by buying in more of the winter bulk fodder requirements, or by winter feeding largely on arable by-products, including straw. Purchased bulk fodder and/or straw balancer concentrates will reduce gross margin per cow but increase gross margin per hectare.

BEEF

Single Suckling (per cow): Upland and Hill

	Upland		Upland		Hill	
System	Spring Calving		Autumn Calving			
Performance Level (1)	Average	High	Average	High	Average	High
	£	£	£	£	£	£
Value of Calf (2)	302	331	379	410	294	330
Calf Sales/Valn. per Cow (3) ...	275	311	345	385	268	310
Headage Payments (4)	187	187	216	187	244	244
LESS Cow and Bull Depreciation and Calf Purchases (5)... ...	47	46	53	52	52	50
OUTPUT	415	452	508	520	460	504
Variable Costs·						
Concentrate Costs (cow and calf)	23	21	55	50	45	42
Miscellaneous Variable Costs (6)	43	43	47	47	37	37
TOTAL VARIABLE COSTS (excluding forage)	66	64	102	97	82	79
GROSS MARGIN per cow, before deducting Forage Variable Costs	349	388	406	423	378	425
Forage Variable Costs	44	40	50	45	40	35
Purchased Bulk Feed	24	18	24	18	15	12
GROSS MARGIN per Cow	281	330	332	360	323	378
Cows per ha (7, 8)...	1·6	1·9	1·2	1·5	1·0	1·2
Forage Ha (Acres) per Cow ...	·62	·53	·83	·67	1·0	·83
	(1·53)	(1·31)	(2·05)	(1·66)	(2·5)	(2·06)
GROSS MARGIN per Forage Hectare	450	625	400	540	325	455
GROSS MARGIN per Forage Acre ...	182	254	162	219	131	184

Notes

1. Performance level relates to variations in two factors: weaner calf weight and stocking rate. "High" refers to the average levels likely to be achieved by the better fifty per cent of producers. It is clearly possible to set still higher "targets".

2. Weight of calves (kg) at sale/transfer: upland spring calving: average 270 (at approx. 7·5 months old), high 290 (same age); upland autumn calving: average 370 (at approx. 11·5 months old), high 390 (same age); hill: average 280, high 300. Price (per live kg): upland spring calving: average 112p, high 114p; upland autumn calving: average 102·5p, high 105p; hill: average 105p, high 110p.

3. Calves reared per 100 cows mated: average 91, high 94.

4. Suckler cow premium and hill compensatory allowance: see page 72. Numbers are assumed to be within available quota. The (lower) extensification premium would be available at the stocking rates assumed for average upland autumn calving herds and hill farms. No allowance has been made for any overshooting of regional reference herd limits.

5. Assumptions. Herd life: spring calving, 6 years; autumn calving and hill, 5 years. Purchase price £650, average cull value £450. Calves purchased: upland average, 4 per 100 cows mated, premium 3, at £140; hill: average 3, premium 2. Bull: purchase price £2,500, cull value £750.

6. Vet. and med. £22; bedding: spring calving £12, autumn £16, hill £6; miscellaneous £9. Where yarded in winter, requirements average 0·5-0·75 tonne per cow for spring calvers and around 0·75 tonne for autumn calvers.

7. The higher stocking density implies better use of grassland. Higher stocking rates can also be achieved by buying in more of the winter bulk fodder requirements, or by winter feeding largely on arable by-products, including straw. Purchased bulk fodder and/or straw balancer concentrates reduce gross margin per cow but increase gross margin per hectare.

8. Forage Hectares (Acres) per cow and Gross Margin per Forage Hectare (Acre) relate to "in-bye equivalent" (3 hectares of rough grazing are taken as being equal to 1 hectare of in-bye land).

BEEF

Double and Multiple Suckling (per cow)

	Output level (1)			
	Double Suckling	Multiple Suckling		
No. of calves reared per cow	1·9	2·5	3·5	4·5
	£	£	£	£
Value of Calf	265	260	255	250
Calf Sales per Cow	504	650	892	1125
Headage Payment (2)	117	117	117	117
Calf Costs (including Replacement				
LESS Calves (3)	115	181	302	425
Cow Depreciation	50	50	55	60
OUTPUT (3)	456	536	652	757
Variable Costs:				
Concentrates	65	80	100	115
Miscellaneous Variable Costs (4) ...	60	70	85	100
TOTAL VARIABLE COSTS (excluding forage)	125	150	185	215
GROSS MARGIN per cow, before deducting				
Forage Variable Costs	331	386	467	542
Forage Variable Costs	45	50	60	65
Purchased Bulk Feed	25	30	35	40
GROSS MARGIN per Cow	261	306	372	437
Cows per ha	1·9	1·85	1·8	1·75
Forage Hectares (Acres) per Cow	·525	·54	·56	·57
	(1·3)	(1·34)	(1·38)	(1·41)
GROSS MARGIN per Forage Hectare ...	495	565	670	765
GROSS MARGIN per Forage Acre ...	200	229	271	310

Notes

1. The different levels of output refer only to different numbers of calves reared per cow. The standards are averages at each level of output. There are wide variations in prices obtained and paid per calf and in concentrate costs: together they can make a very large difference to the gross margin.

2. Headage payment: see page 72.

3. Calf cost assumed: £110 (average steers and heifers, 1 week old). Calf mortality assumed: 5 per cent (double suckling) to 8 per cent (4·5 calves per cow).

4. Miscellaneous variable costs include straw: approx. 1 tonne per cow.

N.B. There is very little survey data available for these enterprises, since multiple suckling in particular is not widely practised. Hence these estimates must be treated with caution.

BEEF

Finishing/Rearing on Suckler-Bred Stores (per head)

	Winter Finishing Average £	Winter Finishing High £	Grass Finishing Average £	Grass Finishing High £	Overwintering and Grass Finishing Average £	Overwintering and Grass Finishing High £	Grazing and Yard Finishing Average £	Grazing and Yard Finishing High £	Overwintering and Selling as Stores Average £	Overwintering and Selling as Stores High £
Sales	510	551	445	450	465	485	525	578	428	463
Less Store (1)	312	334	352	330	285	283	300	278	283	283
Output*	198	247	93	120	180	203	225	300	145	180
Variable Costs:										
Concentrates (2)	88	90	5	3	60	51	58	43	52	47
Miscellaneous (3)	31	29	21	19	36	33	36	33	32	30
Total Variable Costs (excl. Forage)	119	119	26	22	96	84	94	76	84	77
Gross Margin per head before deducting Forage Variable Costs	79	128	67	98	84	119	131	224	61	103
Forage Variable Costs ...	26	28	23	23	41	41	38	38	24	26
Purchased Bulk Feed ...	12	14	—	—	16	16	10	6	10	5
Gross Margin per head*	41	86	44	75	27	62	83	180	27	72
No. per ha	9	10	4	5	3.75	4.50	4	5	11	13
No. per acre	3.6	4	1.6	2	1.5	1.8	1.6	2	4.5	5.3
Gross Margin per Forage Ha* ...	370	850	175	375	100	280	330	900	295	935
Gross Margin per Forage Acre* ...	150	350	70	150	40	115	135	365	120	380
Weight at start (kg)	315	310	335	320	280	280	285	270	280	280
Weight at end (kg)	500	525	445	445	470	485	500	540	400	425
Purchase Price (p per kg LW)	99	98	105	103	102	101	105	103	101	101
Sale Price (p per kg LW) ...	102	105	100	101	99	100	105	107	107	109
Concentrates per head (kg) ...	675	725	40	25	475	425	450	350	400	375
Silage per head (tonnes) ...	3.25	3.75	—	—	3.6	3.6	2.1	2.3	2.3	2.7

*The output and gross margin figures exclude the beef special premium as this will depend, per head, on the overall stocking rate on the farm. Where the above beef enterprises represent the only livestock on the farm the full payment per head (see page 72) is likely to be obtained for the centre three systems but not for the first and last.

All-System Assumptions:

(1) Allowing for mortality at 1 per cent.

(2) Concentrate costs per tonne: winter: average £130, high £125; summer: average £120, high £115.

(3) Including vet. and med. and bedding.

Additional Note: The gross margin per ha figures must be treated with considerable caution, especially with regard to winter fattening/rearing systems: small variations in land requirements and margins per head cause wide variations in the per ha figures, and capital requirements are considerable. Differences in buying and selling prices per kg can be critical.

63

BEEF

Finishing/Rearing on Dairy-Bred Stores (per head)

	Winter Finishing Average £	High £	Grass Finishing Average £	High £	Overwintering and Grass Finishing Average £	High £	Grazing and Yard Finishing Average £	High £	Overwintering and Selling as Stores Average £	High £
Sales	510	535	466	490	470	490	515	578	415	450
Less Store (1)	322	290	361	357	294	291	237	245	275	272
Output*	188	245	105	133	176	199	278	333	140	178
Variable Costs:										
Concentrates (2)	75	72	6	5	54	45	78	56	52	47
Miscellaneous (3)	31	29	20	19	45	41	37	33	32	30
Total Variable Costs (excl. Forage)	106	101	26	24	99	86	115	89	84	77
Gross Margin per head before deducting Forage Variable Costs	82	144	79	109	77	113	163	244	56	101
Forage Variable Costs	26	28	23	23	41	40	38	39	23	26
Purchased Bulk Feed	14	12	—	—	16	16	10	6	10	5
Gross Margin per head*	42	104	56	86	20	57	115	199	23	70
No. per ha	7.5	9	4	5	3.5	4.25	3.5	4.5	11	13
No. per acre	3	3.6	1.6	2	1.4	1.7	1.4	1.8	4.5	5.3
Gross Margin per Forage Ha*	315	935	225	430	70	240	405	895	255	910
Gross Margin per Forage Acre*	127	380	90	175	28	97	165	360	103	370
Weight at start (kg)	335	305	350	350	300	300	230	240	275	275
Weight at end (kg)	520	535	475	495	490	505	500	550	395	420
Purchase Price (p per kg LW)	96	95	103	102	98	97	103	102	100	99
Sale Price (p per kg LW)	98	100	98	99	96	97	103	105	105	107
Concentrates per head (kg)	575	575	50	40	425	375	600	450	400	375
Silage per head (tonnes)	3.4	3.4	—	—	3.6	3.6	3.5	4.5	2.6	3.0

*The output and gross margin figures exclude the beef special premium, as this will depend, per head, on the overall stocking rate on the farm. Where the above beef enterprises represent the only livestock on the farm the full payment per head (see page 72) is likely to be obtained for the centre three systems but not for the first and last.

All-System Assumptions:

(1) Allowing for mortality at 1 per cent.

(2) Concentrate costs per tonne: winter: average £130, high £125; summer: average £120, high £115.

(3) Including vet. and med. and bedding.

Additional Note: The gross margin per ha figures must be treated with considerable caution, especially with regard to winter fattening/rearing systems: small variations in land requirements and margins per head cause wide variations in the per ha figures, and capital requirements are considerable. Differences in buying

BEEF

Traditional Finishing of Strong Store Cattle (per head) (1)

	Summer Finishing £	Winter Finishing £
Sales	520 (2)	546 (3)
LESS Purchased Store	420 (4)	420 (5)
OUTPUT*	100	126
Variable Costs:		
Concentrates	5	52 (6)
Miscellaneous Variable Costs	23	37 (7)
TOTAL VARIABLE COSTS (excluding Forage)	28	87
GROSS MARGIN per Head before deducting Forage		
Variable Costs	72	39
Forage Variable Costs	19	12
GROSS MARGIN per Head*	53	27
No. per ha (acre)	4 (1·6)	9 (3·65)
Forage Hectares (Acres) per Head	·25 (·62)	·11 (·275)
GROSS MARGIN per Forage Hectare*	212	243
GROSS MARGIN per Forage Acre*	86	98

*No headage payment (beef special premium) has been included: although the animal becomes eligible at 22 months old (if on the farm at that age of course) the stocking rate assumed would limit the numbers eligible per farm for summer fattening and especially for winter fattening. Even where available, the payment is likely to be largely cancelled out under these systems by a higher sum paid for the store.

Notes

1. The financial results of this enterprise are highly dependent on the market margin, i.e. the difference between the price per kg paid for the store and the price per kg obtained for the finished animal. Other important factors are the stocking rate and the degree of dependence on cash-crop by-products and the quality of conserved grass (and hence the quantity of concentrates required in relation to the liveweight gain) in the case of winter fattening.

2. 520 kg @ 100p.

3. 520 kg @ 105p.

4. 400 kg @ 105p.

5. 420 kg @ 100p.

6. 400 kg @ £130/tonne.

7. Including straw: average 0·75 tonne per head.

BEEF

Intensive Cereal Bull Beef (per Head)

		Calves reared on farm		Reared calves purchased	
		Average £	High £	Average £	High £
Sales (1)		479	514	500	535
Less Calf (2)		89	88	194	192
Output (3)		390	426	306	343
Variable Costs:					
Concentrates (4)...		266	259	221	214
Other Feed		4	4	4	4
Miscellaneous (5)		43	43	35	35
Total Variable Costs ...		313	306	260	253
Gross Margin per Head ...		77	120	46	90

Notes

1. Weight at slaughter (kg): own-reared calves: average 470, high 485; bought reared calves: average 490, high 505. Price: average 102p per live kg, high 106p. All year round production is assumed. Days (on farm) to slaughter: calves reared on farm: 345; reared calves purchased: 270.

2. £85 per Friesian bull calf (1 week old average of all qualities except the poorest) + mortality (average 5, high 3 per cent). Reared calves purchased at about 3 months old at £190; average mortality 2, high 1 per cent.

3. No headage payment (Beef Special Premium) is included, because of the stocking rate constraint in the regulations. However, in some farm circumstances it may be available for a limited number.

4. £45 calf rearing (to 12 weeks: see p. 59) + finishing ration + £5 food to losses. Finishing ration: 17 parts barley @ £80 per tonne (estimated average price, 1998 calendar year), 3 parts concentrate supplement @ £235 per tonne; plus milling and mixing. Total, £112·50 per tonne.

   Quantity (kg from 12 weeks (115 kg) to slaughter; FCR average 5·1, high 4·75): own-reared calves: average 1810, high 1757; bought reared calves: average 1912, high 1852.

   A difference of £5 per tonne in the cost of barley changes the feed cost by approximately £7·75 per head.

5. Calves reared on farm: vet. and med.11, bedding 14, other 18; reared calves purchased: 10, 11, 14 respectively.

Note: Interest on Capital

As examples of the need to be aware of interest paid or forgone on capital invested in beef production, interest on the cost of the calf and variable costs alone, at 8%, are likely to be in the order of £25 a head for intensive cereal beef and £35 a head for 18-month beef (page 67).

BEEF

18 Month Beef and Grass Silage Beef (per Head)

	18 month		Grass silage	
	Average	High	Average	High
	£	£	£	£
Sales	500	536	536	572
Less Calf	126	124	194	192
Plus Headage Payments*	88	88	44	35
Output	462	500	386	415
Variable Costs:				
Concentrates	138	122	156	126
Other Feed	12	10	12	10
Miscellaneous	59	55	48	45
Total Variable Costs (excl. Forage) ...	209	187	216	181
Gross Margin per Head before deducting Forage Variable Costs	253	313	170	234
Forage Variable Costs	37	37	30	30
Gross Margin per Head	216	276	140	204
No. per ha (acre)	3·25 (1·3)	3·6 (1·45)	7 (2·8)	9 (3·6)
Forage Hectares (Acres) per Head	·31 (·76)	·28 (·69)	0·14 (·35)	0·12 (·27)
Gross Margin per Forage Ha (per year) ...	700	993	980	1835
Gross Margin per Forage Acre (per year) ...	285	405	395	745

Notes
18 Month Beef
Autumn-born dairy-bred calves, beef crosses.
Slaughter weights (kg): average 500, high 520. Sale price per live kg: average 100p, high 103p.
Calf price/value £120 (1 week old bulls); mortality: average 5, high 3 per cent.
Concentrates (kg; average with high performance in brackets). 14; other: first winter 360 (335), at grass 115 (110), second winter 150 (130). Price of concentrates per tonne: first winter (inc. calf rearing) £140 (£130), summer £125 (£115); second winter, £130 (£120). Silage: 4·5 tonnes (average and high): 0·75 tonne first winter, 3·75 tonnes second.
Miscellaneous (average): vet. and med. £19, bedding £20, other £20.
Intensive grazing of fresh leys and good quality silage are needed—especially to achieve the high performance levels.
*Headage Payment. The full beef special premium is only available for all the stock (up to 90 head) if the overall stocking rate on the farm is below 2 livestock units per hectare. Male cattle 6 to 18 months old are counted as 0·6 LU and those under 6 months are excluded. The full (estimated) payment is therefore included, although the high stocking rate would exceed the limit if there were no other livestock on the farm. The actual payment will vary from farm to farm and be reduced if regional limits are exceeded.

Grass Silage Beef
Three months old dairy-bred calves fed indoors on grass silage and concentrates, for slaughter at 14 to 17 months old. Good quality silage is the key to high performance per herd (otherwise concentrates per head rise and/or daily liveweight gain falls). High yields of silage per ha raise gross margins per ha.
Slaughter weights (kg): average 525, high 545. Sale price per live kg: average 102p, high 105p.
Calf price (3 months old): £190. Concentrates per head (kg): average, with high performance in brackets: 1200 (1050); price per tonne £130 (£120). Silage required: approx. 5·5 tonnes per head.
Miscellaneous (average): vet. and med. £9, bedding £20, other £19.
*Headage Payment: see above for 18 month beef. Because of the very high stocking rate with this system only a crude allowance has been included: 50% of the full rate for average, 40% for high.
Note that the gross margin per hectare figures must be interpreted with considerable caution: small differences in silage yields can have a large effect and, more important, the working capital and building requirements per hectare are extremely high: well above even the high needs of 18 month beef.

BEEF
24 Month Beef from Bucket Reared Calves (per Head)

	Autumn-born calf £	Spring-born calf £
Sales (1)	500	525
Less Calf	125	115
Headage Payments*	176	176
Output	551	586
Variable Costs:		
Concentrates	115	135
Miscellaneous	75	82
Forage	55	45
Total Variable Costs	245	262
Gross Margin per Head	306	324
No. per ha (acre)	2 (·8)	2·25 (·9)
Forage Hectares (Acres) per Head	0·5 (1·25)	0·45 (1·1)
Gross Margin per Forage Hectare	610	730
Gross Margin per Forage Acre	247	295

Notes
(1) 500 kg. Autumn-born: 100p per kg; spring-born: 105p.
*Beef special premiums: 2 payments, at 10 and 22 months old.

VEAL

General points. Veal consumption is very low in the UK: approx. 0·06 kg (2 oz) per head per year compared with 2·2 kg (5 lb) in France; UK consumption is only about 0.6% (5,000 tonnes) of EU production (800,000 tonnes). Continental demand is mainly for white veal, produced in veal crates: a system that is illegal in the UK, where the less economic loose housing system is required, producing "pink veal" at heavier weights.

For the above reasons there is little veal now produced in the UK and consequently validated economic data is rarely seen. A wide variety of breeds are used: beef cross heifer calves are perhaps the most suitable and hence most common. Some farmers produce "light veal" at 75-100 kg dw in 4 months, some "heavy veal" at 125-135 kg dw in 6 months.

The following figures could be broadly typical of present UK production.

	£
Sale value (1)	393
Less Calf (2)	105
Output	288
Variable Costs:	
Milk powder (3)	234
Miscellaneous (4)	34
Total Variable Costs	268
Gross Margin per Head (5)	20

Notes
1. Sold at 190 kg liveweight (bought at 45-55 kg), average 102 kg dressed carcass weight; weeks to slaughter 16-20. Killing out percentage, 52-55 per cent. Price assumed: £3·85 per kg dcw (£2·07 per kg liveweight). At post-BSE levels of around £3·50/kg dw the enterprise is totally uneconomic, unless the feed conversion efficiency is superlative and/or the price paid for (good) calves is well below the level assumed.
2. £100 per calf (beef cross heifer, 1 week old); 5 per cent mortality assumed, mainly in first three weeks.
3. Milk powder: £850 per tonne. A conversion rate of 1·95 kg of food per kg liveweight gain is assumed (plus an allowance for losses) = approx. 275 kg total.
4. Miscellaneous: vet and med. 14, straw 12, other 8.
5. The gross margin is obviously highly dependent on calf price, the market price of veal, and feed efficiency.

SHEEP
A. Lowland Spring Lambing (per Ewe)
(Selling lambs off grass)

Performance level	Low	Average	High
Lambs reared per ewe (1)	1·3	1·45	1·65
Average price per lamb (£) (2)	39·5	40·5	41·5
	£	£	£
Lamb sales	51·3	58·7	68·5
Ewe Premium (2)	14·0	14·0	14·0
Wool (3)	2·8	2·8	2·8
Cull ewes and rams	6·8	6·8	6·8
Sub-total	74·9	82·3	92·1
LESS Ewe and ram replacements	19·1	19·1	19·1
OUTPUT	55·8	63·2	73·0
Variable Costs:			
Concentrates (54 kg ewes, 14 kg lambs)		9·8	
Vet. and Med.		4·9	
Miscellaneous and Transport		4·1	
TOTAL VARIABLE COSTS (excluding Forage)		18·8	
GROSS MARGIN per Ewe before deducting Forage Variable Costs	37·0	44·4	54·2
Forage Variable Costs (inc. bought forage and keep)	7·0	7·5	8·0
GROSS MARGIN per Ewe	30·0	36·9	46·2
Stocking Rate (Ewes, with lambs, per forage hectare (acre))	9 (3·65)	12 (4·85)	15 (6·05)
GROSS MARGIN per Forage Hectare	270	445	695
GROSS MARGIN per Forage Acre	109	180	281

Notes

1. *Lambs reared per ewe* (× 100 = lambing percentage) is derived as follows *(average figures* only):

   Lambs born per 100 ewes lambing = 173
   Lambs born per 100 ewes put to ram = 161
   (93% of ewes put to ram bear lambs: 1·5% deaths, 5·5% barren)
   Lamb mortality: 10% (inc. half dead at birth or before seen)
   Lambs reared per 100 ewes lambing = 156
   Lambs reared per 100 ewes put to ram = 145

2. *Lamb Prices/Ewe Premium.* The price assumed for lambs sold for slaughter *for the 1998 mid-season lamb crop* assumes that most of the lambs are sold between mid-June and the end of October. Prices are normally highest in March-May and lowest in August-October; in 1993-5 the average price during the two-month spring peak exceeded 125p/kg/lw, even reaching 155p briefly, with the autumn trough at 80p-90p. However, prices were much higher in 1996 and 1997 (BSE effect). An average market price of 107·5p/kglw has been assumed, giving £41·50 per finished lamb (38·6 kglw). However, the average price given in the above table allows for a proportion (15%) sold or retained in the autumn as *store* lambs. Low performance is £1·25 a lamb less, high £1·25 more.

   A difference in price of £2 per lamb (i.e. a difference of approx. 5·20p per kglw for a 38·6 kglw lamb) causes a difference of £23, £35 and £50 (9, 14, 20) to the low, average and high gross margins per hectare (acre) respectively. Exported lambs could average 15-20 per cent above domestic prices.

The *Sheep Annual Premium* payment per ewe is calculated from the shortfall between the basic price set and the average EU market price for lamb marketed at 12 kg or above. Recent levels have been: 1994, £16·96; 1995, £21·26; 1996, £13·66; 1997 (forecast) £12·50. (Eligible sheep in LFAs received an additional £5·38/head in 1996). Relatively high EU sheepmeat prices were responsible for the low 1996 and (forecast) 1997 premiums. Lower prices, and thus a slightly higher premium, are assumed for 1998.

The premiums are tradable, with restrictions; the prices of *quotas* (premium rights) have varied widely, especially for lowland quota. Typical ranges per unit have been as follows. Lowland: £15 to £25 to buy (but only £6 to £12 in early 1997) and £6 to £8 to lease (but only £1 or £2 in 1997); LFAs: £30 to £42·50 to buy, £8 to £15 to lease.

3. *Wool.* Prices have fallen since their 1995 peak; average payment around 85p/kg in 1997. 3kg/head at 95p has been assumed for 1998.

4. *Breed* will obviously have a large effect on lambing percentage, rate of liveweight gain (reflected in price per lamb), and amount of wool per ewe.

5. *Stocking Density.* The stocking rates assumed are based on land requirements *throughout the year.* With a given level of management one would expect higher stocking rates to be associated with a lower gross margin per ewe. The assumption made in the initial table, however, is that management performance is affecting both factors together.

   N.B. The forage variable costs include purchased forage and keep (where appropriate) (£1·3, £1·7 and £2·0 per ewe at the three performance levels respectively).

   The top one-third gross margin per hectare herds recorded by the Meat and Livestock Commission achieve stocking rates exceeding 15 ewes per hectare. Often such high stocking rates are achieved by substantial use of by-products (e.g. autumn or spring grazing of grass grown primarily for seed) and catch crops (e.g. rape). Otherwise a stocking rate of 15 per hectare (just over 6 per acre) requires a stocking rate of about 24 ewes (with lambs) per hectare in the spring and early summer.

   The top few per cent of flocks in the country achieve gross margins exceeding £750 per hectare (£300 per acre) by a combination of high lambing percentage, high average lamb price and, especially, very high stocking rates.

   Where there are no grazing livestock other than sheep on the farm, some ewes, at the higher stocking rates, are often either agisted (away-wintered) or housed indoors, thus reducing the margin. Agistment costs around 32p per week plus transport, i.e. approx. £8 per year. Depreciation and Interest on new Housing (1·2 sq. m per ewe) is approximately £5 per ewe per year (10-year life); straw, extra hay and perhaps concentrates will also be required for indoor housing.

   On the other hand, with only 7 or 8 ewes per hectare (2·75 to 3·25/acre) on a lowland farm of reasonable quality with no other grazing livestock, there should be surplus grass available in the late spring or early summer; this could be cut for hay or used for seed production.

6. *Flock Depreciation.* (i.e. Market price of replacements less value of culls). It is assumed above that 20 per cent of the ewe flock is culled each year @ £32·50 each and that, allowing for 4 per cent mortality, 24 per cent are purchased or home-reared at £70 each. Rams: 1 per 40 to 45 ewes, 3-year life, purchased @ £300, sold @ £45. The net cost is £11.40 per ewe per year. N.B. Cull ewe prices are approximately £5 per head higher for heavy breeds and £5 lower for light breeds.

   No increase in flock valuation through inflation is included.

7. *Miscellaneous Costs* include lambing and shearing bonus. Contract shearing is approximately 90p per head, including rolling (but can be around £1·10 for small flocks); approx. 50p/ewe for shearing only in upland flocks.

8. *Prices of Specialised Equipment:*

Troughs (2·75 m)	£55 to £60
Racks (2½ to 3 m)	£180 to £200
Foot Baths (3 m)	£90 to £110
Shearer (electric)	£600 to £900
Lamb Creep and Shelter, skids	£550
Netting	67·5p to £1·20 per metre

9. *Fencing:* approximately £1·45 per metre + 70p labour.

10. *Home-reared tegs* (shearlings). Output: value £67 (allowing for culling and mortality) less £35 for the lamb, plus £2 for wool = £34. Variable costs (including forage) = £12·50. Gross margin per head = £21·50, per forage hectare £385 (£155 per acre).

If the figures for home-reared replacement tegs are included in the figures per ewe, the latter are increased approximately as follows: output by £8·50, gross margin (per ewe) by £5·50. The stocking rate in terms of ewes per hectare devoted to sheep will be about 15 per cent less and the overall sheep gross margin per hectare will be slightly reduced.

11. Labour: see page 113.

B. Other Sheep Systems (average performance level only)

System	Early Lambing per ewe	Winter Fattening of Store Lambs per head	Upland Flocks per ewe	Hill Flocks per ewe
Lambs reared per ewe	1·4	—	1·3	1·0
	£	£	£	£
Average price per lamb sold	51·5	50·0	37·7	34·0
Lamb sales	72·1	49·0	49·0	25·5
Ewe premium	14·0	—	19·4*	19·4*
Wool	2·9	—	2·4	1·9
Subsidy/Hill Livestock	—	—	2·6*	5·7*
Sub-total	89·0	49·0	73·4	52·5
Less Livestock Purchases (net of cull sales)	11·5	35·0	13·2	(+) 3·5
Output	77·5	14·0	60.2	56·0
Variable Costs:				
Concentrates	21·0	2·1	6·5	3·5
	(135 kg)	(15 kg)	(45 kg)	(25 kg)
Vet. and Med.	5·1	0·4	4·3	3·6
Miscellaneous and Transport	5·1	1·5	3·6	1·9
Total Variable Costs (excl. Forage) ...	31·2	4·0	14·4	9·0
Gross Margin per ewe (or head) before deducting Forage Variable Costs ...	46·3	10·0	45·8	47·0
Forage Variable Costs (inc. bought forage)	7·1	2·0	6·2	3·1
Gross Margin per ewe (or head)	39·2	8·0	39·6	43·9
Stocking Rate (No. per Forage Ha (Acre))	15·5	50	9·5	—
	(6·25)	(20)	(3·85)	
Gross Margin per Forage Hectare	610	400	375	—
Gross Margin per Forage Acre	247	162	152	—

* The same supplement to the ewe premium (£5·38/ewe) and the same hill sheep compensatory allowances have been assumed as paid in 1997; hardy breed ewes assumed for the hill flocks.

Notes

Early Fat Lambs. In this system, 60 per cent of the lambs are sold before the end of May, and the remainder before the end of August. This may be compared with *Mid-Season* lamb production (see table on page 69), in which 75 - 80 per cent of the lambs are sold in June, July and August, and *Late* lamb production, in which only two-thirds or so of the lambs are sold for slaughter by the end of the normal grazing season, 60 per cent of total lambs being sold for slaughter or as stores in October/

November, or the stores are retained on the farm for winter fattening. The gross margin per ewe tends to be slightly higher with the latter system compared with Mid-Season production, provided the proportion of stores is not too high — but more grass is utilised per ewe, making per hectare results similar.

Winter Fattening of Store Lambs. The gross margin per head is particularly variable, being very dependent on the difference between the purchase and sale price of the lambs. Store lamb prices were exceptionally high in August/September 1996. Some of the forage variable costs consist of bulk feed and agistment.

Hill Sheep. The flock is assumed to be self-maintained; thus only about 0·75 lambs are sold per ewe per annum and the fleece of the yearling ewes are included in wool sales. Only the rams are purchased, costing approx. £2 per ewe per year. Results obviously vary according to the height of the hill and severity of the winter.

Note. The figures for early fat lamb production, upland and hill sheep are largely based on the relative figures for these systems as compared with the lowland spring lambing results obtained from the Meat and Livestock Commission's Flockplan recording and costing service.

GRANTS FOR BEEF AND SHEEP

Note. The green rate used to convert ecu payments into sterling has been frozen at £0·809915 (the rate on 1st January 1997) until 1st January 1999. Hence the 1997 payments will also apply in 1998, unless the ecu rates are altered, which is not anticipated. Previously the payments depended on the ecu value in sterling on the 1st January each year.

Beef Cows. The *Suckler Cow Premium* was £117·36 (144·9 ecu) per cow in 1997 and should be the same in 1998 (see note above). Eligibility is confined to pure beef or beef cross dairy cows or in-calf heifers producing calves for meat. Limited to the number on the farm in 1992 base year (but the "quotas") (premium rights) are tradeable (for values see page 59)); otherwise there is no upper limit to the number eligible or number kept per farm eligible for the premium. The producer must undertake not to deliver any milk or milk products from any of his production units, except that milk producers with less than 120,000 kg (116,500 litres) of quota may apply for the subsidy. The full premium is subject to a maximum stocking rate: 2 livestock units/ha.

Finished Male Cattle. Beef Special Premium: the full rate was £88·04 (108·7 ecu) per head in 1997, and should be the same in 1998 (see note above), but this was reduced very slightly in England and Wales in 1997 and by around 20% in Scotland in 1996 and 1997 because there are regional herd size limits that were exceeded. Payment is limited to 90 animals per producer per year. There are no quality criteria. It is payable on male animals only, at 10 and 22 months of age, at the point of slaughter and at the point of sale for slaughter (auction markets). The producer must have finished the cattle over at least the preceding two months. The above rate (£88·04) is for castrated animals; £109·34 (135 ecu) is the rate for bulls. The maximum carcass weight for intervention is 340 kg. As with the Suckler Cow Premium the full premium is subject to a maximum stocking rate: 2 livestock units/ha.

Extensification Premium. This is an addition to both the Suckler Cow and Beef Special Premiums if the stocking rate is less than 1·4 livestock units/ha; the premium is higher if this is below 1·0 LU/ha. The rates in 1997 and, probably, 1998 (see note above) are £29·16 (36 ecu) and £42·12 (52 ecu) respectively. These rates are reduced if regional herd size limits are exceeded, as for the Beef Special Premium.

Hill Livestock Compensatory Allowances (1997):

(a) Cows. £97·50 per head on eligible cows and in-calf heifers maintained in regular breeding herds on hill land (severely disadvantaged areas) and £69·75 per head on upland (disadvantaged areas) for the purposes of breeding store cattle. Cows kept for selling milk are not eligible.

(b) Sheep. Severely disadvantaged areas: for ewes of an approved breed in specially qualified flocks £5·75 per head (restricted to 6 ewes/ha), other eligible ewes in such flocks £3 (also up to 6 ewes/ha). Disadvantaged areas: £2·65 (restricted to 9 ewes/ha). A supplement to the ewe premium (see page 70) is paid in all less favoured areas: £5·38 (£6·64 ecu).

(c) Limits. The maximum HLCAs payments per hectare are £121·49 in severely disadvantaged areas and £97·65 in disadvantaged areas.

GRAZING AND REARING CHARGES:
CATTLE AND SHEEP

Grazing charges vary widely according to the quality of the pasture and local supply and demand. The following figures are typical (estimated for 1998):

Summer Grazing (per head per week)

Store Cattle and in-calf heifers over 21 months, dry cows, and fattening bullocks over 18 months...	£4·05
Heifers and Steers, 12-21 months	£3·15
6-12 months Cattle	£2·45
Cattle of mixed ages	£3·20
Ewes	35p-55p

Winter Grazing (per head per week)

"Strong" Cattle	£2·45-£3·15
Heifers	£1·90-£2·45
Sheep	35p-55p

Note: the above figures assume the farmer whose land the livestock are on does all the fencing and "looking after". Where the owner of the, say, sheep does the fencing, shepherding, etc., the figures may be halved.

Grass Keep (per hectare, per acre in brackets)

Average in 1997 around £210-225 (£85-90); similar in 1995, 10 to 15% higher in 1996. Main range £150-300 (£60-120).

These figures are highly variable, especially between one part of the country and another, and between one season and another. The charge can be very high where the pasture is good, the supply scarce and the demand strong. Poor quality keep may fetch only £75(30), top quality (fenced and with mains water) more than £350 (140). For top quality grassland, fertilised, well-fenced and watered, with stock seen daily, prices can even exceed £550 (220) for some lots in the west and north-west in years of gross shortage. The *average* price can exceed £350 (140) in some years in parts of the west and west midlands but can fall below £100 (40) in some south-eastern counties.

Winter Keep (Cattle) (per head per week)

Grazing + 9 kg hay and some straw	£7·00
Full winter keep in yards	£7·50-£9·75
Calf rearing for beef (0 to 12 weeks or 0 to 6 months)	£10·25

Heifer Rearing Charges

Points to clarify in any arrangement are: who pays for transport, who pays the vet. and med. expenses, who bears the losses or pays for replacements, how often are payments made (monthly payments save the rearer interest compared with lump sum payments when the heifer is returned)?

Two possible arrangements are:

1. Farmer X sells calf to Rearer at agreed price; the calf is then Rearer's responsibility and he pays for all expenses and bears any losses. Farmer X has first option on heifers, which he buys back two months before calving. Approx. price: £775 above cost of calf for Holstein Friesians, £475 for Channel Islands. Rearer fetches calf; Farmer X supplies transport for heifer.

2. Farmer X retains ownership of calf. Approx. charges: £35 per month from 10 to 14 days old (£38 if two-year old calving), or £31 per month from 6 months old (£36 if two-year old calving), (£46 per month from 10 to 14 days to 6 months). As Rearer has no interest on capital to bear, he supplies transport and pays for vet. and medical expenses. In the case of losses by accident/chance, the rearer either refunds payments or replaces calf (this means Farmer X and Rearer share a loss averaging approx. £30 each per heifer reared, assuming 10 per cent losses at average 6 months old). In the case of losses by negligence, the rearer both refunds payments and replaces calf. (The NFU can supply model agreements).

Calf and Heifer Rearing for Shorter Periods

Calf, 10 days to 3 months, £135 (for food, labour and housing) to £150 (all costs, and rearer bearing losses). Heifers, average from 3 months old to steaming up: approx. £15·50 per month in summer, £43·50 in winter.

RED DEER

Sales:	Selling at 14-16 months per 100 hinds £	Selling calves per 100 hinds £	Finishing stag calves per 200 £
Stag calves	—	4705 (48)	—
Hind calves	—	2700 (38)	—
Stags, 14-16 months	9120 (48)	—	38400
Hinds, 14-16 months	6300 (38)	—	—
Culls (8 hinds, 1 stag)	1000	1000	—
Less purchased stock	—	—	19800
OUTPUT	16420	8405	18600
Variable Costs:			
Supplementary Feed	3905	3100	4095
Forage	1100	700	1000
Vet. and Med	1235	705	600
Miscellaneous	900	600	400
Slaughter Cost	1900	200	4000
TOTAL VARIABLE COSTS	9040	5305	10095
GROSS MARGIN	7380	3100	8505
GROSS MARGIN per Hind (Stag) ...	74	31	42·5
Stocking Rate (No. per ha (acre)) ...	7 (2·85)	8 (3·25)	15 (6)
GROSS MARGIN per hectare	515	250	640
GROSS MARGIN per acre	209	100	258

Notes
Numbers of animals sold given in brackets.
Calves housed from September, hinds from November.
Intensive system, on sown pasture. Self-contained herd.
Herd life (years): hinds 12, stags 8. Hinds per stag: 30 approx.
Calves per 100 hinds: 95 reared (to 4 months).
Supplementary feed: hinds: 7 kg silage/head/day over 165 days plus 0·5 kg concs./ head/day for 30 days; calves: 4 kg silage 195 days plus 0.5 kg concs./head/day 30 days; 2 kg silage 45 days plus 1 kg concs./head/day 45 days; 5 kg silage 195 days plus 0·5 kg concs./head/day 45 days. Concentrates £130/tonne; silage £18/tonne.

Sale weights and values:	Stags		Hinds	
	kg	£/kg	kg	£/kg
Calves	45 lw	2·20 lw	40 lw	1·80 lw
At 14-16 months	48 dw	4·00 dw	42 dw	4·00 dw

Stock: breeding stags £500 plus, hinds £300 plus, yearling hinds £250 plus. Prices reflect good quality stock sold in UK. Tb accreditation brings premium.
Venison prices reflect projected sales for 1997/98 to wholesale buyers. Farm shop and local co-operative sales will vary.
Capital costs: perimeter fencing, £4·20/metre; internal fencing, electric £2/metre, mesh £3·70/metre; handling yard, pens, scales, crush: £6,000—in existing buildings. Total cost of establishing a 100-hind breeding flock is typically in the order of £40,000, including breeding stock and £10,000 for fencing, housing and handling facilities. *Labour:* with an experienced stockman: 400 plus head with additional help when yarding.
Comment: Feed costs are based on exploiting summer compensatory growth and reducing overwinter feed rates and cost. Veterinary figures are based on successful minimal regime.
In 1994 there were 267 deer farms in England and Wales, 86 in Scotland (MAFF). In 1995 there were 28,500 farmed deer in England and Wales, a 30% decline compared with 1993, caused by increased exports from eastern Europe, low prices and the absence of any subsidy. However, demand has increased substantially since, largely because of the BSE in beef scares but also because the low fat content of deer meat is being increasingly recognised. The national herd is still low in overall numbers, due in part to high venison prices. There are signs that customer resistance is reducing retail prices (up to £17·50/kg pre-Christmas 1996) and hence carcass values to a sustainable level (£4/kg). Calf prices need to rise to make breeding herds more viable. Advice is plentiful for newcomers.
Acknowledgement: The above information is provided by J. C. Cordery, Sparsholt College Hampshire.

SHEEP DAIRYING

						per Ewe	
						Average	High
Performance level (yield)	...	...	...	...			
Milk Yield (litres) ...	...	...	...	...	...	250	320
						£	£
Milk Value (1)	...	...	...	...	...	195	250
Value of Lambs (2)	...	...	...	...	...	15	20
Cull Ewes (3)	...	...	...	...	...	5	5
Ewe Premium (4) ...	...	...	...	...	...	15	15
Wool ...	...	...	...	...	...	3	3
OUTPUT ...	...	...	...	...	...	233	293
Variable Costs:							
Concentrates (5)	...	...	...	...		54	
Miscellaneous (inc. vet. and med.)	...	...	...		10	
Forage Variable Costs (6)	...	...	...	...		9	
TOTAL VARIABLE COSTS	...	...	...	...		73	
GROSS MARGIN per Ewe ...	...	...	...	...		160	220
Ewes per ha (acre)	...	...	...	...		12·5 (5)	
GROSS MARGIN per Forage Hectare	...	...	...		2000	2750
GROSS MARGIN per Forage Acre ...	...	...	...		810	1115

Notes

1. *Price.* 78p per litre at farmgate.

2. Lambing % 175 (200 target). Assume a 250 ewe flock. Retain 100 ewe lambs, of which 65 own replacements; sell 35 at £75/head. Balance sold at 3-5 days old at £3+.

3. Cull ewes: 20% culled at £25+/head.

4. Dairy ewes are eligible for 80% of the Annual Ewe Premium; 100% if all lambs are carried on for finishing.

5. *Concentrates.* Milking ewes: 200 days at 1 kg/head/day, 130 days at 0·5 kg/head/day; cost £150/tonne. Ewe lamb replacements: milk powder £24/head, concentrates £11/head.

6. *Forage costs.* Silage: 1 tonne/milking ewe. Grazing includes catch crop of early grass in March/April.

Additional Points

Specific Fixed Costs. Labour, £50/ewe; parlour running costs (inc. water and electricity), £7/ewe.

Capital Costs of Equipment. Complete milking unit for 100 ewes (including yokes, bulk tank, dairy equipment, installation): £5,000-£8,000. Simple unit for 50 sheep: £2,000 plus. These are likely to be minimum costs; they do not include freezing capacity or building work.

Cheesemaking. 5 litres of milk required to make 1 kg of cheese. Wholesale cheese price: approx. £6·50 per kg. Retail price 40 to 60 per cent higher. Cheesemaking equipment £4,000 to £5,000, excluding building (two rooms plus a store). New environmental health regulations have made all processing much more costly. Require separate processing rooms (minimum cost £5,000-£6,000), pasteuriser (£1,000-£4,000), stainless steel or approved plastic utensils (£400-£500), etc.

Acknowledgement. Data supplied by Anthony Hyde, FRICS, MBIAC.

GOAT DAIRYING

Performance level (yield)		Low	per Goat Average	High
Milk Yield (litres) (1)		500	800	1100
		£	£	£
Milk Value (2)		200	320	440
PLUS Value of Kid(s) (3)		7	9	18
PLUS Value of Culls (4)		7	7	7
LESS Cost of Replacements (4)		30	30	30
OUTPUT		184	306	435
Variable Costs:				
Concentrates (5)		50	79	109
Forage (6)		43	68	94
Miscellaneous (7)		36	36	36
TOTAL VARIABLE COSTS		129	183	239
GROSS MARGIN per Goat		55	123	196
Stocking rate: No. per ha(acre) (zero grazed) (8)		6·5 (2·65)	8 (3·25)	9·5 (3·85)
(Equivalent) Gross Margin per ha (acre)		360 (145)	985 (400)	1865 (755)

Notes

1. *Yield.* Per 300 day lactation, kidding each year. Autumn kidders tend to yield less.

2. *Price.* 40p per litre; seasonal variation from 32p in June to 52p in November. 12·5% solids delivered to creamery.

3. *Kid(s).* Prolificacy relates to age, breed, seasonality and feed level. Assumptions: low 140%; average and high 180%. Average week-old kid price for both sexes £5, although many males are destroyed as unsaleable; premium herds average £10 per kid.

4. *Culls and Replacements.* 20% replacement at £150/head; culls £35, average life 5 years. Bucks: 1 per 40-50 does. Does normally mate in autumn, kid 5 months later; young goats can be mated from 6 months onwards.

5. *Concentrates.* Average 0·55 kg concentrate per litre, at £180 per tonne DM.

6. *Forage.* Average 0·9 kg DM forage per litre at £95 per tonne DM (part purchased, part home-grown). Goats can be grazed but are normally storage fed to avoid problems with worms, fencing and milk taints.

7. *Miscellaneous.* Bedding £10, vet and med. £15, sundries £11.

8. *Stocking rate.* Based on home-grown forage.

9. *Labour.* 1 full-time person per 100 goats.

10. *Markets.* There is no government market support for goat produce. Some successful businesses have been built on producer retailing. Bulk purchasers of goats milk are few and far between. The overall market for goat produce (mainly cheese, milk and yogurt) continues to grow at 10-20% per annum. However, natural prolifacy and improved technology would allow a 60% growth in output, which leads to cyclical instability in the prices of both milk and livestock.

Organisations. The British Goat Society registers pedigree animals and publishes a monthly newsletter.

Acknowledgements. The above information has been supplied by Dr. T. Mottram, Bristol University, School of Veterinary Science, Langford, Bristol.

ANGORA GOATS

							Breeding Does (2)	Subsequent Shearing (2)
Yield of Fibre (kg/year) (3)	...	...	...	...			13·71	5·45
Price of Fibre (£/kg) (3)...	...	...	...	...			3·02	2·5

							£ per doe	£ per head
Value of Fibre	...	...	...	...	...	...	41·4	13·63
Value of Kids (1·42 per doe mated (4))					...	...	33·4	—
Value of Cull (5) ...	...	...	...	...	...		4·1	9·2
LESS Replacements (5)	...	...	...	...	...		9·6	10·0
OUTPUT	...	...	...	...	...	...	69·3	12·83
Variable Costs:								
Concentrates (6)	...	...	...	...	...		24·6	6·4
Vet. and Med ...	...	...	...	...	...		6·0	0·6
Miscellaneous (7)	...	...	...	...	...		9·0	2·2
TOTAL VARIABLE COSTS (excl. Forage) ...			...	...			39·6	9·2
GROSS MARGIN per Doe/Head before Forage Costs				...			29·7	3·63
Forage Variable Costs	...	...	...	...	...		8·0	5·3
GROSS MARGIN per Doe/Head	...	...	...	...			21·7	-1·67
Stocking Rate (Does (Inc. followers) per ha (acre))							10 (4)	15 (6)
GROSS MARGIN per ha (acre)	...	...	...	...			217 (88)	-25 (-10)

Notes:

1. Angora goats produce mohair; angora rabbits produce angora; cashgora is produced by angora cross feral goats; cashmere is produced by improved feral goats (valuable "down" has to be separated from guard hairs; thus, with cashmere production, "yield of down" must not be confused with "weight of clip" as percentage down is low and can vary widely). Goat meat is called "chevon".

2. The data for Breeding Does include output and inputs for a proportion (3%) of a buck and the doe's progeny. Progeny are sold after 2 clips for breeding or after 3 clips for meat. Stock may be retained for further shearing, but the annual margins shown above under "subsequent shearing" indicate that this is currently unprofitable.

3. Angora goats are usually clipped twice a year. Yield increases over first four clips, but quality decreases. Prices are volatile, being dependent on fashion and on the world market dominated by South Africa and Texas, both showing some instability at present (1997). Demand and prices for the high quality kid fibre <30 microns in diameter. The following yields and values have been used. Current wholesale values are poor but an allowance has been made for some direct selling for spinning.
   Clip 1: 1·2 kg, £5/kg; clip 2: 2·0 kg, £4/kg; clip 3: 2·5 kg, £3/kg; adult: 3·0 kg, £2-2·50/kg.

4. 1·5 kids born alive per doe mated; 2% mortality to each clip. Number of doe kids sold for breeding equal to number of replacements (unless the flock size is increasing).Value comprises: 0·2 breeders at £45 each, 1·22 kids for meat at £20 each.

5. *Culls.* Breeding stock in commercial flocks are culled after five years on average. Doe: buck ratio averages 35:1. Subsequent shearing stock culled after a further 4 clips. Value of all cull stock: £20 each. Replacement costs: does, £45; bucks, £100. Shearing stock, £20 (as transfer from breeding enterprise). Show grade stock command a premium.

6. *Concentrates.* Price: £160 per tonne. Quantities: Kids—30 kg to Clip 2, 15 kg to Clip 3; Adults—breeding 90 kg per year, shearing 40 kg per year.

7. Veterinary costs can be high. Miscellaneous costs include £1 per shearing per head (it may be more) and bedding materials.

8. Margins are particularly sensitive to the value and number of breeding stock sold, yield and value of fibre, kidding percentage and meat values. When comparing with sheep margins the higher average working capital requirement should be recognised. Fencing requirements similar to sheep, housing a little more.
   Researcher: Angela Edwards.

GRAZING LIVESTOCK UNITS

Dairy cows	1·00	Lowland ewes	0·11
Beef cows (excl. calf) ...	0·75	Upland ewes	0·08
Heifers in calf (rearing) ...	0·80	Hill ewes	0·06
Bulls	0·65	Breeding ewe hoggs,	
		½ to 1 year	0·06
Other cattle (excl. intensive beef):		Other sheep, over 1 year ...	0·08
0-1 year old	0·34	Store lambs, under 1 year	0·04
1-2 years old	0·65	Rams	0·08
2 years old and over ...	0·80		

Source: as advised by MAFF in England and Wales Farm Business Survey

Notes

1. Total livestock units on a farm should be calculated by multiplying the above ratios by the *monthly livestock numbers averaged over the whole year.*

2. The ratios are based on feed requirements. Strictly speaking, when calculating stocking density, allowances should also be made for differences in output (e.g. milk yield per cow or liveweight gain per head), breed (e.g. Friesians *v.* Jerseys), and quantities of non-forage feed consumed.

OTHER LIVESTOCK UNITS

Breeding sows	0·44	Broilers	0·0017
Gilts in pig	0·20	Other table chicken	0·004
Maiden gilts	0·18	Turkeys	0·005
Boars	0·35	Ducks, geese, other poultry	0·003
Other pigs	0·17	Horses	0·80
Cocks, hens, pullets in lay ...	0·017	Milch goats	0·16
Pullets, 1 week to point of lay	0·003	Other goats	0·11

Source: as advised by MAFF in England and Wales Farm Business Survey

CAP Payments: Stocking Rate for Beef Premiums

Note that the above units are not those to be used for calculating stocking rates for the purpose of determining eligibility for the new beef premiums. Only dairy cows, beef and sheep animals qualifying for support payments are included in the calculation and the following livestock units are used: dairy and suckler cows (including replacement in-calf heifers) and male cattle over 2 years old, 1; male cattle 6 months-2 years, 0·6; ewes and goats, 0·15. The number of dairy cows used in the calculation are not the actual number on the farm but are based on the farm's milk quota divided by the average yield in the region (5200 kg in England) . The total number of units are divided by the forage area (ha) declared as such (on which no area payments may be claimed) associated with these enterprises to give the stocking rate in units per hectare.

FORAGE VARIABLE COSTS
(£ per hectare (acre) per annum)

	Grass-Dairying (1)	Grass-Other (1)	Forage Maize (2)	Kale	Fodder Beet
Yield:					
tonnes/ha (tons/acre)	—	—	40 (16) (silage)	50 (20)	65 (26)
Seed	12 (5)	10 (4)	135 (55)	50 (20·5)	160 (65)
Fertilizer...	100 (40)	65 (26)	75 (30)	85 (34·5)	105 (42)
Sprays	8 (3)	5 (2)	40 (16)	55 (22)	160 (65)
Total	120 (48)	80 (32)	250 (101)	190 (77)	425 (172)

	Rape	Turnips	Rape and Turnips	Stubble Turnips	Swedes
Yield:					
tonnes/ha (tons/acre)	—	65 (26)	—	—	65 (26)
Seed	15	15 (6)	30 (12)	25 (10)	25 (10)
Fertilizer	65	75 (30)	75 (30)	70 (28)	80 (32)
Sprays	—	50 (20)	—	—	45 (18)
Total	80 (30)	140 (56)	105 (42)	95 (38)	150 (60)

(1) These are *average* figures only. Intensively grazed grass may have much higher fertilizer costs in particular—possibly approaching £140 (57) for dairying. The seed costs will vary according to the proportion, if any, of permanent pasture and the length of the leys. Fertilizer inputs are often less on permanent pasture too, but this depends largely on the attitude of the farmer/manager, which will also be reflected in the stocking rates and productive levels per animal achieved. Note that the dairying figure is the average for the grass devoted to the *whole herd*, i.e., followers as well as cows; the figure for cows alone will usually be higher.

(2) Contract work on maize: drilling £40 (16); harvesting (inc. carting and clamping) 125 (50). For further details on this crop see "Forage Maize", by Q. Straghan and A. Perry, Genus Management, 1993. The area grown in the UK increased five fold in the past 12 years, to 111,000 ha in 1996.

An area payment is available for forage maize, provided the area is not included in the stocking rate calculation for beef premiums; the set aside requirement applies if the payment is claimed except for small farms where the maize is entered under the simplified scheme. Maize has a separate base area; in 1996 overshooting caused the area payment to be cut to 76% of the claimed area.

Standing maize crops are generally sold for between £600 and £1,100/ha (£240-440/ acre) according to the quality of the crop and the seasonal demand.

Labour: grass, pages 106-7; kale, page 108; conservation labour, page 106-7. Conservation machinery, page 116.

Silage and Hay

Estimated average costs (for 1998) of producing and harvesting, on a full costs basis (i.e. including rental value of the land, all labour, share of general overheads, etc.) are:

Hay: £75 per tonne; Silage: £21·50 per tonne.

Approximately half the silage cost is for growing the grass and half for harvesting and storage. The % breakdown of total costs is as follows:

Variable Costs	Fertilizer	Seeds and Sprays	Contract	Sundries
Silage	23	1	10	5
Hay	18	1	2	2

Fixed Costs	Rent	Labour	Tractors	Deprec. & Reps.	FYM/Lime
Silage... ...	21	10	16	9	5
Hay	25	16	19	12	5

Sale Value of hay and (far less common because of its bulk) silage vary widely according to the region and type of season (supply/demand situation), quality and time of year. Silage is typically valued at about £25 a tonne.

Ensiled whole crop wheat (40 to 50% DM): £30 to £40 per tonne.

Relative Costs of Grazing, Conserved Grass, etc. (1987)

Source: ICI (M. E. Hutchinson, Henley Manor Farm)

	Yield DM tonnes/ha (acre)	Cost per tonne DM (£)	MJ per kg DM	Pence per MJ of ME in DM
Grazed Grass	11·1 (4·5)	38·6	11·8	0·33
Kale (direct drilled)	6·9 (2·8)	42·0	11·0	0·38
Forage Turnips (direct drilled) ...	6·9 (2·8)	38·1	10·2	0·37
Grass Silage	11·1 (4·5)	69·1	10·9	0·63
Big Bale Silage	11·1 (4·5)	74·1	10·9	0·68
Extra Silage	2·5 (1·0)	7·0	10·9	0·34
Purchased Hay (1)	—	76·5	8·8	0·87
Brewers' Grains (2)	—	108·5	10·0	1·09
Concentrates (3)	—	155·2	12·8	1·21

(1) At £65/tonne. (2) At £24/tonne. (3)14% CP, delivered in bulk, £133·50/tonne.

Notes

1. In interpreting the above comparative figures for use in planning feed use on the individual farm it is important to remember two points: (a) that own land, labour and capital for equipment are required for home-produced fodder but not for purchased feed, and much more storage is required, and (b) the limitation on the consumption of bulk fodder by ruminant livestock—although this very much depends upon its quality/digestibility.
2. Later data may be obtained from the Kingshay Farming Trust (Tel. 01460 72977).

Relative Value of Feeds

(based on their energy contents fed to dairy cows)

	Weight equivalent (1)	Relative Value (2)		Weight equivalent (1)	Relative Value (2)
Good hay	154	52	Fresh brewers' grains	589	13·5
Medium hay	165	48·5	Pressed sugar beet pulp	515	15·5
Dried grass	143	56	Dried distillers' grains	108	74
Swedes	767	10·5	Molassed dried beet pulp	107	75
Potatoes	449	17·75	Wheat middlings	113	71
Mangolds	857	9·25	Flaked maize	87	92
Cabbage	1030	7·75	Maize germ meal (14%)	88	91
Oats	119	67	Barley straw	218	37
Wheat	98	81·5	Oat straw	228	35
Sorghum	102	78·5	Wheat straw	245	32·5
Maize	97	82·5	Pea haulm straw	211	38
			Wheat bran	133	60

(1) equivalent to 100 of barley   (2) value (£) compared with feed barley at £80 per tonne.

Source (of Weight Equivalents): ADAS (D. Morgan)

See also Feedingstuffs: Nutritive Values, page 192.

FODDER CROPS, GRASSES AND CLOVERS:
SEED PRICES (1997) AND SEED RATES

Crop	Price	Seed Rate per hectare
Fodder Kale	£8·50 to £12 per kg	3·4 to 4·5 kg
Swedes	£18·00 to £25·00 per kg	3·0 to 4·0 kg
Turnips	£4·25 per kg	3·0 to 4·0 kg
Stubble Turnips	£4·50 per kg	7·0 kg broadcast
Rape	£2·20 to £2·50 per kg	3·8 kg drilled
		7·5 kg broadcast
Mustard	£1·40 per kg	22 to 28 kg
Rape and Turnips	£30 to £35 per hectare	1·25 kg rape
		3·75 kg turnips
Rape, Kale and Turnips	£56 per hectare	7·5 kg rape, 2·5 kg kale,
		1·25 kg turnips
Fodder Turnip	£4·00 to £6·25 per kg	5 kg broadcast
Forage Maize—Silage	£100 to £140 per hectare	110,000 to 120,000 seeds
Forage Maize—zero		
grazed	£110 to £160 per hectare	130,000 to 160,000 seeds
Arable Silage	£110 per hectare	125 kg oats, 60 kg tares
Tares	£60 per 50 kg	—
Westerwold Ryegrass	£2 per kg	35 kg
Italian Ryegrass	£2·20 to £2·60 per kg	33 to 50 kg
Perennial Ryegrass	£2·30 to £3·30 per kg	22 to 33 kg
Hybrid Ryegrass	£2.50 to £2.70 per kg	30 to 40 kg
Cocksfoot	£2·35 per kg	20 to 25 kg
Timothy	£2·50 to £2·60 per kg	7 to 9 kg
Meadow Fescue	£2·65 per kg	11 to 13 kg
Broad Red Clover	£4·00 to 4·90 per kg	18 to 22 kg
Alsike Clover	£2·75 per kg	18 to 22 kg
White Clover	£4·50 to £11·25 per kg	3·5 kg
Kent Wild White Clover	£9.50 per kg	—
Lucerne	£4·90 per kg	18 to 22 kg
Rye	£30 per 50 kg	175 kg
Rye and Ryegrass	£120 per hectare	125 kg rye
		22 kg Italian Ryegrass
1 year leys	£75 to £80 per hectare	—
2-3 year leys	£75 to £80 per hectare	—
3-5 year leys	£90 to £100 per hectare	—
Permanent Grass	£100 to £120 per hectare	—
Red Clover Ley	£86 per hectare	—
Wye College mixture	£59 per hectare	—
Horse grazing	£77 per hectare	—
Game Cover mixture	£46 per hectare	—

N.B. Grass seed prices are likely to remain firm during 1997-98.

4. PIGS AND POULTRY

PIGS

1. Breeding and Rearing (to 30 kg liveweight):
per sow per year and per 30 kg pig reared

Performance Level		Average			High	
		per sow	per pig		per sow	per pig
		£	£		£	£
Weaners: 21 (1) @ £35 (3) ...		735	35·00	24 (2) @ £35 (3)	840	35·00
Less Livestock Depreciation (4) ...		25	1·20		30	1·25
Output		710	33·80		810	33·75
Variable Costs:						
Food (5)		415	19·75		415	17·30
Miscellaneous (6)		45	2·15		50	2·10
Total Variable Costs		460	21·90		465	19·40
Gross Margin (per year)		250	11·90		345	14·35

Notes

1. Weaners per sow—average: 9·5 reared per litter, 2·2 litters per year = 21 weaners per sow per year.
2. Weaners per sow—high: 10·2 reared per litter, 2·35 litters per year = 24 weaners per sow per year.
3. Price—assumed pig cycle average. (See footnote (N.B.) on p. 83). Prices for average quality 30 kg weaners have varied from £25 to over £50 in recent years.
4. Average livestock depreciation assumes an in-pig gilt purchase price of £160, a cull value per sow of £135 and a 45% replacement rate (i.e. approx. 6 litters per sow life). Sow mortality 4·5%. Boars purchased at £600, sold at £130. "High" compared with "Average": higher gilt and boar purchase prices and slightly fewer sows per boar assumed.
5. Food—2·15 tonnes per sow: sow 1·25, boar (per sow) 0·05, other feed (per sow) 0·85. Price of feed consumed: £192·50 per tonne; (average of 60% sow (and boar) feed (at £150-160) and 40% piglet and rearing feed (at £240-260), and of home-mixed and purchased compounds). High performance: slightly higher percentage of creep feed but lower feed cost per tonne, as higher proportion home-mixed.
6. Average: vet. and med. £25, transport £1·5, straw and bedding £10, miscellaneous £8·5. (Electricity and gas (£17·5) and water (£3·5) additional).
7. *Direct Labour Cost* per sow: average £125, good £100; per weaner: average £5·95, good £4·15. See further page 113. *Other Fixed Costs:* approx. £105.
8. *Building Costs:* see pages 149-150.

N.B. *Outdoor Breeding:* see page 85.

PIGS

2. Feeding (from 30 kg liveweight): per pig

A. Average Performance

	Pork £	Cutter £	Bacon £
Sale Value	62·70	73·45	75·90
LESS Weaner Cost*	35·00	35·00	35·00
Mortality charge	0·75	0·95	1·05
OUTPUT	26·95	37·50	39·85
Variable Costs:			
Food	21·45	26·45	28·45
Miscellaneous	1·15	1·40	1·75
TOTAL VARIABLE COSTS	22·60	27·85	30·20
GROSS MARGIN	4·35	9·65	9·65
Liveweight (kg)	77·5	88·5	92·5
Deadweight (kg)	55	65	69
Killing out (%)	71	73·5	74·5
Price per kg deadweight (p)	114	113	110
Price per kg liveweight (p)	80·9	83·0	82·1
Food Conversion Rate	2·7	2·9	2·95
Food per pig (kg)	128	170	184
Average Cost of Food per tonne	£167·50	£155·50	£154·50
Food Cost per kg Liveweight Gain ...	45·2p	45·2p	45·5p
Liveweight Gain per day (kg)	·62	·65	·61
Feeding period (weeks)	11	13	14·5
Mortality (per cent)	2·7	2·9	3·1
Direct Labour Cost per pig	£3·00	£3·80	£3·95
B. High Performance (Food Conversion)			
Food Conversion Rate	2·4	2·55	2·55
Food per pig (kg)	114	149	159
Food Cost per pig	£19·10	£23·15	£24·55
Food Cost per kg Liveweight Gain ...	40·2p	39·6p	39·3p
Gross Margin per pig	£6·70	£12·95	£13·55
Direct Labour Cost per pig	£1·95	£2·50	£2·60

Notes
* Weaner cost assumes on farm transfer. If purchased (i.e., feeding only) transport and purchasing costs have to be added: these are very variable but average about £1·50 per weaner.
Labour: see page 113.
Building Costs: see pages 150-151.
Acknowledgement: Main data source: Pig Yearbook (Meat and Livestock Commission), 1997 and previous years, but the pig and feed price assumptions are entirely the author's responsibility. Small differences in the relationship between these can of course cause large differences in margins. Big variations can occur between farms in feed costs per tonne, according to whether the food is purchased as compounds or home-mixed, bought in bulk or in bags, size of unit, etc. The weaner price is crucial as regards the relative margins between breeding and rearing and finishing.
Sensitivity Analysis. The effect on gross margins per pig (£) of changes in important variables (other things being equal) are as follows (per porker, cutter and baconer respectively). Price: 5p per kg dw difference: 2·75, 3·25, 3·45. Food Cost/tonne: £10 difference: 1·28, 1·70, 1·84. FCR: 0·1 difference: 0·79, 0·91, 0·96. The effect of differences in the cost per weaner is obvious.
N.B. No attempt has been made in this section to forecast the actual position of the pig cycle during 1998. The figures represent only what the average trend figures are likely to be in that year, given neither an "up" nor a "down" stage prevailing for much of the year. The UK Average All Pigs Price (Adjusted Euro Spec. UK average; p/kg dw) fell as low as 90p early in 1994 and reached 151p in July 1996. A rapid drop, to 103p in February 1997, was halted by severe outbreaks of swine fever on the Continent. The level assumed above is approx. 112·50p.

3. Combined Breeding, Rearing and Feeding: per pig

	Pork £		Cutter £		Bacon £	
Level of Performance*	Average	High	Average	High	Average	High
Sale Value	62·70	62·70	73·45	73·45	75·90	75·90
Sow/boar deprecn. ...	1·20	1·25	1·20	1·25	1·20	1·25
Mortality charge ...	0·75	0·65	0·95	0·80	1·05	0·85
OUTPUT	60·75	60·80	71·30	71·40	73·65	73·80
Food	41·20	36·40	46·20	40·45	48·20	41·85
Miscellaneous	3·30	3·25	3·55	3·50	3·90	3·85
TOTAL VARIABLE COSTS	44·50	39·65	49·75	43·95	52·10	45·70
GROSS MARGIN per pig	16·25	21·15	21·55	27·45	21·55	28·10
GROSS MARGIN per sow	340	510	455	660	455	675
Labour	8·95	6·10	9·75	6·65	9·90	6·75

* Performance levels refer to breeding and rearing differences as on page 82 and, for feeding, differences in food conversion rate (and labour cost) only.

4. Further Performance Data

(Meat and Livestock Commission Pigplan results, year ended Sept. 1996).

Level of Performance	Average	Top Third	Top 10%
Breeding			
Sow replacements (%)	44·9	45·9	46·3
Sow sales and deaths (%)	44·2	42·3	41·3
Sow mortality (%)	4·4	3·7	2·9
Litters per sow per year	2·26	2·34	2·41
Pigs reared per litter	9·60	9·99	10·38
Pigs reared per sow per year	21·7	23·4	25·0
Weight of pigs produced (kg)	6·6	6·5	6·7
Average weaning age (days)	25	24	24
Sow feed per sow per year (tonnes)	1·34	1·34	1·33
Feed per pig reared (kg): sow feed	68	63	58
piglet feed ...	0·36	0·32	0·42
Sow feed cost per tonne	£148·7	£146·8	£147·9
Sow feed cost per sow per year	£199·1	£197·2	£196·4
Feed cost per pig reared	£10·16	£9·42	£8·83
Rearing:			
Weight of pigs at start (kg)	6·6	6·6	6·5
Weight of pigs produced (kg)	34·0	36·6	32·4
Mortality (%)	2·5	2·0	2·0
Feed conversion ratio	1·79	1·75	1·60
Daily gain (kg)	·452	·488	·458
Feed cost per tonne	£289·0	£209·6	£200·8
Feed cost per kg gain (p)	41·05	36·74	32·09
Feed cost per pig reared	£11·25	£11·02	£8·31
Feed per pig reared (kg) (1993/4)	51·4	53·6	46·0

84

Level of Performance	Average	Top Third	Top 10%
Feeding:			
Weight of pigs at start (kg)	18·2	16·4	14·5
Weight of pigs produced (kg)...	86·3	85·9	87·5
Mortality (%)	4·0	3·6	3·0
Feed conversion ratio	2·59	2·39	2·39
Daily gain (kg)	·587	·631	·620
Feed cost per tonne	£172·9	£164·7	£154·3
Feed cost per kg gain (p)	44·8	39·3	36·9
Feed cost per pig reared	£30·52	£27·31	£26·94
Feed per pig reared (kg) (1993/4)	163	151	141
Carcase weight (kg)	66·2	66·0	68·2

(FCR for rearing and feeding combined, according to sale weight (kg), 2-year averages:
65-75, 2·25 ; 75-85, 2·34 ; 85-100, 2·50).

Source: Pig Yearbook 1997 (MLC).

5. Outdoor Breeding

The following comparison between Outdoor and Indoor Breeding Herds is from The MLC's
Pig Yearbook (2-year averages, 1994/5 and 1995/6):

	Outdoor	Indoor
Av. no. of sows and gilts	478	214
Sow replacements (%)	45·1	43·2
Sow sales and deaths (%)	44·1	42·9
Sow mortality %)	3·1	5·4
Mortality of pigs born alive (%)	10·9	11·8
Average age at weaning (days)	24	25
Live pigs born per litter	10·79	10·87
Pigs reared per litter	9·61	9·58
Litters per sow per year	2·24	2·26
Pigs reared per sow per year	21·5	21·7
Sow feed per sow per year (tonnes)	1·462	1·248
Sow feed cost per tonne £	147·4	141·0
Sow feed cost per sow per year (£)	215·5	176·0
Feed per pig reared (kg)	74·5	62·5
Feed cost per pig reared (£)	11·02	8·95

Comparative data are also available in University of Exeter Pig Production reports including
the following per sow (two-year averages of 1991/2 and 1992/3 (the latest available)).

	£	£
Gross Margin	219	290
Labour	106	146
(Hours)	(21)	(27)
Land Charges	12	2
Buildings and Equipment	22	31
Other Fixed Costs	33	66
Net Margin	46	45

Stocking Rate for outdoor pigs is mainly between 12 and 25 per ha (5 and 10 per acre),
20 (8) being the most common. Good drainage is essential. A low rainfall and mild climate
are also highly desirable.

It is estimated that outdoor pigs now represent around 20% of the UK breeding herd and
that the proportion is continually increasing. One 1994 estimate updated is that the cost
of establishing a 200-sow herd indoors is £1,450 a head, compared with £235 a head outdoors
(PIC). Re labour, MLC data substantiates the significantly lower requirement for outdoor
compared with indoor breeding.

EGG PRODUCTION

(brown egg layers, 52 week laying period)

Performance Level	Cages Average		High		Free Range Average	
	per bird	per doz eggs	per bird	per doz eggs	per bird	per doz eggs
	£	p	£	p	£	p
Egg Returns	11·28	47·0	12·10	47·0	16·15	68·0
LESS Livestock Depreciation	2·14	8·9	2·14	8·3	2·42	10·2
OUTPUT (per year)	9·14	38·1	9·96	38·7	13·73	57·8
Variable Costs:						
Food	6·36	26·5	6·36	24·7	7·51	31·6
Miscellaneous	0·95	4·0	0·95	3·7	0·91	3·8
TOTAL VARIABLE COSTS	7·31	30·5	7·31	28·4	8·42	35·4
GROSS MARGIN	1·83	7·6	2·65	10·3	5·31	22·4

Notes

Hen-housed data are used throughout, i.e. the total costs and returns are divided by the number of birds housed at the commencement of the laying period.

A. Cage Production

1. The yields assumed are:

    Average ... ... 288 (24 dozen)

    High ... ... 309 (25·75 dozen)

2. The average price assumed (for 1998), 47p per dozen, includes all quantity and quality bonuses. Farmer to shop and consumer prices are well above packer to producer levels and normally 35p and 65p per dozen premiums respectively are required.

3. Livestock depreciation—the average point of lay pullet is priced at £2·40 (17 weeks old) less £0·36 for culls; (allowance has been made for mortality).

4. The food price assumed (for 1998) is £148 per tonne. The feed cost is dependent on breed, housing and environmental conditions, quantity purchased and type of ration. Quantity of feed used = 43 kg.

5. *Direct Labour Costs:* average £1·30 per bird, premium 98p. See page 113.

    Housing Costs: see page 150. Deadstock depreciation averages about £1 per caged bird.

B. Free Range Production

1. Egg yields: 285 (23·75 dozen).

2. Average price: 68p per dozen. An additional premium of 2p per dozen may be paid by packers for eggs produced to welfare specifications.

3. Quantity of feed used = 47·5 kg. Price £158 per tonne.

4. *Direct Labour Costs:* average £3·15 per bird, dependent on automation.

Acknowledgement. See page 89.

REARING PULLETS

(Average per bird reared)

	£
Value of 17 week old bird	2·40
Less Chicks 1·02 (1) @ 52p (including levy)	0·53
Output	**1·87**
Variable Costs:	
Food: 6·25 kg @ £150 per tonne	0·94
Miscellaneous (2)	0·52
Total Variable Costs	**1·46**
Gross Margin	**0·41**

1. Assumes 3 per cent mortality, but 2 per cent allowed in price.
2. Excluding transport (11p), but including gumboro vaccination and in some cases voluntary salmonella testing.

Labour 25p; *deadstock depreciation* 30p.

TABLE POULTRY

A. *Broilers* (per bird sold at 43 days)

	p
Returns: 2·30 kg per bird @ 60·5p per kg lw	139·2
Less Cost of Chick	25·5
Output	**113·7**
Variable Costs:	
Food: 4·25 kg per bird @ £184 per tonne	78·2
Heat, Light, Miscellaneous	11·8
Total Variable Costs	**90·0**
Gross Margin	**23·7**

Capital cost of housing and equipment: £4·75 per broiler space (depreciation cost approximately 3·25p per bird sold).

Labour: 3·9p, excluding catching and cleaning out (3·7p) but includes management; see page 113.

Housing Costs: see page 150.

B. Turkeys (per bird sold) (1)

Size (2)	Light £	Medium £	Heavy £
Returns (Christmas) (3)	12·88	15·45	18·11
Returns (All Year Average) (3)	10·00	12·00	16·58
LESS Cost of Poult	2·16	2·29	2·24
OUTPUT (Christmas)	10·72	13·16	15·87
OUTPUT (All Year Average)	7·84	9·71	14·34
Variable Costs:			
Food (£188 per tonne)	3·07	4·57	6·72
Miscellaneous	1·58	1·87	2·20
TOTAL VARIABLE COSTS	4·65	6·44	8·92
GROSS MARGIN (Christmas)	6·07	6·72	6·95
GROSS MARGIN (All Year Average)	3·19	3·27	5·42
Killing Age (weeks)	16	20	22
Deadweight (kg)	5·0	6·0	10·2
Food Conversion Factor	2·8	3·5	3·0
Food per bird (kg)	15·4	22·5	32·5

(1) 6, 8 and 10% mortality allowed for in cost of poult and feed figures for light, medium and heavy weights respectively.

(2) Light and medium: hen birds; heavy: stags. (As hatched).

(3) Price per kg dw: Christmas: hens 240-275p, stags 165-190p; All Year Average: hens 180-220p, stags 150-175p. Usually the heavier the bird the lower the price.

Note

Considerable variations occur between individual strains and because of different production systems and feeding regimes. The figures should therefore be used only as rough guidelines.

C. Roasters (Capons) (per bird sold at 12 weeks; Christmas–males only)

	£
Returns 4·7 kg @ £2·20 per kg	10·34
LESS Cost of Chick	0·52
OUTPUT	9·82
Variable costs:	
Food: 14·2 kg per bird @ £188 per tonne	2·94
Miscellaneous	0·56
TOTAL VARIABLE COSTS	3·50
GROSS MARGIN	6·32

10% mortality allowed for in cost of chick and feed figures.

D. Ducks (Aylesbury type: per bird sold at 7 weeks)

	£
Returns: 3·3 kg @ £1·90 per kg dw	6·27
Less Cost of Duckling	1·20
Output	5·07
Variable Costs:	
Food: 9·4 kg per bird @ £200 per tonne	2·07
Miscellaneous	0·84
Total Variable Costs	2·91
Gross Margin	2·16

N.B. Returns: see note below.

E. Geese

	£
Returns: 5·5 kg @ £4·00 per kg dw	22·00
Less Cost of Gosling	4·00
Output	18·00
Variable Costs:	
Food: 18·0 kg @ £195 per tonne	3·86
Miscellaneous	1·08
Total Variable Costs	4·94
Gross Margin	13·06

N.B. Feed costs for both ducks and geese allow for mortality.

Returns for both ducks and geese are based on London (Smithfield) Christmas prices — individual growers may well find oven-ready prices are as high as £5·00 and £6·40 per kg respectively for Grade A quality birds sold direct to consumers.

Acknowledgement: The figures in the whole of the poultry section are provided by Tony Warner, AAW Poultry Consultancy, Newport, Shropshire.

RAINBOW TROUT

(per tonne of fish)

	£
Sales: 1 tonne of fish @ £2·05 per kg	2,050
Less 3,440 fingerlings @ 4·8p each	165
Output	1,885
Variable Costs:	
Food: 1·1 tonnes @ £610/tonne	670
Vet. and med	60
Marketing and transport	110
Total Variable Costs	840
Gross Margin	1,045

Notes

Fish growing to 350g from fingerlings at 4·5g.

Prices are expected wholesale, 1997, but most fish farmers sell at least some of their production direct to retailers, caterers and consumers at prices up to £4·20 kg, but with added marketing costs.

Fingerlings price: 4·0 to 5·5p each according to quantity ordered and time of year.

Average feeding period, 10 months. Mortality, from fingerling to market size, 17%. Food conversion ratio, 1·1:1. The price for fish food is for a pigmented high oil expanded pellet.

Current capital costs for construction of earth pond unit approx. £1,000 per tonne of holding capacity, to include buildings, holding systems and installation of water supply and services, but excluding land.

Labour requirement: the basic norm has in the past been 1 man per 50 tonnes of fish produced per annum on a table fish farm, but with mechanisation this can now be as high as 100 tonnes.

Acknowledgement: Data provided by Dr. John Springate, Roche Products Ltd., Heanor.

II. LABOUR

1. LABOUR COST

1. Statutory Minimum Wage Rates
(from June 1, 1997)

The minimum weekly rates relate to a 39-hour standard week of normal hours worked on any five days between Monday and Saturday. (1, 2) The rates apply to both men and women.

Grades I & II	Appointment Grade I		Appointment Grade II		Craft NVQ3 Grade (3)		Craft Certificate Grade (4)	
Age	Weekly rate	Overtime per hour	Weekly rate	Overtime per hour	Weekly rate	Overtime per hour	Weekly rate	Overtime per hour
	£	£	£	£	£	£	£	£
19 and over	217·15	8·35	201·07	7·73	189·81	7·30	184·98	7·11

	Full and Part-time Standard Workers			Casual Workers (5)		Night work Supplement	Standby Payments (6)
Age	rate per standard week	rate per hour excluding overtime	overtime rate per hour	rate per hour excluding overtime	overtime rate per hour	rate per hour	rate per day
	£	£	£	£	£	p	£
19 & over	160·85	4·12	6·19	3·06	4·59	82	16·50
18	136·73	3·51	5·26	2·60	3·90	70	14·02
17	112·60	2·89	4·33	2·14	3·21	58	11·55
16	96·51	2·47	3·71	1·84	2·75	49	9·90
15 & under	80·43	2·06	3·09	1·53	2·30	41	8·25

1. Holidays with pay. The number of days holiday that workers are entitled to in a year depends on the number of "qualifying periods" completed during their employment during that year. For those working full-time, 5 days a week, all year, this amounts to 4 weeks and a day. There are rules as to timing. The rates of holiday pay are given on page 92.
2. Rates of pay over the above rates are paid to workers 18 years old or more for flexible working contracts: 5% more where basic hours are worked on 4 or 5 days, 7% more where they are worked on 6 days.
3. National Vocational Qualification (NVQ) Level 3 craft grade (18% premium above the basic rate).
4. In 1996 26·7 per cent of the regular whole-time adult (19 years old and over) male labour force in England and Wales were classified as craftsmen (NVQ3) (plus 5·8 per cent as Grade I and 6·75 per cent as Grade II). However, many other workers receive basic wages above the "ordinary" rates.
5. Casual workers: employed on temporary basis by the hour or day; excludes workers continuously employed for more than 20 weeks.
6. Part standby duty days are paid at half these rates.
7. Pre-college students are paid at 75% of the appropriate minimum rate for the first year. Modern apprentices receive 75% of the normal basic rate for a full-time standard worker for the first six months. Young trainees are paid at the appropriate overtime rate for hours in excess of their training course. Foreign students are paid at special rates for the first 13 weeks.
8. Certain benefits are reckonable in part payment of the minimum wage rates, at specified values, e.g. a cottage or house (£1·50/week—though can be varied on application), board and lodging. There are specified provisions for sick pay, paid bereavement leave and paid paternity leave (3 days).

Holiday Pay

With the exception of casual workers holiday pay must be paid to all types of worker when they take holidays to which they are entitled. For full-time standard and full-time flexible workers the minimum rates are 25% higher than the minimum basic pay rates for a 39 hour week, i.e. excluding overtime. For part-time workers holiday rates are the same as basic pay rates based on the average of the total hours worked, including overtime, over the 12 months ending on the last 5th April. For new workers average hours are based on the days worked since 6th April.

2. Average Earnings (1)

Type of Worker	Average Total Earnings				Total Hours (3)
	1996		1998 (est.) (2)		
	Annual	Per Week	Annual	Per Week	Per Week
	£	£	£	£	
All Hired Men	13,010	250·19 (4)	13,975	269	47·4
Foremen	15,825	304·37	17,025	327	47·5
Dairy Herdsmen	15,650	300·95	16,825	324	53·1
Other Stockmen	13,110	252·07	14,100	271	46·4
Tractor Drivers	13,960	268·42	15,000	289	49·7
General Farm Workers ...	12,180	234·26	13,100	252	46·8
Horticultural Workers ...	10,965	210·84	11,775	227	42·4

1. Hired regular whole-time workers, England and Wales.
2. 1996 earnings, plus approx. 7·5 per cent.
3. Hours worked plus statutory holidays (in 1996).
4. Prescribed weekly wage for hours worked: £222·13.

Source: MAFF Statistics (Survey of Earnings and Hours), with author's forecasts.

3. Typical Annual Labour Cost 1997/98
(regular worker of 20 or more[1]: from June 1, 1997 to (approx.)
May 31, 1998)

		Average Annual Cost £	Average Weekly Cost £	Average Hourly Cost (2) £
Minimum Wage (non-craftsman rate) (3)		8,525	163·95	4·75
National Insurance Contribution (10% of earnings) (4)	855			
Employer's Liability Insurance (1%)	85	940	18·10	
Minimum Cost		9,465	182·05	5·28
Overtime, average 8·4 hours per week @ £6·19 (+ NIC, ELI)		3,000	57·70	
		12,465	239·75	5·59
"Premium" over basic rate, average £30 per week (+ NIC, ELI)		1,730	33·25	
Total Cost (5, 6)		14,195	273·00	6·36

(NIC = National Insurance Contribution; ELI = Employer's Liability Insurance)
1. Assuming not paid craft grade rates (but note the "premium" assumed exceeds the craft grade "premiums").
2. Hours, excluding overtime, based on 46 weeks (of 39 hours) per year, i.e. statutory holidays and a few days' illness have been deducted.
3. Including additional holiday pay.
4. Employer's NIC reduces from 10% to 7% if the employee's total weekly earnings fall below £210 a week (see page 179).
5. Annual cost (or net value) of cottages, value of perquisites, contribution towards payment of the council tax, etc., would have to be added where appropriate.
6. Total average worker's gross *earnings* on the above assumptions = £12,790 a year, £245·95 a week, £5·73 an hour.

4. Assessing Annual Labour Requirements

The regular labour staff required for a farm is sometimes assessed by calculating the total number of Standard Man-Days (Man-Work Units), as given on page 192. The number of days supplied by casual labour are first deducted, then 15 per cent is added for general maintenance work; no allowance is made for management, for which 7.5% may be added if required. It is assumed that 300 Standard Man-Days are provided annually per man; allowance is made for any manual labour supplied by the farmer himself. Alternatively, no addition is made for maintenance work and 300 SMD are assumed to be provided by stockmen and 250 by other workers. (1 SMD = 8 labour hours a year.)

This is a very rough and inaccurate calculation since it makes no allowance for seasonality and the special circumstances of an individual farm, such as soil type, level of mechanization, and condition and layout of the buildings.

The following sections supply the type of data that should be used in assessing labour requirements.

2. LABOUR HOURS AVAILABLE FOR FIELD WORK
(per man per month)

	Total Ordinary Hours (1)	Adjusted Ordinary Hours (2)	% Workable	Available Ordinary Hours (3)	Available Overtime Hours (4)	**Total Available Hours**	Total Available "8-hour Days" (5)
January	177	148	50	74	28 (61)	**102** (135)	13 (17)
February	160	134	50	67	33 (55)	**100** (122)	12½ (15)
March	172	149	60	89	69 (82)	**158** (171)	20 (21½)
April	161	139	65	90	86	**176**	22
May	171	151	70	106	110	**216**	27
June	170	150	75	112	112	**224**	28
July	177	157	75	118	113	**231**	29
August	169	150	75	112	104	**216**	27
September	172	152	70	106	82 (69)	**188** (195)	23½ (24½)
October	177	153	65	99	63 (83)	**162** (182)	20 (23)
November	172	144	50	72	26 (59)	**98** (131)	12 (16½)
December	161	135	50	67	25 (65)	**92** (132)	11½ (16½)

(1) 40 hour week, less public holidays. No deductions have been made for other holidays because they may be taken at various times of the year.

(2) After deducting (a) for illness (10 per cent Nov. to Feb., 7½ per cent March, April and Oct., 5 per cent May to Sept.), and (b) for contingencies and non-delayable maintenance (½ hour per day).

(3) Adjusted Ordinary Hours × percentage Workable.

(4) Maximum 4 overtime hours per day summer, 3 hours winter, and 12 to 14 hours' work at weekends, according to season. Same adjustments for illness and percentage workable as for ordinary hours. Figures in brackets indicate hours available if headlights used up to limit of overtime stated. The percentage overtime (without headlights) available from weekend work as opposed to evenings = (January to December respectively): 100, 78, 58, 50, 40, 40, 41, 42, 53, 67, 100, 100.

(5) Total available hours ÷ 8.

Notes

1. *These figures relate to medium land. The percentage workability will be higher with light soils and less with particularly heavy soils.* On heavy soils, of course, the land may be virtually 100 per cent unworkable between late November and early March (or still later, according to the season), particularly if undrained. A rough estimate of variations in workability according to soil type (compared with the figures in the above table) are as follows. Heavy land—March, October, November: one-third less; April: one-fifth less; September: 10 per cent less; May to August: no difference. Light land—October to April: one-sixth more; May and September: 10 per cent more; June to August: no difference.

2. When these figures are used for farm planning, it must be remembered that indoor work, e.g. livestock tending or potato riddling, can be continued over the full working-week, i.e. the hours available are the Adjusted Ordinary Hours, plus overtime. Also, some handwork in the field has to continue even in rain, e.g. sprout picking.

3. To be precise, percentage workability varies according to the particular operation, e.g. compare ploughing and drilling.

4. Furthermore, some operations are limited by factors other than soil workability, e.g. combine-harvesting by grain moisture content.

5. Factors touched upon briefly above are discussed fully in Duckham's "The Farming Year".

3. SEASONAL LABOUR REQUIREMENTS FOR CROPS AND GRASS

On the following pages, data on labour requirements for various farm crops and types of livestock are given. Two levels are shown: average and premium. *The average figures relate to the whole range of conditions and farm size. The premium rates do not denote the maximum rates possible,* for instance by the use of especially high-powered tractors under ideal conditions, but relate to rates of work estimated to be obtainable over the whole season, averaging good and bad conditions, with the use of wide implements, largish tractors (75 to 90 kW) (100-120 hp) and high capacity equipment in 8 hectare fields and over, where no time is wasted. **Most farmers with more than 200 hectares (500 acres) of arable land are likely to achieve the premium levels shown. Those with over 400 hectares (1,000 acres) will have still bigger machines and therefore faster work rates, and thus require about 10 to 20 per cent less labour than even the premium levels given.**

The rates of work include morning preparation, travelling to and from the fields, and allow for minor breakdowns and other stoppages. They relate broadly to medium and medium-heavy land; some jobs, such as ploughing, may be done more quickly on light soils. Operations such as combine harvesting can obviously vary according to many factors to do with the topography and other natural features of the farm.

The usual times of year when each operation takes place are shown; these relate to lowland conditions in the south-eastern half of Britain. They will obviously vary between seasons, soil types, latitude and altitude. In particular, on light land, land can be ploughed over a longer winter period and a high proportion of cultivations for spring crops may be completed in February in many seasons. All such factors must be allowed for in individual farm planning. Conditions in different seasons will also affect, for instance, the number and type of cultivations required in seedbed preparation. Typical monthly breakdowns of requirements are given for various crops.

To illustrate the type of questions that need to be asked for full details of seasonal labour requirements on the individual farm, "Critical Questions affecting Timing" are listed for cereals and maincrop potatoes. Similar questions would, of course, need to be asked for other crops.

WINTER CEREALS

Operations	Labour-Hours per hectare		Time of Year
	Average	Premium	
Plough (1)	1·4	1·0	July to October (according to previous crop)
Cultivate (often power harrow)	1·0	0·7	September to October (according to previous crop) (half August if ploughed in July)
Drill (often with power harrows), Roll	1·3	0·9	Mid-September to 3rd week October (according to previous crop and soil)
Apply Fertilizer	0·4	0·3	
Spray	0·3	0·2	October-November
Top Dress (three times (2)) ...	1·2	0·9	March and April
Spray (three or four (2)) ...	1·0	0·7	Spring/early summer
Combine, Cart Grain, Barn Work	2·7	2·1	Mid-August to approx. 10th September
Later Barn Work (3)	0·7	0·4	September to June
Total	10·0	7·2	
Straw: Bale	1·3	0·8	Mid-August to end
Cart	3·7	2·8	September

Typical Monthly Breakdown

Month	Average	Premium	Notes
October	2·6	1·9	Approx. 60% of Ploughing,
November ...	—	—	Cults., Drill, Harrow
December ...	—	—	
January	—	—	
February ...	—	—	
March	0·5	0·3	Part Top Dress
April	1·1	0·8	Part Top Dress, Spraying
May	0·3	0·3	Spraying
June	0·3	0·2	Spraying
July	—		
August	1·8 (+2·5 Straw)	1·4 (+1·8 Straw)	$^2/_3$ of harvesting (4)
September (harvest) ...	0·9 (+2·5 Straw)	0·7 (+1·8 Straw)	$^1/_3$ of harvesting (4)
September (prepn. drill)	1·8	1·2	40% of Ploughing, Cults., Drill, Harrow

Notes
1. Some cereal crops are direct drilled or drilled after reduced, or minimal, cultivations, i.e. without traditional ploughing. Direct drilling reduces man-hours per hectare by about 2·5 (average) or 1·8 (premium), and minimal cultivations by about 1·2 (average) and 0·9 (premium).
2. Winter wheat; winter barley will often have one less top dressing and spraying and oats two less.
3. Later barn work excluded from monthly breakdown.
4. Winter wheat (see page 98 for harvest times for winter barley and oats).

Seasonal Labour Requirements

SPRING CEREALS

Operations	Labour-Hours per hectare		Time of Year
	Average	Premium	
Plough (1)	1·4	1·0	September-March (according to previous crop and soil type)
Cultivate (often power harrow)	1·0	0·7	March (½ in second half February on light land)
Apply Fertilizer	0·4	0·3	
Drill (often with power harrows), Roll	1·3	0·9	March (¼ at end February on light land)
Top Dress (once, some possibly twice)	0·5	0·3	
Spray (two or three)	0·7	0·5	May
Combine, Cart Grain, Barn Work	2·6	2·0	Last three-quarters of August (affected by variety as well as season)
Later Barn Work (2)	0·6	0·4	September to June
Total	8·5	6·1	
Straw: Bale (unmanned sledge)	1·3	0·8	Mid-August to end
Cart	3·7	2·8	September

Typical Monthly Breakdown

Month		Average	Premium	Notes
October	...	0·4	0·3	Ploughing. How much in
November	...	0·8	0·5	October depends on
December	...	0·2	0·2	area of Winter Wheat, Potatoes, etc.
January	...	—	—	
February	...	—	—	
March	...	2·7	1·9	All Cults. Drilling, Rolling (nearly half in February on light land)
April	... ...	—	—	
May	... ...	1·2	0·8	Spray and top dress
June	... ...	—	—	
July	... ...	—	—	
August (3)	...	2·6 (+2·7 Straw)	2·0 (+1·9 Straw)	
September	...	— (+2·3 Straw)	— (+1·7 Straw)	

Notes
1. See note 1 on page 96.
2. Later barn work excluded.
3. Spring barley; spring wheat and oats partly September (see page 98).

In a *normal* (i.e. neither early or late) *season*:

WINTER WHEAT
Drilling mid-September to 3rd week October.
Harvesting mid-August to approx. 10th September.

WINTER BARLEY
As for winter wheat, except that:
Ploughing unlikely to start before cereal harvest, as usually follows a cereal crop.
Harvesting some weeks earlier: mid July to approx. 10th August.

WINTER OATS
As for winter wheat, except that:
Drilling usually first full half of October.
Harvesting earlier (first half of August).

SPRING BARLEY
Drilling end of February to end of March or early April.
Harvesting last half/¾ of August.

SPRING WHEAT
As for spring barley, except that:
Drilling is on average one or two weeks earlier (should be finished in March)—lose more if late than barley.
Harvesting, on average, is two weeks later: last week of August/first half of September (two-thirds in September).

SPRING OATS
As for spring barley, except that:
Drilling is usually a little earlier.
Harvesting is later than spring barley, earlier than spring wheat: end of August/beginning of September.

Seasonal Labour Requirements

Critical Questions affecting Timing (Autumn-sown Cereals)
1. Previous crops (affects time available and need for ploughing and cultivations).
2. Will the crop be ploughed traditionally, chisel ploughed, minimally cultivated, or direct drilled?
3. Earliest and latest drilling date, by choice.
4. Effect on yield if drilling is delayed.
5. Autumn weed control?
6. In the spring: (a) whether crop is rolled, and when,
   (b) whether crop is harrowed, and when,
   (c) time of top dressings,
   (d) number of spray applications.
7. (a) Average period for harvesting.
   (b) Earliest dates for starting and finishing harvest, and latest dates for starting and finishing harvest, ignoring extreme seasons (one year in ten).

Critical Questions affecting Timing (Spring-sown Cereals)
1. Previous crops.
2. Will the crop be ploughed traditionally, chisel ploughed, minimally cultivated, or direct drilled?
3. Months when winter ploughing is possible, on average. (Where relevant).
4. Is spring ploughing satisfactory? (Where relevant).
5. Average period of cultivations and drilling.
6. Earliest dates for starting and finishing spring cultivations/ drilling and latest dates for starting and finishing cultivations/ drilling, ignoring extreme seasons (one year in ten).
7. Effect on yield if drilling is delayed.
8. Is the crop rolled (a) within a few days of drilling or (b) later?
9. (a) Average period of harvesting.
   (b) Earliest dates for starting and finishing harvest, and latest dates for starting and finishing harvest, ignoring extreme seasons (one year in ten).

Seasonal Labour Requirements

MAINCROP POTATOES

Operations	Labour-Hours per hectare Average	Premium	Time of Year
Plough	1·4	1·0	September to December
Cultivating, Ridging, Destoning/ Clod sep. (as required) ...	6·5	5·0	March, early April
Plant and Apply Fertilizer (1)	4·5	3·5	Last quarter of March, first
Apply Herbicide	0·3	0·2	three-quarters of April
Spray for Blight (av. 4 times)	1·2	0·9	July, first half August
Burn off Haulm	0·3	0·2	End September, early October
Harvest, Cart, Clamp (2) ...	15·0	10·0	End September, October
Work on Indoor Clamp ...	4·8	3·2	November
Riddle, Bag, Load	40·0	30·0	October to May
TOTAL	74·0	54·0	

(1) Automatic planter. Hand-fed planters: approx. 12 hours plus 8 that could be casual labour.

(2) Mechanical harvester, excluding up to 25 hours for picking off on harvester—usually casual labour. None may be needed on clod- and stone-free soils. Hand harvesting: additional approx. 80 hours of casual labour.

Typical Monthly Breakdown

Month				Average	Premium	Notes
October	...	...	...	12·2	8·2	80% of harvest, ½ burn off
November	...	...	...	5·9	4·0	Clamp work and ¾ plough
December	...	...	...	0·3	0·2	¼ plough
January	...	...	...	—	—	
February	...	...	...	—	—	
March ...	...	...	...	7·8	6·0	All fertilizer, ½ cults., ¼ plant
April	...	...	...	3·5	2·7	½ cults., ¾ plant
May	...	...	...	—	—	
June	...	...	...	—	—	
July	...	...	...	0·9	0·7	3 blight sprays
August	...	...	...	0·3	0·2	1 blight spray
September	...	...	...	3·1	2·0	20% harvest, ½ burn off

Note: These figures exclude casual labour and riddling.

EARLY POTATOES

Operations	Labour-Hours per hectare		Time of Year
	Average	Premium	
Plough	1·4	1·0	September to December
Cultivating, etc.	6·5	5·0	Late February, early March
Plant and Apply Fertilizer ...	4·5	3·5	Late February, early March
Apply Herbicide	0·3	0·2	1st half March (some in February on light land or in early season)
Further Spraying	0·3	0·2	
After-Cultivation/Spray ...	0·3	0·2	April, early May
Harvest, bag, load	30·0(1)	25·0(2)	2nd week June onwards All June or till mid-July

(1) Excluding 80 hours picking—usually casuals.

(2) Excluding 60 hours picking—usually casuals.

SECOND EARLY POTATOES

Operations	Labour-Hours per hectare		Time of Year
	Average	Premium	
Plough	1·4	1·0	September to December
Cultivating, etc	6·5	5·0	March
Plant and Apply Fertilizer	4·5	3·5	March
Apply Herbicide	0·3	0·2	Half 2nd half March, half 1st half April
Further Spraying	0·9	0·7	End April, May, early June
Harvest	15·0(1)	10·0(2)	Mid-July to end August

(1) Spinner or elevator-digger, excluding picking and riddling—usually casual labour.

(2) Mechanical harvester, excluding picking off on harvester and riddling—usually casual labour.

Seasonal Labour Requirements

SUGAR BEET

Operations	Labour-Hours per hectare Average	Premium	Time of Year
Plough	1·4	1·0	September to December
Seedbed Cults	3·4	2·4	Mainly March (some early April. Some late February
Load, Cart, Apply Fertilizer ...	0·8	0·6	in good seasons)
Drill (and Flat Roll)	2·0	1·3	Between mid-March and mid-April
Spray (herbicide: pre- and post-emergence)	0·6	0·4	Late March/April
Spray (× 2)	0·6	0·4	May/June
Spray (aphis)	0·3	0·2	July
Harvest (machine)	15·0	10·0	End September, October, November
Load	3·4	2·7	End September to early January
TOTAL	27·5	19·0	

Typical Monthly Breakdown

Month	Average	Premium	Notes
October ...	7·7	5·2	45% harvest; + loading
November ...	8·7	5·9	45% harvest; ¾ ploughing; + loading
December ...	1·0	0·8	¼ ploughing; + loading
January ...	0·5	0·4	Loading
February ...	—	—	
March ...	4·1	2·8	Fertilizer, most of cults., some drilling
April	2·7	1·9	Some cults., most of drilling
May	0·3	0·2	Spray
June	0·3	0·2	Spray
July	0·2	0·2	Spray
August	—	—	
September ...	2·0	1·4	10% harvesting; + loading

VINING PEAS

Operations	Labour-Hours per hectare		Time of Year
	Average	Premium	
Plough	1·4	1·0	September to December
Cults., Fert. and Drill	2·5	1·8	Mid-Feb. to April
Post Drilling and Spraying ...	1·5	1·0	
Harvesting	20·0	15·0	July and early August

Note
Drilling is staggered in small areas through the season, ranging from early varieties to late varieties.

DRIED PEAS

Month	Labour-Hours per hectare		Operation
	Average	Premium	
October	1·4	1·0	⎫
November ...	0·9	0·6	⎬ Stubble cult., Plough
December ...	0·2	0·2	⎭
January	—	—	
February	0·2	0·1	Cult. twice, harrow; drill and fert. (80 per
March	3·4	2·4	cent March); light harrow and roll;
April	0·6	0·4	spray
May	2·5	1·8	⎫
June	0·2	0·2	⎬ Scare pigeons; spray
July	2·2	1·4	⎫ Possible spray desiccant; combine and
August	2·5	1·6	⎬ cart, dry
September ...	1·0	0·5	⎭ Stubble cult.

Assumes direct combining.

FIELD BEANS

A. Winter Beans

Operations	Labour-Hours per hectare		Time of Year
	Average	Premium	
Broadcast Seed	0·6	0·4 ⎫	
Apply Fertilizer	0·4	0·3 ⎪	
Plough	1·4	1·0 ⎬ September/October	
Power Harrow	1·0	0·8 ⎪	
Spray (pre-emergence) ...	0·3	0·2 ⎭	
Spraying (two or three times)	0·8	0·5	Spring
Combine and cart and barnwork	3·6	3·0	August

B. Spring Beans

Operations	Labour-Hours per hectare		Time of Year
	Average	Premium	
Plough	1·4	1·0	September to December
Cultivate (often power harrow)	1·0	0·7 ⎫	
Apply Fertilizer...	0·4	0·3 ⎪ End Feb, early March	
Drill, Roll	1·3	0·9 ⎬	
Spray (two or three times) ...	0·8	0·5 ⎭	
Combine and cart and barnwork	3·6	3·0	September

OILSEED RAPE

(Autumn Sown)

Month	Labour-Hours per hectare		Operation
	Average	Premium	
October ... ... ⎫			
November... ... ⎬ 0·6		0·4	Spray herbicide and insecticide if necessary
December... ... ⎭			
January	—	—	
February	—	—	
March ... ... ⎫			
April ... ... ⎬ 1·0		0·6	Top dress twice
May ... ... ⎭	—	—	
June	—	—	
July	2·9	2·1 ⎱	Windrow (1st half July); combine (½ 2nd
August	2·6	1·8 ⎰	half July; ½ 1st half Aug.); straw, dry
August	2·0	1·3 ⎱	Cults. (× 2), spray, drill, fert.; harrow, roll,
September ...	3·3	2·1 ⎰	barn work (0·5)

104

Seasonal Labour Requirements

HERBAGE SEEDS (first production year)

A. Undersown

Operations	Labour-Hours per hectare		Time of Year
	Average	Premium	
Undersow	0·6	0·4	March, April
Roll	(0·6	0·4)	Straight after drilling
Load, Cart, Apply Fertilizer {	0·4	0·3	September
	0.4	0·3	Late February, March
Harvest (by Combine): Mow	1·4	0·9	3 to 4 days before combining
	4·5	3·5	*Ital. Ryegrasses and Early Perennials: late July.*
			Intermed Perennials: late July/ early August.
Combine and Cart			*Late Perennials/White Clover: mid-August*
	6·0	4·5	Meadow Fescue: early July
	7·0	5·0	Cocksfoot: early July
	10·0	7·0	Timothy: mid-August
			Red Clover: late September

B. Direct Drilled in Autumn

Operations	Labour-Hours per hectare		Time of Year
	Average	Premium	
Plough	1·4	1·0 ⎫	Depends on previous crop—
Seedbed Cults	2·2	1·6 ⎬	Usually July or August
Load, Cart, Apply Fertilizer ...	0·4	0·3 ⎭	
Drill (with harrows behind) ...	0·8	0·6	As early as previous crop allows. This may be up to mid-September for ryegrasses without detriment to the subsequent yield.
Roll (soon after drilling) ...	0·6	0·4	Meadow fescue and cocksfoot are best sown no later than July
Harvest	See above (Undersown)		and it is risky to sow timothy much later than this.

105

GRASS

A. Production

Operations	Labour-Hours per hectare Average	Premium	Time of Year
Plough	1·4	1·0	Autumn drilling: may not plough
Seedbed Cults.	2·2	1·6	
Load, Cart, Apply Fertilizer ...	0·4	0·3	
Drill*	0·7	0·5	Mid-March to mid-April (1) or end July to mid-Sept.
Roll	0·6	0·4	Soon after drilling
Load, Cart, Apply Fertiliser*:			
(three lots)	1·2	0·9	March to mid-August (2)
Top*	1·4	0·9	Mid-June to mid-July; if grazed only

Notes

1. Direct drilling in spring may continue to mid-May to enable extra cleaning cultivations or the application of farmyard manure.

2. P. and K. may be applied in September—especially on undersown ley in year sown.

* Only these operations apply where the seeds are undersown in a spring cereal crop soon after drilling. One extra harrowing and rolling are needed if undersown in an autumn-sown cereal crop.

B. Conservation

Operations	Labour-Hours per hectare Average	Premium	Time of Year
Hay (5·5 tonnes per hectare)			
Mow	1·2	0·9	
Turn, etc	2·6	1·9	Two-thirds June, one-third
Bale	1·3	0·9	July
Cart	6·0	4·5	
	—	—	
Total per hectare	11·1	8·2	
Total per tonne	2·0	1·5	
Silage (17 tonnes per hectare)			
Mow	1·2	0·9	
Turn, etc	0·7	0·5	Two-thirds May, one-third
Load	2·3	1·7	June
Cart	3·0	2·3	
Clamp...	2·3	1·7	
	—	—	
Total per hectare	9·5	7·1	
Total per tonne	0·56	0·42	

Specialized Equipment Prices for Grass Conservation: see page 116.

Seasonal Labour Requirements

Typical Monthly Breakdown

A. Production (figures averaged over the life of the ley)

	1-year ley undersown		3-dear ley undersown		1-year ley direct drilled in spring		3-year ley direct drilled in autumn (1)	
	Av.	Prem.	Av.	Prem.	Av.	Prem.	Av.	Prem.
March	0·9	0·5	0·7	0·5	0·6	0·3	0·6	0·3
April	0·9	0·5	0·7	0·5	0·6	0·3	0·6	0·3
May	0·6	0·3	0·6	0·3	0·6	0·3	0·6	0·3
June	0·6	0·3	0·6	0·3	0·6	0·3	0·6	0·3
July	0·6	0·3	0·6	0·3	0·6	0·3	0·6	0·3
August	0·3	0·2	0·3	0·2	5·0	3·4	1·9	1·4
September ...	0·6	0·3	0·3	0·2	3·2	2·2	1·4	1·0

Note
1. On land ploughed after a cereal crop, drilled early August to mid-September.

	1-year ley direct drilled in autumn (1)		3-year ley direct drilled in spring		Permanent Pasture	
	Av.	Prem.	Av.	Prem.	Av.	Prem.
March	3·0	2·1	1·4	1·0	0·6	0·3
April	1·8	1·2	0·9	0·7	0·6	0·3
May	0·3	0·3	0·6	0·3	0·6	0·3
June	0·6	0·3	0·6	0·3	0·6	0·3
July	0·6	0·3	0·6	0·3	0·6	0·3
August	0·3	0·2	0·2	0·2	0·3	0·2
September ...:	—	—	—	0·2	0·2	0·2
October	0·9	0·5	0·6	0·3	—	—
November ...	1·4	1·0	1·0	0·3	—	—
December ...	0·7	0·5	0·6	0·2	—	—

B. Conservation

	Hay				Silage			
	per hectare		per tonne		per hectare		per tonne	
	Av.	Prem.	Av.	Prem.	Av.	Prem.	Av.	Prem.
May	—	—	—	—	6·3	4·7	0·37	0·28
June	7·4	5·6	1·3	1·0	3·2	2·4	0·19	0·14
July	3·7	2·6	0·7	0·5	—	—	—	—

Seasonal Labour Requirements

KALE (growing only)

A. *Maincrop*

Operations	Labour-Hours per hectare Average	Premium	Time of Year
Plough	1·4	1·0	September onwards
Seedbed Cults.	2·2	1·6	March, April, early May
Fertilizer	0·4	0·3	April, early May
Drill	1·3	1·0	May
Roll	0·6	0·4	Straight after drilling
Spray (weedkiller)	0·3	0·2	6 weeks after drilling

B. Catch Crop

Kale may be drilled up to the first week of July; the crop will be smaller but either an early bite or silage crop may have been taken from a ley earlier in the year, or the ground may have been fallowed and thoroughly cleaned during the spring and early summer. The smaller crop is also easier to graze using an electric fence.

The above operations will still apply although the times of the year will obviously be different, but there may be an additional three or so rotavations and two or three heavy cultivations if fallowed for the first half of the year or ploughed after an early bite. This means approximately an extra 10 (average) or 8 (premium) man-hours per hectare in April, May, June.

FIELD-SCALE VEGETABLES

(Labour hours per hectare unless otherwise stated)

Cabbage Transplanting.	Hand 150-160. Spring cabbage, Sept.-Oct.; summer, April; autumn, May-June
	Machine (3·5 gang). Spring cabbage 75, summer 85, autumn 100.
	Pulling and dipping plants. 20 per hectare transplanted.
Cabbage Harvesting.	Early spring cabbage, 210, Feb.-April; hearted spring, 250, April-June; summer, 220, June-July; autumn, 220, Oct.-Dec.
Brussels Sprouts Transplanting.	45 (machine) to 55 (hand), May-June.
Brussels Sprouts Picking.	320-400: picked over 3-5 times, maximum approx. 3 hectares per picker per season. Early sprouts, Aug.-Dec.; late, Nov.-Mar.
Peas Hand Pulling.	475-525 (150 per tonne). Early, June; maincrop, July-Aug.
Runner Beans (Picked)	Harvesting. 625 (175 per tonne), July-Sept.
Runner Beans (Stick)	Harvesting. 675, July-Sept.
Runner Beans (Stick)	Erecting Canes and String. 100-150, May-June.
Carrot Harvesting.	Elevator-digger: 260 (1 man + 12 casuals, 20 hours per hectare). Earlies, July-Aug.; maincrop, Sept.-Feb. Harvester: 30 (3 men, 10 hours per hectare). Riddle and Grade: (1½ per tonne), Dec.-Feb.
Beetroot Harvest and Clamp.	25, Oct.-Dec. 12-15 man-hours per tonne to wash and pack.

Source: The Farm as a Business, Aids to Management, Section 6: Labour and Machinery (M.A.F.F.). (N.B. This data is now very dated, but it is still the latest known to the author.)

108

4. LABOUR FOR FIELD WORK: Gang Sizes and Rates of Work

Basic information on *Rates of Work is* given on pages 119 to 121, where both "average" and "premium" rates for many operations are listed.

The following data relate to rates of work with gangs of different sizes. The rates of work are *averages* for good and bad conditions throughout the season, including preparation time and travelling to the field, and *assume an 8-hour day, unless otherwise stated.* Obviously these rates can be exceeded by overtime work in the evenings.

Combine Harvesting

Gang size can vary from 1 to 4 men per combine (excluding straw baling) according to the number of men available, size and type of combine, distance from grain store, crop yield, type of grain drier, and degree of automation in the grain store. The main possibilities are:

1 man: all jobs (trailer in field)
2 men: 1 combining, 1 carting and attending to grain store
3 men: 1 combining, 2 carting and attending to grain store
3 men: 1 combining, 1 carting, 1 attending to grain store
4 men: 1 combining, 2 carting, 1 attending to grain store

Three men is most typical, although two is quite feasible with a fully automated grain store with in-bin or floor drying, unless transport times are excessive owing to distance or lack of good connecting roads. Four men is most usual with two combines, but an extra man may be needed with a continuous drier.

Except in the case of the small area cereal producer operating on his own, the rate of work will normally depend on the speed of the combine, sufficient tractors and trailers being provided to ensure that combining does not have to stop because of their absence.

Assuming a 9-hour combining day, typical rates of work are:

Size of combine (metres cut)	No. of Men	Ha/day
3 to 4·2...	1	4·5 to 7·75
	2 or 3	6 to 10
4·25 to 5·4	2 or 3	8 to 12
5·5 and over	3 or 4	10 to 15

Straw Carting

2 men, 1 or 2 tractors and trailers	"traditional system"	2·5 to 3·25 ha a day
3 men, 1 to 3 tractors and trailers		3·25 ha a day
1 man, 1 tractor with front and rear carriers		2·5 ha a day
2 men, flat 8/10 accumulator mechanised system		10 to 15 ha a day
2 or 3 men, big bale system		8 to 15 ha a day

Potato Planting

Hand planting (chitted seed) 3 men, 16 women	2 ha a day
Hand planting (unchitted seed) 2 men, 12 women	2 ha a day
(women working a 6-hour day only)	
2-row planter (chitted seed) 3 workers	1 ha a day
3-row planter (chitted seed) 4 or 5 workers	1·75 ha a day
2-row planter (unchitted seed) 3 workers	1·5 ha a day
3-row planter (unchitted seed) 4 workers	2·25 ha a day
2-row automatic planter (unchitted seed) 1 worker	2·5 ha a day
(part-time help loading and carting seed additional; this may be full time if fertilizer is applied with an attachment to the planter)	

Potato Harvesting

Hand harvesting (piecework) 3 to 5 men, 10 to 15 women	0·65 to 0·85 ha a day
(women working a 6-hour day only)	
Machine harvesting (1-row) 4 men, 3 women	0·65 to 0·9 ha a day
Machine harvesting (2-row) 5 men, 3 women	1 to 1·5 ha a day
(lower end of range for heavy land, upper end for light land and good work organization)	

Potato Riddling

3 to 5 workers	10 to 15 tonnes a day

Sugar Beet Harvesting (1-row)

Gang can vary from 1 to 5 (1 or 2 on harvester, 2 or 3 carting, 1 at clamp) but is usually 3 or 4.

3 or 4 men	0·9 ha a day
2 men	0·8 ha a day
1 man	0·7 ha a day
(add 20 per cent for light loams and silts)	

Vining Peas

Drilling (2 men)	7 to 10 ha a day
2·5-3 m. cutter (1 man)	2 ha a day
Pea pod picker, and carting, 5 or 6 men	0·4 ha a day
(large-scale growers: two 12 hour shifts worked per day)	

Carting Hay Bales

2 men, 1 or 2 tractors and trailers	7 to 9 tonnes a day
3 men, 1 to 3 tractors and trailers	9 to 14 tonnes a day

Silage-Making with Forage Harvester (excl. mowing, but inc. clamping; 15 tonne/ha crop)

1 man gang (1)	1·25 ha a day
2 man gang (1,3)	2·25 ha a day
3 man gang (1,3)	3·5 ha a day
4 man gang (2,3)	4·5 ha a day
(1) trailers towed behind, in line	
(2) trailers towed alongside	
(3) man with buckrake at clamp full-time	

Farmyard Manure Spreading

1 man: front loader and mechanical spreader	28 tonnes a day
4 men: front loader and 3 mechanical spreaders	90 tonnes a day

5. LABOUR FOR LIVESTOCK

DAIRY COWS

Herd size (no. of cows)	60	80	100 or more
		hours per cow per month	
January	3·3	2·9	2·5
February	3·3	2·9	2·5
March	3·3	2·9	2·5
April	3·0	2·7	2·4
May	2·7	2·4	2·2
June	2·7	2·4	2·1
July	2·7	2·4	2·1
August	2·7	2·4	2·1
September	2·7	2·4	2·2
October	3·0	2·8	2·4
November	3·3	2·9	2·5
December	3·3	2·9	2·5
Total per cow per year...	36	32	28
Total hours per year	2160	2560	2800
Total hours per week	42	49	54
Total cost per annum	£14,450	£17,575	£20,025
Total cost per week	£278	£338	£385
Total cost per cow per annum ...	£241	£220	£200
Cost per litre: 5000 litres/cow ...	4·82p	4·39p	4·01p
Cost per litre: 5500 litres/cow ...	4·38p	3·99p	3·64p
Cost per litre: 6000 litres/cow ...	4·01p	3·66p	3·34p
Cost per litre: 6500 litres/cow ...	3·71p	3·38p	3·08p
Cost per litre: 7000 litres/cow ...	3·44p	3·14p	2·36p

Note

These *costs* (note, not *earnings*) are *estimates for 1998* and are based on the average number of *direct* hours of work per cow for different herd sizes obtained from University costings; they do not include fieldwork, such as hay and silage making. The costs include craftsman addition and any other premiums paid, overtime, national insurance payments, and holidays with pay. They also include the cost of relief milking, including during annual holidays.

Earnings. The average earnings of all "dairy herdsmen" in 1996, according to MAFF Statistics, were £300·95/week (£15,650/year), for a 53·1 hour week. Wage inflation is likely to raise this to approximately £324/week (£16,825/year) in 1998.

DAIRY FOLLOWERS AND BEEF

Note.

No recent survey work has been published on labour requirements for beef animals and dairy followers. The following data can therefore only be taken as "best estimates". They are for average performance under average conditions. Substantial variations can occur from farm to farm, e.g. through economies of scale with widely differing herd sizes.

A. *Calves* (per head, early weaning)

Age Group	Labour hours per month Average	Premium
0-3 months	2·3	1·6
3-6 months	0·9	0·6
(av. 0-6 months	1·6	1·1)
6-12 months, yarded	1·1	0·8
6-12 months, summer grazed	0·3	0·2
(av. 0-12 months, during winter (1)	1·3	0·9)
(av. 0-12 months, during summer (1)	0·9	0·6)

Note
1. Assuming 6- to 12-month olds yarded in winter and grazed in summer, and calvings or calf purchases fairly evenly spaced throughout the year.

B. *Stores* (per head)

Yearling, yarded	1·0	0·7
2 year olds and over, yarded	1·4	0·8
Outwintered store	0·7	0·5
12 months and over, summer grazed	0·2	0·1

C. *Dairy Followers*

(Per "replacement unit", i.e. calf + yearling + in-calf heifer.) (1)		
During winter	2·9	2·0
During summer	1·2	0·8

Note
1. Assuming calvings fairly evenly spaced throughout the year and heifers calving at 2 to 2·5 years old.

D. *Beef Finishing* (per head)

Yarded	1·9	1·3
Summer Grazed	0·2	0·1
Intensive Beef (0-12 months)	1·35	1·0

E. *Suckler Herds* (per cow)

Single suckling (av. whole year)	0·9	0·6
Multiple suckling (av. whole year)	2·9	2·1

SHEEP
(per ewe)

	Labour hours per month	
	Average	Premium
January	0·3	0·25
February	0·3	0·25
March	1·0 (1)	0·75
April	0·4	0·3
May	0·3	0·25
June	0·4 (2)	0·3
July	0·2	0·15
August	0·2	0·15
September	0·25	0·15
October	0·25	0·15
November	0·2	0·15
December	0·2	0·15
Total	4·0 (3)	3·0

Notes
1. Assuming mainly March lambing.
2. 0·3 if shearing is by contract.
3. A full-time shepherd can look after 400 ewes, with lambs (average), to 600 (premium), with help of extra man at lambing time (4 to 6 weeks) and extra men during dipping (one day) and at shearing time. The above labour-hour figures would thus be higher if only full-time shepherds were considered, since 400 ewes per man equals more than 5·5 hours per ewe per year. (With a full-time assistant a shepherd can look after 1,000 ewes or more.)

PIGS

	Labour hours per month	
	Average	Premium
Breeding and Rearing, per sow	2·0	1·5
(Average 110 sows per worker, Premium 150)		
Feeding only, per 10 pigs	1·9	1·4
No. at a time, per worker:		
Average 1,200 per man, Premium 1,600		
No. per year, per worker:		
Average: 5,000 porkers, 4,000 cutters, 3,500 baconers		
Premium: 6,750 porkers, 5,500 cutters, 4,750 baconers		
Breeding, Rearing and Feeding, per sow		
Porkers, average 70 sows per worker (with progeny),		
premium 95	3·2	2·4
Cutters, average 65 sows per worker (with progeny),		
premium 90	3·5	2·6
Baconers, average 60 sows per worker (with progeny),		
premium 80	3·7	2·8

POULTRY
(large-scale, automated)

	Labour hours per month
Laying hens: 12,000 per full-time worker	1·65 per 100
Broilers: 32,500 at a time per full-time worker*	
(225,000 a year)	1·0 per 100

*N.B. additional help needed for catching and cleaning out (included in labour hours per month).

III. MACHINERY

1. AGRICULTURAL MACHINERY PRICES

(Estimated Spring 1998 prices for new machinery, net of discounts and excluding V.A.T.)

1. Tractors

(a) Two-Wheel Drive   £
27-34 kW (36-45 hp)	12,000-14,000
35-41 kW (47-55 hp)	14,000-16,000
43-49 kW (57-66 hp)	16,000-17,500
50-56 kW (67-75 hp)	17,500-19,000
57-66 kW (76-89 hp)	19,000-22,000
67-75 kW (90-100 hp)	22,000-28,000

(b) Four- Wheel Drive
43-50 kW (57-67 hp)	18,000-21,000
56-65 kW (75-87 hp)	21,000-25,000
66-75 kW (88-100 hp)	25,000-33,000
76-90 kW (101-120 hp)	33,000-40,000
95-100 kW (127-134 hp)	42,000-49,000
115-134 kW (154-180 hp)	49,000-54,000
140-165 kW (187-220 hp)	58,000-64,000
170-200 kW (228-268 hp)	65,000-71,000

(c) High Road Speed
86-105 kW (115-140 hp)	47,000-57,000
112-139 kW (150-185 hp)	60,000-66,000

(d) Crawlers
60-64 kW (80-85 hp), steel track	20,000-22,000
90-120 kW (120-160 hp), rubber track	60,000-65,000
150-206 kW (200-275 hp), rubber track	90,000-110,000

2. Cultivating Equipment

(a) Ploughs
Mounted	2-furrow	2,000-2,400
	3-furrow	2,800-3,200
	4-furrow	3,300-4,300
	5-furrow	4,500-5,500
Reversible	2-furrow	4,000-5,000
	3-furrow	5,000-6,000
	4-furrow	6,000-8,000
	5-furrow	8,000-10,000
	6-furrow (semi-mounted)	13,000-16,000
	7-furrow (semi-mounted)	17,000-21,000

(b) Furrow Presses
1·3-1·5 m double row	2,200-2,400
1·7-1·9 m double row	2,400-2,700
2·1-2·5 m double row	2,700-3,200
2·7-3·1 m double row	3,300-3,700
3·3-3·5 m double row	4,400-5,500

(c) Front Presses
1·5 m single row	1,400-1,600
3·0 m single row	2,100-2,500
4·0 m single row— hydraulic folding	3,400-4,000

(d) Other Cultivating Equipment

Sub Soiler 2-3 leg	2,000-2,500
Soil Looseners (2·25-3·25 m)	3,300-3,800
(3·5-4·2 m)	6,500-7,500
Vibrating Compaction Breaker (2·5-3·0 m)	4,000-4,500
(3·7-4·5 m)	5,500-6,500
Straw Incorporating Cultivator (3-4 m)	3,500-4,500
Stubble Cultivator (2·5-3·0 m):	2,100-3,000
(3·4-4·3 m): hydraulic folding ...	3,600-4,000
(4·8-5·7 m): hydraulic folding ...	5,000-5,800
Spring-tine Cultivator (3-4 m):	1,600-2,300
(5-6 m): hydraulic folding	3,500-4,000
Combination Harrows (2·5-4 m)	2,500-4,000
(5-6 m): hydraulic folding	6,000-7,000
Levelling Harrows (2·5-4·2 m)	1,300-2,000
(3·7-6·1 m): hydraulic folding ...	3,000-4,500
Disc Harrows (3-4 m): trailed	8,000-9,000
(4·5-5·5 m): trailed, heavy duty, folding	12,000-14,000
Harrows (5-6 m): light-medium, hydraulic folding	2,000-2,200
Rotovator (up to 80 kW tractor)	5,000-6,000
(80-100 kW tractor)	6,000-7,000
Power Harrow (2·5-3 m)	4,500-5,500
(3·5-4 m)	7,000-8,000
(4·5-5 m, with crumbler roller) ...	10,000-13,000
(6·0 m, with crumbler roller) ...	18,000-20,000
Roller Packer for power harrow (2·5-4 m)	1,200-1,700
(4·5-6 m)	2,000-2,600
Rolls: triple gang, hydraulic folding (6 m)	5,500-6,500
five gang, „ „ (12m)	12,000-13,000

3. Fertilizer Distributors, Seed Drills, Sprayers

(a) Fertilizer Distributors

Mounted Spinner (500-750 litre)	1,600-1,800
(800-1200 litre): twin disc, hydraulic control	2,800-3,200
Pneumatic Spreader (800-1200 litre): twin disc, electric control	4,800-5,200
trailed (12m boom), 4,000 litre hopper	17,000-18,000
trailed (18m boom), 6,000 litre hopper	23,000-25,000

(b) Seed Drills

Grain: mounted	2·5-3 m, 21-25 row	4,000-5,000
trailed	3 m, 18-24 row	6,000-7,000
	4 m, 24-32 row	7,000-8,000
mounted	3-4 m, pneumatic, 24-32 row	8,000-10,000
	6-8 m, pneumatic, 48-64 row	17,000-25,000
Mounted grass seed broadcaster (2·4-4·6 m)		1,000-1,200

(c) Combine Grain and Fertilizer Drills

Trailed, 3 m, 18-24 row	6,500-7,500
4 m, 24-32 row	7,500-8,500

(d) Combined Cultivator and Drill

4-4.5 m, 32 row	30,000-32,000

(e) Combined Power Harrow and Pneumatic Drill

3-4 m, 24-32 row	12,000-14,000

(f) Sprayers

Mounted, 200-300 litre tank, 6-8 m boom	1,200-1,400
Mounted, 600-800 litre tank, 12 m boom	2,000-2,500
Mounted, 800-1,000 litre tank, 24 m hydraulic boom ...	12,000-15,000
Mounted, Air Assisted, 800-1,000 litre tank, 12 m boom ...	12,000-15,000
Trailed, Air Assisted, 2,000-2,500 litre tank, 12 m boom ...	15,000-19,000
Trailed, 1,500-2,000 litre tank 12 m boom	9,000-12,000
Trailed, 2,500-3,000 litre tank 24 m boom	15,000-20,000
Self-propelled, 12-20 m boom, lightweight	24,000-30,000
Self-propelled, 24 m boom, 4-wheel drive	40,000-50,000

4. Grass Conservation and Handling Equipment

(a) Silage Equipment

Forage Harvester: mounted	9,000-11,000
Forage Harvester: trailed	15,000-20,000
Maize Harvester, mounted, 2 row	6,000-8,000
Self-propelled (3-4·5 m pick-up 165-265 kW)	80,000-100,000
Maize attachment, 4-6 row	14,000-20,000
Silage Trailer, 6 tonne	3,000-3,500
Silage Trailer, 10 tonne, tandem axle	4,500-5,000
Buckrake (push off)	1,100-1,300

(b) Haymaking Equipment

Mower (1·6-2·0 m, drum)	1,500-2,000
Mower (2·0-2·5 m, disc)	3,500-5,000
Mower (drum) Conditioner, mounted (1·8-2·5 m)	5,000-6,000
Mower (disc) Conditioner (2·4-2·8 m)	6,000-7,000
Tedder (5-7 m, 4-6 rotors)	4,000-5,000
Windrower, (3-4 m)	2,200-2,500
Balers and Bale Handling: see 5(b) below	

(c) Silage Handling Equipment

Silage shear bucket (1-1·2 m³)	1,600-2,000
Silage grab	1,300-1,500
Big Bale Silage Feeder, mounted	3,500-4,500
Forage Feeder Wagon (6-7 m³)	6,000-7,000
Mixer-feeder Wagon (8-12 m³)	15,000-17,000
Feed Trailer	800-1,000

5. Grain and Straw Harvesting and Handling Equipment

(a) Combines

Engine size kW (hp)	Cutterbar width metres (feet)	
75-89 (100-119)	3·0-3·6 (10-12)	65,000-75,000
90-111 (120-149)	3·6-6·0 (12-19)	70,000-80,000
112-148 (150-199)	3·6-6·0 (12-19)	80,000-100,000
149-185 (200-249)	4·2-6·1 (14-20)	100,000-120,000
186-224 (250-299)	6·1-7·6 (20-25)	120,000-140,000
Over 225 (Over 300)	6·9-9·0 (23-29)	140,000-160,000
(For self-levelling models add 6,000-8,000)		

(b) Straw Disposal Equipment

Straw Chopper (trailed), (2-3 m)	4,000-5,000
Straw Chopper attachment for combines	4,000-5,000
Chaff Spreader attachment for combines	1,500-2,000

(c) Pick-up Balers (twine tying)

Small rectangular bales	8,000-9,000
Small rectangular bales, heavy duty models	10,000-12,000
Big round bales, twine tying	14,000-15,000
net wrap	15,000-16,000
High density rectangular bales	48,000-55,000

(d) Bale Handling Equipment

Big Bale Wrapper: mounted	4,000-5,000
trailed	7,000-8,000
Big Square Bale Wrapper	14,000-17,000
Bale Trailers, 5-8 tonne	2,200-3,000
Accumulator, flat 8, mechanical...	1,400-1,600
Loader, flat 8	700-800
Big Bale Spike	200-250
Big Bale Handler	500-700
Big Bale Shredder...	3,000-3,500

(e) *Drying, Handling, Food Processing Equipment*
Grain driers and Grain storage: see pages 132, 151

Cleaner/grader, 10-20 tonnes/hour	6,000-9,000
Grain augers 100 mm, 3·3-7·3 m	450-550
Grain augers 150 mm, 6-8·5 m, with trolley	1,400-1,600
Grain conveyors, (25t/hour) (excl. motor) ...	1,000-1,200 + 90-100 per m
Bucket elevator, (25-30t/hour)	1,800-2,000 + 125-150 per m
Hammer Mill, 7·5-15 kW	1,400-1,700
Crushing Mill, 2-5·5 kW	1,500-2,000
Mixer, 750-1000 kg	2,200-2,500
Mill and Mixer, 1000kg, 3·7-5·5 kW	4,000-4,500
Seed Dresser, 3 tonne	2,000-2,500

6. Potato, Sugar Beet and Vegetable Machinery

(a) *Potato Machinery*

Stone separator, 1·8-2·0 m	22,000-25,000
Bedformer, 1·5-2 m	2,300-2,600
Bed cultivator, 1·8 m	4,500-5,500
Ridger, 3-5 row	800-1,200
Planter: 2 row automatic, mechanical drive	4,500-5,500
2 row automatic, hydraulic drive	6,500-7,500
3 row automatic, hydraulic drive	10,000-12,000
Fertilizer attachment, 2 row	1,300-1,500
Haulm pulveriser: 2 row	4,000-4,500
2 row cross conveyor	6,000-7,000
Elevator-Digger, 2 row	4,500-5,000
Harvesters: semi-mounted, 1 row, manned/unmanned ...	13,000-15,000
trailed, 1 row, manned	25,000-27,000
trailed, 2 row, manned/unmanned ...	45,000-50,000
Elevator (rubber belt)	6,000-7,000
Flat belt conveyor, 3-8 m	1,500-2,500
Swinging head elevator	9,000-10,000
Soil elevator (rubber belt)	3,000-3,500
Self-unloading hopper, 3-5 tonnes	5,000-6,000
Hopper cleaner, 2-4 tonnes	2,500-4,000
Clod separator	5,000-6,500
Sizer, 5-10 tonnes/hour	6,000-8,000
Sponge drier, 0·9-1·2m	5,000-6,000
Barrel washer, 6-8 tonnes/hour	6,500-7,500
Roller inspection table, 1·2 × 2·4 m	2,500-3,000
Weigher, automatic, 8-10 tonnes/hour	4,000-5,000
Box tipper	3,250-4,000
Box filer, automatic	9,000-10,000
Bag stitcher (hand held)	750-900

(b) *Sugar Beet Machinery*

Precision Drill:	6 row-12 row (mechanical)	8,000-15,000
	12 row-18 row (pneumatic)	18,000-25,000
Hoe:	6 row-12 row (heavy duty)	3,500-6,500
Harvesters:	Trailed, 3-4 row	30,000-33,000
	Trailed, 2 row, tanker	35,000-40,000
	Trailed, 3 row, tanker	42,000-47,000
Self-propelled, 6 row (including power unit) elevator		120,000-130,000
Cleaner-loader, with engine, 60 tonnes per hour ...		18,000-20,000
Fodder beet harvester		4,000-4,500

(c) *Vegetable Machinery*

Onion windrower		7,000-8,000
Root crop digger: 1 webb		4,500-5,000
2 webbs		6,000-7,000
Top lifting vegetable harvester: single row, bunker ...		35,000-40,000
	twin row, bunker/elevator ...		65,000-70,000
	four row, elevator		90,000-100,000
Leek harvester		11,000-12,000

7. General

Trailer, 4 tonne tipping	1,600-1,800
Trailer, 6 tonne tipping; grain/silage	2,500-3,000/3,000-3,500
Trailer, 10 tonne tipping, tandem axle; grain/silage	4,000-4,500/4,500-5,000
F.Y.M. Spreaders, (4-6 m³)	2,500-3,000
F.Y.M. Spreaders, (6-8 m³)	4,000-5,000
Loaders, front mounted...	3,000-4,500
Pallet loader, self levelling (1,000-1,600 kg)	4,500-5,500
Materials Handler, telescopic boom (2·5-3·0 tonne)...	28,000-33,000
Skid steer loader (500-600 kg)	12,000-14,000
Slurry Stores (metal), including base but before grant (assumes large store for 200 cows with a 15-week storage period; stores for 70-80 cows are £160-180 per cow)	£130 per cow
Slurry Tanker-Spreaders (4,000-5,000 litre)	3,500-4,000
Slurry-Tanker-Spreaders, tandem axle (6,000-10,000 litre) ...	6,000-8,000
Slurry pump	2,000-2,500
Cattle crush	500-700
Cattle crush with weigher	1,000-1,200
Cattle trailer (twin-axle)	1,700-2,000
Yard scrapers	500-600
Rotary brush (2-2·5 m)...	1,800-2,200
Grassland roll, ballastable (2·5-3 m)	800-900
Pasture topper (2·0-3·0 m)	1,500-2,000
Pasture aerator (2·5-3 m)	1,700-2,200
Hedger: hydraulic angling; flail head...	7,000-8,000
Ditcher: fully slewing	4,000-5,000
Carrier box	300-400
Post hole digger/driver	800-1,000/1,200-1,600
Saw bench	650
Log splitter	400-500

118

2. TYPICAL CONTRACTORS' CHARGES, AVERAGE FARMERS' COSTS AND RATES OF WORK FOR VARIOUS FARM OPERATIONS

Contractors' charges vary widely according to many factors: those given below are estimates for 1998. Farmer-contractors often charge less, since their overheads and machinery fixed costs are largely covered by their own farming operations, but the service may not always be so complete, including specialist advice.

Farmers' own costs (which include the value of the farmers' own manual labour) vary even more widely; those given below (estimated for Spring 1998) are averages in every respect—covering different types of soil, size of farm, and so on; they are based on accounting cost procedures in that labour, tractor and machinery fuel, repairs and depreciation are included—but no allowance has been added for general farm overheads, interest on capital, supervision/management or under-occupied labour during slack times. They assume four-wheel drive 75-90 kW (100-120 hp) tractors for ploughing, heavy cultivation and other work with a high power requirement. Four-wheel drive 55-65 kW (75-87 hp) tractors are assumed to be used for most other operations. The figures should not be used for partial budgeting.

For a typical set of farm operations, excluding harvesting, the breakdown of the farmers' costs averages approximately 30% labour, 45% tractors and 25% implements/machines. The larger the farm the lower the labour element and the higher the machine element, and vice versa.

The contract charges and average farmers' costs are put side-by-side for tabular convenience, not to facilitate comparisons. Apart from the fact that contractors' charges must cover expenses omitted from the farmers' cost, the advisability or otherwise of hiring a contractor for a particular job depends on many factors, varying widely according to farm circumstances; furthermore, there are advantages and disadvantages not reflected in a cost comparison alone.

Four-wheel drive 120-150 kW (150-200 hp) tractors are assumed where appropriate to achieve the "Premium" rates of work (which will be achieved on most farms with more than 200 hectares (500 acres) of arable land); obviously, still larger wheeled tractors and crawlers could achieve still faster rates of work, particularly on light land. See further page 95, first paragraph.

All charges and costs below are *per hectare* unless otherwise stated.

Operation	Contract Charge	Average Farmers' Cost	Rate of Work (hectares per 8 hr. day) Average	Premium
		£	£	
Ploughing (light/heavy soils) ...	36·00-45·00	32·50-42·00	5-6½	7½-9
Ploughing with furrow press ...	42·00-52·00	39·00-50·00		
Deep Ploughing (over 300 mm)	50·00-62·00	52·00-65·00	3-3¾	5-6½
Rotovating...	47·00-57·00	55·00 (ploughed land)	4½	6
		83·00 (grass)	3	4

Operation	Contract Charge	Average Farmers' Cost	Rate of Work (hectares per 8 hr. day) Average	Premium
	£	£		
Subsoiling	48·00	31·00	6	10
Stubble Cultivating	27·00	16·75	12	16
Heavy Disc Cultivating	28·00	22·50	10	15
Disc Harrowing ...	18·00	11·75	12	16
Power Harrowing	31·00	24·25	9	12
Spring tine Harrowing	19·00	12·00	12	18
Seedbed Harrowing	15·00	9·75	12	20
Rolling (flat 3-4 tonne)	21·00	17·00	6	10
(ring, set of 3, 6 m) ...	12·00	10·25	14	22
Fertilizer Distributing (including loading and carting):				
Broadcast (125-375 kg/ha) ...	8·00-11·00 (fert. in field)	7·25	20	30
Broadcast (500-1,250 kg/ha) ...	—	12·00	15	20
Pneumatic (125-375 kg/ha)...	—	9·75	30	45
Drilling:				
Cereals (direct into stubble) ...	34·00 (seed & fert. in field)	31·50	8	10
Cereals (plain, 1 man)	21·00	15·25	12	16
Grass (broadcast)	16·00	12·00	11	15
Roots (4-row)	—	51·00	3½ (4 row)	5 (6 row)
Sugar Beet—precision drill ...	35·00	30·50	6 (6 row)	10 (12 row)
Power Harrowing and Drilling Cereals	42·00	34·00	8	11
Destoning potato land	160·00	128·00	3·25	4
Potato Planting automatic	—	97·50	2½ (2 row)	3¼
Potato Ridging	34·00	22·50	5½	7
Spraying (excl. materials):				
Low Volume (up to 175 l/ha) ...	10·00	5·90	35	55
Medium Volume (200-300 l/ha) ...	12·00	6·60	30	45
High Volume (over 800 l/ha) ...	—	12·50	25	35
Tractor Hoeing Sugar Beet	—	28·00	5	8
Combine Harvesting Cereals:			(hectares per hour)	
100 ha/year	75-85	90·00	¾-1	1-1½
200 ha/year	75-85	71·00		
300 ha/year	75-85	64·00		
Carting to barn add	16·50	13·00		
Combine Harvesting:				
Oilseed rape (direct)	80-90	as cereals + 10%	²/₃-1	¾-1¼
Beans	75-85	as cereals + 10%	²/₃-1	¾-1¼
Peas	85-90	as cereals	¾-1	1-1½
Windrowing Oilseed Rape	35·00	—	1·2	1·4
Pick-up Baling (incl. string) ...	19-23p per bale	17p per bale	0·8 per hour	1·25 per hour
Big Baling (round)	1·50-2·00 per bale	1·60 per bale	—	—
Crop Drying (inc. pre-cleaning) (per tonne)				
Cereals:				
by 6 per cent	13·00	7·00	—	—
by 10 per cent	16·50	8·50	—	—
Oilseed Rape:				
by 5 per cent	17·00	9·00	—	—
by 10 per cent	22·50	11·50	—	—
Cleaning without drying (per tonne)	8·00	—	—	—
Mobile Seed Cleaning (cereals) (per tonne) (including chemicals)	70-90	—	—	—
Grain Storage (per tonne per week)	27p	(see page 132)	—	—
Handling into store (per tonne)	£1·50	£1		
Handling out of store (per tonne)	£1·50	£1		

Operation	Contract Charge	Average Farmers' Cost	Rate of Work (hectares per 8 hr. day) Average	Premium
	£	£		
Potato Harvesting	—	1,000-1,100 (incl. carting, store, casuals)	0·75	1
Sugar Beet Complete Harvesting ...	155	149(excl. carting)	3·5	4·5
...	195	187(incl. carting)		
Grass Mowing/Topping (inc. Set-aside)	21·00	18·00	8	12
Swath Turning/Tedding	14·00	12·50	11	15
Forage Harvesting (inc. mowing): Full chop harvester, 17·5 tonnes/ha (driver only)	45·00	—	—	—
Forage harvesting, carting and ensiling grass 17·5 tonnes/ha	110	—	—	—
Forage harvesting, carting and ensiling maize 25-30 tonnes/ha...	125	—	—	—
F.Y.M.: Tractor and Spreader ...	20·00 per hour	—	—	—
F.Y.M.: Tractor and Loader	16·00 per hour	—	—	—
Lime Spreading	3·00 per tonne	—	—	—
Hedge Cutting (flail head)	16·00 per hour	—	—	—
Tractor Hire (inc. driver and fuel):				
2 wheel drive, 56 kW (75 h.p.) ...	110	—	—	—
2 wheel drive, 75 kW (100 h.p.)	115	—	—	—
4 wheel drive, 56 kW (75 h.p.) ...	125	—	—	—
4 wheel drive, 90 kW (120 h.p.)	135	—	—	—
Crawler, 90 kW (120 h.p.)	160	—	—	—
Trailer (with driver and tractor) ...	130	13·00 per hour	—	—

(Tractor Hire rows bracketed as "per 8 hour day")

Contract Charge for All Operations (Cereals and Combinable Break Crops, "stubble to stubble" i.e. up to and including Combine Harvesting and Carting the Grain to Store): £220 to £270/ha (£90-110/acre). (Variation according to such factors as distance away, area contracted, size of fields, type of terrain, quality of soil and level of inputs (as affecting weight of crop to be harvested and carted). The charge is typically close to £222·50/ha (90/acre) where a proportion of the profit is also taken by the contractor or a neighbouring farmer after payment of a prior charge to the landowner of around £110/ha; the percentage share of total gross margin less these two deductions has been typically 70% to the contractor and 30% to the landowner.

Tractor Power Requirements

		hp/acre av.	prem.	hp/ha av.	prem.	kW/ha av.	prem.
Combinable crops:	heavy land	·75	·6	1·85	1·5	1·4	1·1
	light land	·5	·4	1·25	1	·9	·75
Mixed cropping:	heavy land	1	·8	2·5	2	1·85	1·5
	light land	·75	·6	1·85	1·5	1·4	1·1

Grain Haulage Costs
Averaged £3·50 per tonne for a 10 mile journey + 35p per tonne for each additional mile travelled, in 1996. Average cost per tonne of grain £5·32. (Home-Grown Cereals Authority).

3. TRACTOR HOURS

(per annum)

Crops

	per hectare Average	Premium
Cereals	9	7
Straw Harvesting	3·5	2·5
Potatoes	25	15
Sugar Beet	20	12
Vining Peas	20	12
Dried Peas	10	8
Field Beans	9	7
Oilseed Rape	9	7
Herbage Seeds:		
1 year undersown or 3 year direct drilled	7	5
1 year direct drilled	11	8
Hops (machine picked)	125	—
Kale (grazed)	8	6
Turnips/Swedes: folded/lifted	12/35	10/25
Mangolds	50	35
Fallow	12	7
Ley Establishment:		
Undersown	2	1
Direct Seed	7	4
Making Hay	12	8
Making Silage:		
1st Cut	12	8
2nd Cut	9	6
Grazing:		
Temporary Grass	3	2·5
Permanent Grass	2	1·5

Livestock

	per head Average
Dairy Cows...	6
Other Cattle over 2 years	5
Other Cattle 1-2 years	4
Other Cattle ½-1 year	2·25
Calves 0-½ year	2·25
Yarded bullocks	3
Sheep, per ewe	1·25
Store sheep	0·8
Sows...	1·75
Other pigs over 2 months	1
Laying Birds	0·04

Notes

1. For Livestock, annual requirements are the per head requirements above multiplied by average numbers during the year (i.e. average numbers at end of each month).

2. As with labour, the number of tractors required by a farm depends more on the seasonal requirements and number required at any one time than on total annual tractor hours. These can be calculated from the seasonal labour data provided earlier in this book. The soil type and size/power of tractors purchased are obviously other relevant factors.

4. TRACTOR COSTS
(Estimates for Spring 1998)

	Two-Wheel Drive 43-49 kW (56-66 h.p.)		Four-Wheel Drive 56-65kW (75-85 h.p.)	
Initial Cost	£16,750		£23,000	
	per year £	per hour £	per year £	per hour £
Depreciation	1,340	2·68	1,840	3·68
Tax and Insurance	187	0·37	228	0·46
Repairs and Maintenance	838	1·68	1,150	2·30
Fuel and Oil	562	1 12	897	1·79
Total	2,927	5·85	4,115	8·23

	Four-Wheel Drive			
	76-90 kW (101-120 h.p.)		115-134 kW (154-180 h.p.)	
Initial Cost	£36,000		£51,000	
	per year £	per hour £	per year £	per hour £
Depreciation	2,880	5·76	4,080	8·16
Tax and Insurance	314	0·63	413	0·83
Repairs and Maintenance	1,800	3·60	2,550	5·10
Fuel and Oil	1,242	2·48	1,725	3·45
Total	6,236	12·47	8,768	17·54

	Crawlers			
	60-64 kW (80-86 h.p.)		90 kW (120 h.p.)	
Initial Cost	£21,000		£60,000	
	per year £	per hour £	per year £	per hour £
Depreciation	1,680	3·36	4,800	9·60
Tax and Insurance	180	0·36	437	0·87
Repairs and Maintenance	1,050	2·10	3,000	6·00
Fuel and Oil	883	1·77	1,325	2·65
Total	3,793	7·59	9,562	19·12

Depreciation is based on the assumption that a tractor is sold or traded in for one-fifth of its original cost after ten years. Annual Repair Costs have been calculated at 5 per cent of initial cost. No interest on capital has been included.

The hourly figures are based on a use of 500 hours a year. A greater annual use than this will mean higher annual costs but possibly lower hourly costs. Early replacement at a given annual use will increase depreciation costs per hour but should reduce repair costs. The hourly figures are averages for all types of work: heavy operations such as ploughing obviously have a higher cost than light work.

5. ESTIMATING ANNUAL MACHINERY COSTS

Annual machinery costs consist of depreciation, repairs, fuel and oil, contract charges, and vehicle tax and insurance. These can be budgeted in three ways, assuming there is no available information on past machinery costs on the farm:

(a) *Per hectare,* by looking up an average figure for the district, according to the size and type of farm. Approximate levels are shown in the tables of fixed costs (pages 133-138). This is obviously a very rough and ready measure.

(b) *Per standard tractor hour.* The crop area and livestock numbers can be multiplied by the appropriate standard (average) tractor hours per hectare and per head as given on page 122. The total can then be multiplied by the machinery cost per standard tractor hour as calculated from farm surveys. The following average figures (estimated for mid-1998) are based on 1993-96 levels in South-East England.

Farm Type				Cost per Standard Tractor Hour
Mainly Sheep/Cattle, over 100 ha ...	...	...		£9·00
Mainly Sheep/Cattle, under 100 ha	...	...	}	£12·00
Sheep/Cattle and Arable, over 100 ha	...	...		
Dairy, Sheep/Cattle and Arable	...	...		
Mainly Dairying, under 60 ha	...	...	}	£15.00
Dairying and Arable	...	...		
Sheep/Cattle and Arable, under 100 ha	...	...		
Mainly Dairying, 60-100 ha ...	...	...		£17·50
Mainly Arable, over 200 ha	...	...		£18.50
Mainly Dairying, over 120 ha	...	...		£20·00
Mainly Arable, 100-200 ha ...	...	...	}	£25.00
Intensive Arable—Field Vegetables ...	...	...		
Mainly Arable, under 100 ha	...	...	}	£35.00
Intensive Arable—Fruit	...	...		

Premium levels are about 10 per cent lower.

Depreciation is based on the historic cost of the machinery and equipment. The capital element of leasing (but not the interest) is included in depreciation. With depreciation calculated on the current (i.e. replacement) cost the above figures are raised by approximately 10%.

The percentage composition of the total cost varies with size and type of farm but averages approximately:

	Depreciation	Repairs	Fuel/Elec.	Contract	VTI*
A.	32·5	25	15	22·5	5
B.	40	22·5	12·5	20	5

A = Depreciation based on historic cost.
B = Depreciation based on current cost.

*Vehicle tax and insurance.

This method may be used as a check on the per hectare calculation.

(N.B. The standard tractor hour is used only as a convenient measure of machinery input. *The costs incorporate not only tractor costs but all other power and machinery expenses, including field machinery and implements, fixed equipment, landrovers, vans, use of farm car, etc.*)

(c) *Fully detailed calculation,* costing and depreciating each machine in turn, including tractors, estimating repairs and fuel costs for each, and adding the charges for any contract work.

The following tables, giving, for different types of machine, estimated life, annual depreciation, and estimated repairs according to annual use, are mostly taken from "Profitable Farm Mechanisation", by C. Culpin.

ESTIMATED USEFUL LIFE (YEARS) OF POWER OPERATED MACHINERY IN RELATION TO ANNUAL USE

Equipment	Annual Use (hours)				
	25	50	100	200	300
Group 1: Ploughs, Cultivators, Toothed harrows, Hoes, Rolls, Ridgers, Potato planting attachments, Grain cleaners	12+	12+	12+	12	10
Group 2: Disc harrows, Corn drills, Grain drying machines, Food grinders and mixers	12+	12+	12	10	8
Group 3: Combine harvesters, Pick-up balers, Rotary cultivators, Hydraulic loaders	12+	12+	12	9	7
Group 4: Mowers, Forage harvesters, Swath turners, Side-delivery rakes, Tedders, Hedge cutting machines, Semi-automatic potato planters and transplanters, Unit root drills, Mechanical root thinners	12+	12	11	8	6
Group 5: Fertilizer distributors, Combine drills, Farmyard manure spreaders, Elevator potato diggers, Spraying machines, Pea cutter-windrowers	10	10	9	8	7

Miscellaneous:										
Beet harvesters	...	...	...	...	...	11	10	9	6	5
Potato harvesters	...	...	...	...	...	—	8	7	5	—
Milking machinery	...	...	...	...	...	—	—	—	12	10

	Annual Use (hours)					
	500	750	1,000	1,500	2,000	2,500
Tractors	12+	12	10	7	6	5
Electric motors	12+	12+	12+	12+	12	12

DEPRECIATION: AVERAGE ANNUAL FALL IN VALUE
(per cent of new price)

(Source: V. Baker, Bristol University)

Frequency of renewal. Years	Complex. High Depreciation Rate e.g. potato harvesters, mobile pea viners, etc.	Established machines with many moving parts, e.g. tractors, combines, balers, forage harvesters	Simple equipment with few moving parts, e.g. ploughs, trailers
	%	%	%
1	34	26	19
2	24½	19½	14½
3	20*	16½*	12½
4	17½†	14½	11½
5	15‡	13†	10½*
6	13½	12	9½
7	12	11	9
8	11	10‡	8½†
9	(10)	9½	8
10	(9½)	8½	7½‡

* Typical frequency of renewal with heavy use.

† Typical frequency of renewal with average use.

‡Typical frequency of renewal with light use.

VALUATION AND DEPRECIATION OF MACHINERY BY TYPE

(% of total machinery valuation per farm, 1995/96;
% depreciation in brackets; both based on replacement costs)

Type of Farm	Mainly Cereals	Mixed Cropping	Dairy & Arable	ALL FARMS
Tractors	35 (36)	30 (31)	35 (37)	29 (30)
Vehicles	10 (10)	11 (12)	15 (16)	15 (17)
Harvesters	15 (18)	13 (16)	7 (9)	10 (12)
Other Equipment and Plant	40 (36)	46 (41)	43 (38)	46 (41)

Source: M. C. Murphy, Report on Farming in the Eastern Counties of England, 1995/96. University of Cambridge, Agricultural Economics Unit, 1997.

DEPRECIATION: PERCENTAGE RATES

A. Straight-Line

Years Retained	Trade-in, Second-hand or Scrap Value as % of New Price							
	5	10	20	25	33	40	50	60
3	—	—	—	—	—	20	16½	13½
4	—	—	—	—	17	15	12½	—
5	—	—	—	15	13½	12	—	—
6	—	—	13½	12½	11	10	—	—
8	—	11	10	9½	—	—	—	—
10	9½	9	8	—	—	—	—	—
12	8	7½	—	—	—	—	—	—
15	6½	—	—	—	—	—	—	—

Example: If a machine costing £10,000 is retained for 8 years, at the end of which the trade-in value is 20% of the new price (i.e. £2,000), the average depreciation per annum has been £8,000 ÷ 8 years = £1,000 (i.e. 10% of the new price).

B. Diminishing Balances

Years Retained	Trade-in, Second-hand or Scrap Value as % of New Price							
	5	10	20	25	33	40	50	60
3	—	—	—	—	—	26	21	16
4	—	—	—	—	24	20	16	—
5	—	—	—	24	20	17	—	—
6	—	—	23	20	17	14	—	—
8	—	25	18	16	—	—	—	—
10	25	20	15	—	—	—	—	—
12	22	17	—	—	—	—	—	—
15	18	—	—	—	—	—	—	—

Example: If a machine costing £10,000 is retained for 4 years, at the end of which the trade-in value is 40% of the new replacement price, the annual depreciation on the diminishing balances method is: Year 1, £2,000 (i.e. 20% of £10,000); Year 2, £1,600 (i.e. 20% of £8,000 (the written-down value)); Year 3, £1,280 (i.e. 20% of £6,400); Year 4, £1,024 (20% of £5,120). The total written-down value at the end of Year 4 is therefore £4,096 (i.e. £10,000 less the total depreciation of £5,904). This is approximately 41% of the new price. (Taking the percentages in the above table to decimal places would give the trade-in prices stated more precisely).

Note. The trade-in value taken for purposes of the calculation must exclude any "disguised" discount on the price of the new machine.

Calculations of data collected as part of the Farm Management Survey in 1982/83 found the following to be the best estimates of the real diminishing balance rates of depreciation for machines sold during that year: (source: S. Cunningham, University of Exeter, Agricultural Economics Unit, 1987):

Tractors	15%	Potato harvesters	21%
Combine harvesters	15%	Forage harvesters	21%
Balers	18%	Beet harvesters	23%

For other machinery and equipment an average rate of 15% is suggested (author).

Tax Allowances on Machinery. See pages 172-3.

ESTIMATED ANNUAL COST OF SPARES AND REPAIRS AS A PERCENTAGE OF PURCHASE PRICE* AT VARIOUS LEVELS OF USE

	Approximate Annual Use (hours)				Additional use per 100 hours ADD
	500	750	1,000	1,500	
	%	%	%	%	%
Tractors	5·0	6·7	8·0	10·5	0·5

	Approximate Annual Use (hours)				Additional use per 100 hours ADD
	50	100	150	200	
	%	%	%	%	%
Harvesting Machinery:					
Combine Harvesters, self-propelled and engine-driven	1·5	2·5	3·5	4·5	2·0
Combine Harvesters, p.t.o. driven, metered-chop forage harvesters, pick-up balers, potato harvesters, sugar beet harvesters	3·0	5·0	6·0	7·0	2·0
Other Implements and Machines:					
Group 1:					
Ploughs, Cultivators, Toothed harrows, Hoes, Elevator potato diggers — Normal Soils	4·5	8·0	11·0	14·0	6·0
Group 2:					
Rotary cultivators, Mowers, Pea cutter-windrowers	4·0	7·0	9·5	12·0	5·0
Group 3:					
Disc harrows, Fertilizer distributors, Farmyard manure spreaders, Combine drills, Potato planters with fertilizer attachment, Sprayers, Hedge-cutting machines	3·0	5·5	7·5	9·5	4·0
Group 4:					
Swath turners, Tedders, Side-delivery rakes, Unit drills, Flail forage harvesters, Semi-automatic potato planters and transplanters, Down-the-row thinners	2·5	4·5	6·5	8·5	4·0
Group 5:					
Corn drills, Milking machines, Hydraulic loaders, Potato planting attachments	2·0	4·0	5·5	7·0	3·0
Group 6:					
Grain driers, Grain cleaners, Rolls, Hammer mills, Feed mixers Threshers	1·5	2·0	2·5	3·0	0·5

* When it is known that a high purchase price is due to high quality and durability or a low price corresponds to a high rate of wear and tear, adjustments to the figures should be made.

6. IRRIGATION COSTS
(Estimated for 1998)

A. Capital Costs
(before deducting grant)

1. *Pumps* (delivering from 50 to 150 cubic metres per hour from a surface water source)

Tractor driven, with accessories	£2,800-3,500
Diesel units	£10,000-20,000
Electrically driven units (excluding power supply)	£6,000-13,000

2. *Pipelines (per m)*

Portable: (excl. valves) 75 mm, £5·30; 100 mm, £7·30; 125 mm, £10·00; 150 mm, £14·50; (incl. valves) 75 mm, £9·00; 100 mm, £12·00; 125 mm, £14·00; 150 mm, £20·00.

Permanent (P.V.C. pipe bar rating, supply and laying): 100 mm, £23·00; 150 mm, £30·00. Hydrants: 100 mm, £500; 150 mm, £600.

3. *Application Systems*

Self travellers: hose reel equipment capable of irrigating 10 hectares in a 10-day cycle (two moves each day and operating for 22 hours per day) cost £8,000. Larger machines capable of irrigating 20, 32, 50 and 60 hectares in a 10-day cycle cost approximately £12,000, £17,000, £22,000 and £27,000 respectively.

Sprinkler lines: a 1 hectare setting of a conventional hand-moved sprinkler line costs £6,000 to £9,000 depending on application requirements. For each hectare cover of sprinklers 30 to 40 hectares can normally be irrigated in a 10-day cycle.

4. *Total*

If no source works are needed, as with water from a river, or pond, total capital costs can be as low as £1,000 for each hectare requiring irrigation at regular intervals, but are more typically £1,400 to £2,000.

5. *Source Works*

Boreholes typically cost £160 to £200 per m depth and require expensive submersible pumps. An overall cost, including electricity supply, pump and well head, to irrigate 4 hectares with 25 mm of water per day would be in the region of £20,000 to £30,000. £500 to £800 per hectare can easily be added to capital costs.

The least expensive large reservoirs typically cost £1 per cubic metre of storage capacity, with smaller reservoirs costing as much as £4.00 per cubic metre where lining is required. £1 per cubic metre equals £1,000 per hectare irrigated if enough water is stored to apply 100 mm per hectare.

B. Operating Costs

A typical depreciation and interest cost for a self traveller capable of covering 30 ha in a 10-day cycle where only limited source works are provided would be £55 per application of 25 mm per hectare. Running costs, including labour (2 man-hours per hectare), repairs, fuel, etc. would cost £32.

Abstraction charges vary widely, depending on the region, season and whether or not the source is supported by National Rivers Authority operations. Winter abstraction charges typically range from £1 to £3 per 1,000 m³ and summer rates from £15 to £25 per 1,000 m³ for sources which are not supported by National Rivers Authority operations. Abstraction charges during the summer can be up to £70 per 1,000 m³ in areas where supplies are supported by National River Authority operations. A charge of £2 per 1,000 m³ equals 50p per 25mm hectare, whilst a charge of £20 per 1,000 m³ would cost £5 per hectare per 25 mm application. Mains water at 50p per m³ would cost £125 per application of 25 mm per hectare.

Total costs per application of 25 mm per hectare, based on limited source works and summer abstraction rates, would be in the region of £90 to £95 for a self traveller system. Costs for sprinkler lines are likely to be between 10 and 20 per cent higher, largely because of greater labour requirements (5 man-hours per hectare).

Source works at £1,400 per hectare, together with mainly permanent pipelines, would increase the above figure for depreciation and interest to £93 per 25 mm per hectare, but abstraction and variable costs would be lower, giving a total cost of £110 to £115 per application of 25 mm per hectare.

Where irrigation capacity is under-utilised the effective cost per 25 mm of water applied per hectare can be very much higher.

Note:

The (approximate) imperial equivalents for metric values commonly used in irrigation are as follows:

1 cubic metre=1,000 litres=220 gallons.

A pump capacity of 100 cubic metres per hour is equivalent to 22,000 gallons per hour (366 gallons per minute).

In terms of water storage 1,000 cubic metres (1 million litres) is equivalent to 220,000 gallons (1 million gallons=4,546 cubic metres).

1,000 cubic metres is sufficient to apply 25 millimetres of water over 4 hectares, which is approximately equivalent to applying 1 inch over 10 acres.

7. FIELD DRAINAGE

(Estimated for 1998)

1. Installation (costs per metre of excavating a trench, supplying and laying the pipe and backfilling with soil).

		£ per metre
Plastic pipes:	60mm diameter	1·00—1·25
	80mm diameter	1·15—1·40
	100mm diameter	1·75 2·10
	125mm diameter	2·10—2·80
	150mm diameter	3·30—3·40
	300mm diameter	5·75—7·75

The above rates apply to schemes of 5 hectares or more; smaller areas and patching up work can cost up to 50% more.

Supplying and laying permeable backfill to within 360mm of ground level will add between £1·50 and £2·00 per metre to costs.

Digging new open ditches (1·8m top width, 0·9m depth) costs £1·50-£2·00 per metre compared with improving existing ditches at £1·00 to £1·50 per metre.

Subsoiling or mole draining will cost in the region of £45-£60 per hectare.

2. *Total*

Costs per hectare for complete schemes will vary depending on the distance between laterals, soil type, size of area to be drained, region of the country and the time of year when the work is to be undertaken. The cost of a scheme with 20m spacing between laterals and using permeable backfill will typically be in the range £1,400 to £1,600 per hectare (£565-£650 per acre). Backfilling with soil, rather than with permeable material such as washed gravel, may reduce the cost by almost half but is only possible on certain types of soil. Equally, certain soil types which are particularly suitable for mole drainage may permit spacing between laterals to be increased to 40m or even 80m in some instances. Where this is possible costs will be reduced proportionately.

Grant aid is no longer available for field drainage.

8. GRAIN DRYING AND STORAGE COSTS
(Estimated for 1998)

A. Drying

Capital Costs: vary widely according to type and capacity of drier; assuming 125 to 150 hours of use per season and driers with a rated capacity of 8 to 25 tonnes per hour at 5% extraction, a typical range is £22 to £36 per tonne dried annually.

Annual fixed costs: depreciation and interest £2·50 to £4·50 per tonne.

Running costs: fuel and repairs, £2.20 to £3·20 per tonne (6 per cent moisture extraction) for oil-fired driers or where little heat is used in ventilated plants; £6.00 to £8·00 for electrically-heated driers. Little labour is required for modern automatic driers unless grain has to be passed over the drier several times.

Total operating costs: average £5·90 to £8·90 per tonne (6 per cent) for cereals; costs for oilseed rape are likely to be £2 to £3 per tonne higher when drying in ventilated bins, because of higher labour requirements.

B. Storage

Capital Costs: from less than £70 per tonne (on-floor storage in a purpose-built building) to £220 per tonne for an elaborate plant, including pit, elevator, conveyors, storage bins etc. in a new building.

Typical costs are given on page 150.

Depreciation and Interest: £160 per tonne depreciated over 10 years, with 10 per cent interest, equals £26·00 per annum; over 15 years, at 7 per cent interest, £17·50. (In highly mechanized bulk plants, part of this may be charged against harvesting rather than entirely against storage).

Fuel and Repairs: £1·75 per tonne.

Extra Drying: Additional drying costs will be borne if storage necessitates further moisture reduction. Average £1·60 per tonne where own drier, £3·50 if dried on contract, for an additional 4 per cent moisture extraction.

Loss of Weight: the value of the weight of grain lost should be considered as an additional cost of storage if storage requires extra drying. 2 per cent = £2·00 to £2·50 per tonne.

Interest on Grain Stored: from 58p (£100 per tonne grain, at 7 per cent) to 98p (£130 per tonne grain, at 9 per cent) per month.

Contract Storage: typically £1·10 per tonne per month with a handling charge of around £1·50 per tonne for loading into store and out of store.

IV. OTHER FIXED COSTS DATA
1. WHOLE FARM FIXED COSTS

The following are a *broad indication* of the levels of fixed costs (£) per hectare (acre) for various types and sizes of farm, estimated for 1998, *including the value of unpaid family manual labour,* including that of the farmer and his wife.

All of these costs can of course vary widely according to many factors, especially the intensity of farming, e.g. the number of cows per 100 farm hectares on the mainly dairying and dairying and arable farms, or the hectares of intensive crops such as potatoes, sugar beet and vegetables per 100 farm hectares on the mixed cropping farms.

Furthermore, *the figures provided are only averages. "Premium" farms of the same level of intensity can have labour, machinery and general overhead costs at least 20% lower.* However, the most profitable farms are often more intensive and therefore have higher fixed costs associated with the great intensity—but with substantially higher total farm gross margins; it is the net amount (TGM-TFC) that matters.

More specific data relating to local types of farm can be derived from reports published annually by the agricultural economics departments of certain Universities and Colleges; those in England and Wales (based on the Farm Business Survey) are given below (all have been consulted in compiling the data presented).

North: Farming in Northern England (University of Newcastle-upon-Tyne).
Yorkshire: Farming in Yorkshire (Askham Bryan College).
North-West: An Economic Review of Farming in the North-West (University of
    Manchester).
East Midlands: Farming in the East Midlands (University of Nottingham).
Eastern Counties: Report on Farming in the Eastern Counties (University of Cambridge).
South-East: Farm Business Statistics for South-East England (Wye College, University of
    London).
South: Farm Business Data (University of Reading)
South-West: Farm Incomes in South-West England (University of Exeter).
Wales: Farm Business Survey in Wales (University College of Wales, Aberystwyth).
The addresses and telephone numbers of the above are given on pages 213/214.
Data for Scotland and Northern Ireland are available from the Scottish Agricultural College and
Department of Northern Ireland respectively. Their addresses are given on page 214.

The term "fixed costs" is used here as it is in gross margin analysis and planning: a full explanation of the differences between fixed and variable costs in this context is given on pages 1 and 2. *Note that all casual labour and contract work have been included under fixed costs.* In calculating enterprise gross margins on the individual farm these costs are normally allocated as variable costs if they are specific to a particular enterprise and vary approximately in proportion to its size, i.e. are approximately constant per hectare of a particular crop or per head of livestock. Otherwise they are included as fixed costs. In both cases, however, they could be regarded as substitutes for regular labour and/or the farmer's own machinery—which are both items of fixed cost. It is therefore simpler if both are included, fully, as fixed costs. If one is comparing results from accounts set out on a gross margin basis, and some or all of the casual labour and contract work have been included as variable costs (especially on cropping farms, e.g. for potato harvesting by casual labour or contractor's machine), the necessary adjustments need to be made in making the comparisons.

Notes

Unpaid Labour. Refers to the value of family manual labour, including that of the farmer and his wife.

Depreciation. This is based on the "historic" (i.e. original) cost of machinery, not on the current (i.e. replacement) cost. Although the latter is a truer refection of the *real* loss of value of machinery (as is apparent when replacement becomes necessary), virtually all farm accounts use the historic cost method. Hence the use of the latter facilitates efficiency comparisons. It should, however, be noted that depreciation is based on current costs in the University/College reports listed on the previous page; on average this increases the figure by about a quarter. Both this item and *Repairs* include vehicles.

Leasing Charges: The capital element, but not the interest, is included in depreciation; the proportion paid as interest varies according to the rate of interest paid and the length of the leasing period, but is typically 15 to 20 per cent.

Rental Value. Estimated rent for owner-occupied land, based on actual rents of farms of similar type and size (established tenancies; i.e. not new / farm business tenancies). 'Landlord-type' expenses average about 40 per cent of the estimated rent.

General Overheads include general farm maintenance and repairs, office expenses, water, insurance, fees, subscriptions, etc. 'Farm maintenance', i.e. repairs to property (buildings, roads, etc.), average approximately one-quarter of total general farm overhead expenses.

In making comparisons with fixed costs taken from farm accounts it is important to note that in the figures below unpaid manual labour and a rental value for owner-occupied land are included; (but not paid management or interest charges).

Labour, machinery and buildings are the main items of "fixed" costs subject to change with major alterations in farm policy. Each is the subject of a separate section in this book.

		Mainly Dairying	
	Under 50 ha (Under 125 acres)	50-100 ha (125-250 acres)	Over 100 ha (Over 250 acres)
Regular Labour (paid) ...	150 (61)	250 (101)	285 (115)
Regular Labour (unpaid) ...	460 (186)	250 (101)	95 (39)
Casual Labour	35 (14)	20 (8)	15 (6)
Total Labour	645 (261)	520 (210)	395 (160)
Machinery Depreciation... ...	125 (51)	115 (47)	110 (45)
Machinery Repairs	90 (36)	85 (34)	85 (34)
Fuel, Elec., Oil	70 (29)	62·5 (25)	55 (22)
Contract	90 (36)	90 (36)	85 (34)
Vehicle Tax and Insurance ...	15 (6)	12·5 (5)	10 (4)
Total Power and Machinery ...	390 (158)	365 (148)	345 (139)
Rent/Rental Value	180 (73)	170 (69)	165 (67)
General Overhead Expenses ...	220 (89)	190 (77)	170 (69)
Total Fixed Costs	1435 (581)	1245 (504)	1075 (435)

	Dairying and Arable		
	Under 100 ha (Under 250 acres)	100-200 ha (250-500 acres)	Over 200 ha (Over 500 acres)
Regular Labour (paid)	210 (85)	250 (101)	230 (93)
Regular Labour (unpaid) ...	220 (89)	90 (36)	30 (12)
Casual Labour	20 (8)	15 (6)	10 (4)
Total Labour	450 (182)	355 (143)	270 (109)
Machinery Depreciation... ...	120 (49)	105 (43)	100 (41)
Machinery Repairs	70 (28)	70 (28)	70 (28)
Fuel, Elec., Oil	55 (22)	50 (20)	45 (18)
Contract	52·5 (21)	50 (20)	37·5 (15)
Vehicle Tax and Insurance ...	12·5 (5)	10 (4)	7·5 (3)
Total Power and Machinery ...	310 (125)	285 (115)	260 (105)
Rent/Rental Value	170 (69)	160 (65)	155 (63)
General Overhead Expenses ...	155 (63)	140 (57)	125 (51)
Total Fixed Costs	1085 (439)	940 (380)	810 (328)

	Mainly Cereals*		
	Under 100 ha (Under 250 acres)	100-200 ha (250-500 acres)	Over 200 ha (Over 500 acres)
Regular Labour (paid)	70 (28)	90 (36·5)	95 (38·5)
Regular Labour (unpaid) ...	175 (71)	90 (36·5)	45 (18·5)
Casual Labour	10 (4)	15 (6)	15 (6)
Total Labour	255 (103)	195 (79)	155 (63)
Machinery Depreciation ...	85 (35)	85 (35)	85 (35)
Machinery Repairs	57·5 (23)	50 (20)	47·5 (19)
Fuel, Elec., Oil	35 (14)	30 (12)	30 (12)
Contract	65 (26)	50 (20)	25 (10)
Vehicle Tax and Insurance ...	12·5 (5)	10 (4)	7·5 (3)
Total Power and Machinery ...	255 (103)	225 (91)	195 (79)
Rent/Rental Value	150 (61)	145 (59)	140 (57)
General Overhead Expenses ...	110 (45)	90 (36)	70 (28)
Total Fixed Costs	770 (312)	655 (265)	560 (227)

* With combinable break crops.

	Mixed Cropping*		
	Under 100 ha	100-200 ha	Over 200 ha
	(Under 250 acres)	(250-500 acres)	(Over 500 acres)
Regular Labour (paid)	45 (18)	125 (51)	170 (69)
Regular Labour (unpaid) ...	190 (77)	70 (28)	25 (10)
Casual Labour	20 (8)	10 (4)	10 (4)
Total Labour	255 (103)	205 (83)	205 (83)
Machinery Depreciation... ...	90 (37)	105 (43)	105 (43)
Machinery Repairs	65 (26)	65 (26)	65 (26)
Fuel, Elec., Oil	35 (14)	35 (14)	35 (14)
Contract	30 (12)	42·5 (17)	35 (14)
Vehicle Tax and Insurance ...	15 (6)	12·5 (5)	10 (4)
Total Power and Machinery ...	235 (95)	260 (105)	250 (101)
Rent /Rental Value	170 (69)	165 (67)	160 (64)
General Overhead Expenses ...	110 (45)	100 (40)	95 (38)
Total Fixed Costs	770 (312)	730 (295)	710 (287)

* With potatoes and/or sugar beet and/or field vegetables; grade 1 or 2 land.

	Mainly Sheep/Cattle (lowland)		
	Under 100 ha	100-200 ha	Over 200 ha
	(Under 250 acres)	(250-500 acres)	(Over 500 acres)
Regular Labour (paid)	70 (28)	75 (30)	95 (39)
Regular Labour (unpaid) ...	265 (108)	125 (51)	75 (30)
Casual Labour	20 (8)	10 (4)	5 (2)
Total Labour	355 (144)	210 (85)	175 (71)
Machinery Depreciation... ...	65 (26)	60 (24)	50 (20)
Machinery Repairs	60 (24)	40 (16)	35 (14)
Fuel, Elec., Oil	40 (16)	30 (12)	25 (10)
Contract	40 (16)	25 (10)	17·5 (7)
Vehicle Tax and Insurance ...	10 (4)	10 (4)	7·5 (3)
Total Power and Machinery ...	215 (87)	165 (67)	135 (54)
Rent/Rental Value	130 (53)	125 (51)	115 (47)
General Overhead Expenses ...	105 (42)	75 (30)	65 (26)
Total Fixed Costs	805 (326)	575 (233)	490 (198)

	Sheep/Cattle and Arable		
	Under 100 ha (Under 250 acres)	100-200 ha (250-500 acres)	Over 200 ha (Over 500 acres)
Regular Labour (paid)	45 (18)	60 (24)	100 (41)
Regular Labour (unpaid) ...	190 (77)	130 (53)	65 (26)
Casual Labour	15 (6)	10 (4)	5 (2)
Total Labour	250 (101)	200 (81)	170 (69)
Machinery Depreciation ...	57·5 (23)	60 (24)	55 (22)
Machinery Repairs	40 (16)	45 (18)	40 (16)
Fuel, Elec., Oil	25 (10)	22·5 (9)	22·5 (9)
Contract	35 (14)	22·5 (9)	20 (8)
Vehicle Tax and Insurance ...	12·5 (5)	10 (4)	7·5 (3)
Total Power and Machinery ...	170 (69)	160 (65)	145 (59)
Rent/Rental Value	140 (57)	135 (55)	130 (52)
General Overhead Expenses ...	100 (40)	85 (34)	75 (30)
Total Fixed Costs	660 (267)	580 (235)	520 (210)

	Arable and Pigs/Poultry*		
	Under 100 ha (Under 250 acres)	100-200 ha (250-500 acres)	Over 200 ha (Over 500 acres)
Regular Labour (paid)	400 (162)	380 (154)	260 (105)
Regular Labour (unpaid) ...	185 (75)	90 (36)	25 (10)
Casual Labour	15 (6)	10 (4)	5 (2)
Total Labour	600 (243)	480 (194)	290 (117)
Machinery Depreciation... ...	115 (47)	105 (43)	100 (41)
Machinery Repairs	105 (42)	75 (30)	65 (26)
Fuel, Elec., Oil	110 (45)	80 (32)	65 (26)
Contract	50 (20)	32·5 (13)	30 (12)
Vehicle Tax and Insurance ...	15 (6)	12·5 (5)	10 (4)
Total Power and Machinery ...	395 (160)	305 (123)	270 (109)
Rent/Rental Value	170 (69)	165 (67)	160 (65)
General Overhead Expenses ...	240 (97)	210 (85)	110 (45)
Total Fixed Costs	1405 (569)	1160 (469)	830 (336)

* The number of pigs in relation to the total farm area varies widely, and so, therefore, can these per hectare (per acre) figures.

						Livestock Rearing	
						Upland	Hill
						(per *adjusted* hectare (acre))*	
Regular Labour (paid)	...	...	...	...	...	75 (31)	42·5 (17)
Regular Labour (unpaid)	...	...	...	...	...	90 (36)	75 (31)
Casual Labour	...	...	...	...	...	10 (4)	7·5 (3)
Total Labour	...	...	...	...	...	175 (71)	125 (51)
Machinery Depreciation	...	...	...	...	...	50	32·5
Machinery Repairs	...	...	...	...	...	27·5 (11)	15 (6)
Fuel, Elec., Oil	...	...	...	...	...	15 (6)	12·5 (5)
Contract	...	...	...	...	...	22·5 (9)	7·5 (3)
Vehicle Tax and Insurance	...	...	...	...		5 (2)	2·5 (1)
Total Power and Machinery	...	...	...	...		120 (49)	70 (28)
Rent/Rental Value	...	...	...	...	...	75 (30)	45 (18)
General Overhead Expenses	...	...	...	...		70 (28)	45 (18)
Total Fixed Costs	...	...	...	...	...	440 (178)	285 (115)

*Divisors for per actual/ area figure = upland 1·5, hill 2·25.

Large (Lowland) Farms

The following data are based on the Cambridge University Farm Business Survey results for non-fenland farms in 1995/6 approximated for 1998 (with historic cost depreciation):

	All Farms		Farms excluding livestock	
	400-500 ha	Over 500ha	400-500 ha	Over 500 ha
	(1000-1250 acres)	(Over 1250 acres)	(1000-1250 acres)	(Over 1250 acres)
Regular Labour (paid)	170 (69)	168 (68)	130 (53)	137 (55·5)
Regular Labour (unpaid)	15 (6)	2 (1)	15 (6)	2 (1)
Casual Labour	—	—	—	1 (0·5)
Total Labour	185 (75)	170 (69)	145 (59)	140 (57)
Power and Machinery	280 (113)	245 (99)	245 (99)	220 (89)
Rent/Rental Value	150 (61)	145 (59)	150 (61)	145 (59)
General Overhead Expenses	100 (40)	85 (34)	85 (34)	65 (26)
Total Fixed Costs	715 (289)	645 (261)	625 (253)	570 (231)

N.B. **Horticultural holdings**—see page 30.

2. RENTS

The following figures relate to farms let with a combination of crops, grass and rough grazing in England; they include housing and buildings, as available. They are per hectare (with per acre in brackets) to the nearest 50p per ha and 25p per acre.

On land with full agricultural tenancies (under the Agricultural Holdings Act 1986) the average increase in rents (including farms with no change) in 1996 compared with 1995 was 7.0%. This compares with 6.5% in 1995 and 2.9% in 1994.

In the following table the average recorded regional and national levels for 1996 are given both for full agricultural tenancies and for all rent agreements, including under the new farm business tenancies. In addition the author's estimate is included for rents newly agreed in 1998 for full (traditional) tenancies.

| | 1996 | | 1998 |
Region	Full agric. tenancies	All rents	Full agric. tenancies (est. new rents)
West Midlands	129 (52·25)	152·5 (61·50)	155 (46·5)
Eastern	123 (49·75)	130 (52·75)	148 (60)
South East	120 (48·75)	130·5 (53·00)	144 (58)
East Midlands	117·5 (47·50)	129 (52·25)	141 (57)
South West	109·5 (44·25)	122 (49·25)	131 (53)
Yorks/Humberside	86 (34·75)	94·5 (38·25)	103 (42)
North West	78·5 (31·75)	101·5 (41·00)	94 (38)
North East	51·5 (20·75)	61·5 (25·00)	62 (25)
England	102 (41·25)	116·5 (47·25)	123 (50)

It has to be borne in mind that rough grazing, including upland, is included in the above: hence the low figure (most notably) for the northern farms. **The average rent for lowland, excluding woodland and rough grazing, for land under full agricultural tenancies is likely to be approximately £140 per ha, £57·50 per acre, in 1998; (£150 (£60) where a new rent is set that year).** The levels on large mixed arable farms (i.e. including potatoes, sugar beet and/or vegetables) on very good soil, or well-equipped dairy farms, will tend to average £170 to £200 per ha, £70 to £80 per acre. Variations according to soil type (land classification) and size are shown below.

Farm Business Tenancy rents are likely to be higher still, as has been seen in 1996; it seems probable that future levels offered will be substantially lower than in that year, unless 1994-96 levels of agricultural prosperity (unexpectedly) reoccur. Farmers who already own land, with little or no mortgage, can afford to offer a higher figure than bidders with no other farm.

The following data all relate to 1996.

Average Rent by Type of Agreement

	£ per ha (acre)	Agreements in sample
Full Agricultural Tenancy	102 (41·50)	2516
Farm Business Tenancy less than one year	292 (118·25)	46
Farm Business Tenancy for at least one year	173 (70·00)	513
Other agreement less than one year	202 (81·50)	728
Other agreement for at least one year	112 (45·25)	1065

139

Average Rent by Rented Area

Total rented area of holding	Full agric. tenancies	All rents	Agreements in sample
	£ per ha (acre)		
Less than 10ha	143·5 (58·25)	179 (72·50)	369
10 to 49·9 ha	111·5 (45·25)	148 (59·75)	920
50 to 99·9 ha	114 (46·25)	126 (51·00)	1068
100 to 249·9 ha	109 (44·25)	118 (47·75)	1308
250 ha and above	79·5 (32·00)	83·5 (33·75)	1203

Average Rent by Length of Term

Fixed Term agreements:	£ per ha (acre)	Agreements in sample
Less than one year	206 (83·25)	777
1 year to less than 5	147 (59·50)	839
5 years to less than 10	132 (53·50)	181
10 years to less than 25	140 (56·75)	101
25 years and over	113·5 (46·00)	69
No fixed term	98·5 (39·75)	938
Lifetime agreements	103 (41·50)	1963

Average Rent by Type of Property
(Full agricultural tenancies only)

	£ per ha (acre)
Land only	89·5 (36·25)
Land, buildings &/or dwellings	98·5 (39·75)

Average Rent by Farm Type

Farm type	Full agric' tenancies	All rents	Agreements in sample
	£ per ha (acre)		
Cereals	121·5 (49·25)	133 (54·00)	1471
General Cropping	121·5 (49·25)	134 (54·25)	423
Dairy	131 (53·00)	154 (62·25)	806
Cattle and Sheep (Lowland)	76·5 (31·00)	96 (39·00)	715
Cattle and Sheep (LFA)	32·5 (13·25)	44 (17·75)	652
All mainly LFA farms	44·5 (18·00)	56 (22·75)	883
All other farms	118 (47·75)	133 (53·75)	3985

Source of Data

MAFF (Government Statistical Service): Annual Survey of Tenanted Land - England - 1996. There were 4,868 agreements included in the survey, covering 420,000 ha (1,037,325 acres), which is some 11.6% of the recorded rented farmland in England. This survey has replaced the Annual Rent Enquiry.

3. LAND PRICES

Sale Value of Farmland, England and Wales (£ per hectare (acre))

(1) **Auction Sales (with Vacant Possession only)**

(a) Oxford Institute/Savills series*

Year	Current Prices	Real Values**	Year	Current Prices	Real Values**
1937-9	60 (24)	1328 (537)	1980	4265 (1726)	6227 (2520)
1945	111 (45)	1474 (597)	1981	4272 (1729)	5596 (2265)
1950	198 (80)	2146 (868)	1982	4557 (1844)	5468 (2224)
1955	198 (80)	1732 (701)	1983	5145 (2082)	5917 (2395)
1960	304 (123)	2365 (957)	1984	4888 (1978)	5377 (2176)
1965	581 (235)	3840 (1554)	1985	4781 (1935)	4924 (1993)
1970	605 (245)	3195 (1293)	1986	4193 (1697)	4193 (1697)
1971	647 (262)	3119 (1262)	1987	4944 (2001)	4746 (1921)
1972	1473 (596)	6628 (2682)	1988	6716 (2718)	6135 (2482)
1973	1871 (757)	7727 (3127)	1989	6558 (2654)	5558 (2249)
1974	1572 (636)	5596 (2265)	1990	6346 (2568)	4913 (1988)
1975	1332 (539)	3810 (1542)	1991	6007 (2431)	4393 (1778)
1976	1814 (734)	4462 (1806)	1992	5441 (2202)	3836 (1552)
1977	2449 (991)	5192 (2101)	1993	5456 (2208)	3785 (1532)
1978	3279 (1327)	6427 (2601)	1994	5028 (2035)	3408 (1379)
1979	4371 (1769)	7562 (3060)	1996	8797 (3560)	5630 (2278)

*Savills since 1988. ** At 1986 general price levels.

Since 1970, figures based on sales reports in the *Estates Gazette* and the *Farmers Weekly*, plus some unpublished sales, with a minimum size of 10 hectares.

(b) Farmland Market series

Size Group (hectares)	10-20	20-40	40-60	60-80	80-100	100-140	Over 140	All Farms
1973	2530	2080	1815	1805	1805	1735	2100	1975 (799)
1974	2245	1745	1490	1565	1415	1335	1280	1685 (682)
1975	2115	1545	1340	1165	1200	1190	1090	1485 (601)
1976	2560	2015	1855	1830	1670	1610	1730	1965 (795)
1977	2825	2660	2365	2425	2230	2530	2325	2525 (1020)
1978	3970	3425	3125	3265	3180	3480	3595	3380 (1368)
1979	6280	4385	4220	3975	4330	4890	4315	4515 (1828)
1980	5585	4905	4270	4305	4405	4435	4130	4705 (1904)
1981	6135	4680	3880	4315	3760	4710	4355	4500 (1821)
1982	6455	4950	4465	4065	4705	4510	4325	4815 (1949)
1983	6825	5630	5160	5110	5095	5495	5130	5450 (2206)
1984	6565	5815	5300	5520	5435	5360	4625	5480 (2218)
1985	8410	5190	4455	4555	4210	4405	4645	5245 (2123)
1986	7825	5180	3930	3745	N/A	3155	N/A	4185 (1949)
1987	7280	7115	5130	4285	4325	N/A	N/A	5980 (2421)
1988	13255	9035	6225	5825	5320	6220	4275	7205 (2916)
1989	14140	9260	6660	6610	5770	5980	5260	7520 (3044)
1990	8225	6680	7440	6420	5820	N/A	N/A	6505 (2635)
1991	7335	7790	6575	4455	4985	N/A	N/A	6460 (2615)
1992	8920	6255	4280	4890	N/A	4400	N/A	5650 (2285)
1993	8910	7185	5410	5305	4725	N/A	5585	5890 (2385)
1994	10265	6095	5565	5335	5535	5220	N/A	5765 (2335)
1995	13115	9755	7705	6765	7075	N/A	5855	7785 (3150)
1996	19005	10140	10145	7015	N/A	8605	N/A	9745 (3945)

Bare land prices (over 2 ha): 1987, £3955 (1600); 1988, £5040 (2040); 1989, £5620 (2275); 1990,£7885 (3190); 1991, £4800 (1945); 1992, £3970 (1605); 1993, £4320 (1750); 1994, 4940 (2000); 1995, 5960 (2410); 1996, 6780 (2745).

(2) Current Agricultural Prices (CALP and CALP/RICS) series (vacant possession only)

Cover sales of 5 ha and above but excludes land sold for development or forestry, gifts, inheritances and compulsory purchases. Includes sales of bare land as well as land with dwellings, buildings, etc. (see (iii) (d) below).

CALP series (England only) data collected jointly by ADAS (Agricultural Development and Advisory Service) AMC (Agricultural Mortgage Corporation) and CLA (Country Landowners Association) and were published by the AMC until 1993. A CALP/RICS Farmland Price Index (England and Wales) began in 1995.

(i) *CALP Annual Figures*

	Average price (A)	Average price (B): in 1993 £	Index (of B) (1978 = 100)
1978	3160 (1280)	8905 (3605)	100
1979	4140 (1675)	10295 (4165)	116
1980	3975 (1610)	8375 (3390)	94
1981	3940 (1595)	7420 (3005)	83
1982	4125 (1670)	7155 (2895)	80
1983	4630 (1875)	7675 (3105)	86
1984	4555 (1845)	7195 (2910)	81
1985	4340 (1755)	6460 (2615)	73
1986	3675 (1485)	5300 (2145)	59
1987	3780 (1530)	5220 (2115)	59
1988	5350 (2165)	7045 (2850)	79
1989	5595 (2265)	6835 (2765)	77
1990	4440 (1795)	4955 (2005)	56
1991	4145 (1676)	4370 (1770)	49
1992	3658 (1480)	3715 (1505)	42
1993	3608 (1460)	3608 (1460)	41

Total value of sales divided by total area sold.

(ii) *CALP/RICS Farmland Price Index*

In the 3 months ended

March	1995	5160 (2088)
June	1995	5349 (2165)
September	1995	5469 (2213)
December	1995	5269 (2132)
March	1996	5737 (2322)
June	1996	7275 (2944)
September	1996	7011 (2837)
December	1996	7210 (2918)
March	1997	7014 (2839)
June	1997	7127 (2884)

Average unweighted prices; (value of milk quota excluded).

Note: Regional, size-group, land classification and type of property variations: annual figures for 1988 to 1992 inclusive (vacant possession only) were included in the previous four editions of this book but data after 1992 are regretfully unavailable.

(3) **Inland Revenue Returns** (England only; Oct. 1-Sept. 30 years)

Year[1]	Vacant Possession Farms[2]	Bare Land	Tenanted Farms[2]	Bare Land
1980/1	3568 (1444)	3325 (1346)	2334 (945)	2354 (953)
1981/2	3503 (1418)	3281 (1328)	2644 (1070)	1340 (542)
1982/3	3766 (1524)	3525 (1427)	2549 (1032)	2210 (894)
1983/4	3761 (1522)	3835 (1552)	2389 (967)	2511 (1016)
1984/5	4258 (1723)	3466 (1403)	2879 (1165)	2310 (935)
1985/6	4055 (1641)	3477 (1407)	2192 (887)	2217 (897)
1986/7	3703 (1499)	3023 (1223)	2141 (866)	1777 (719)
1987/8	3750 (1518)	3140 (1271)	2252 (911)	2476 (1002)
1988/9	4739 (1918)	3521 (1425)	3178 (1286)[3]	1929 (781)
1989/90	5355 (2167)	4080 (1651)	2143 (867)	2093 (847)
1990/91	5515 (2231)	3750 (1517)	2090 (846)	2505 (1014)
1991/92	5015 (2030)	3370 (1363)	2505 (1015)	1465 (592)
1992/93	4405 (1785)	3120 (1265)	1680 (680)	2045 (830)[3]
1993/94	4319 (1748)	3235 (1309)	2102 (851)	1116 (452)
1994/95	4661 (1886)	3608 (1460)	1860 (753)	1720 (696)
1995/96	5058 (2047)	3936 (1593)	2605 (1054)	1490 (603)
1996-last ¼	6223 (2158)	5053 (2045)	NA	3030 (1226)

1. There is a delay between the dates when a price is agreed and when it is notified to the Inland Revenue and thus included in the above figures; this time-lag is thought to average about 9 months; hence, for example, the 1994/95 figures roughly approximate to 1994 calendar year prices.
2. Farms = Land and Buildings, including the farmhouse.
3. High figure caused by a few untypically high-priced transactions.

The above figures relate to all sales of agricultural properties of 5 ha and over except those for development and other non-agricultural purposes. They include any sales at prices below ruling open market value (as between members of a family), sales where the vendor retains certain (e.g. sporting) rights, sales in which the farmhouse represents a substantial part of the total value, and sales of land which may, in the purchaser's view, have an element of development value.

Vacant Possession Premium
On the basis of the Inland Revenue Returns above the average price of tenanted land as a percentage of vacant possession land in the five years 1991/92 to 1995/96 was 46% for both whole farms and bare land. In individual years the figure varied from 38% to 52% for whole farms and from 35% to 68% for bare land.

Source: MAFF Statistics (Government Statistical Service).

Woodland
Average price range of average quality established lowland woodland: £1250-1500/ha (£500-600/acre).

Land Classification
% of total area, England and Wales, by grades. 1, 2·3%; 2, 16·9%; 3a, 19·3%; 3b, 35·4%; 4, 15·0%; 5, 11·1%.

4. BUILDINGS

A. Building Costs

Building costs are notoriously variable. Many factors influence a contractor's price, including distance from his yard, size of contract, site access, site conditions, complexity of work, familiarity with the type of work and his current work load. There will also be differences in efficiency and standard of work between contractors and, as is often the case with farm buildings, the absence of detailed specification by the client may mean that different contractors will not have quoted for identical buildings. The number of extras that are found to be required after a contract has been agreed will also vary.

The costs given below can only be taken as an approximate guide. They refer to new buildings, erected by contractor on a clear level site and exclude VAT and any grants that may be available. Prices are forecasts for mid 1997.

Sources of Further Information

The costs below are based on information gathered by the SAC Buildings Design Unit, Aberdeen, cross-checked with other sources to ensure general applicability. More detailed information is available in the following publications. The books and journals giving general building cost information generally assume knowledge of how to take off quantities for building work.

Specialised Information on Farm Building Costs

Farm Building Cost Guide published annually by the Building Design Unit, SAC, Craibstone, Aberdeen.

Standard Costs Part 1: Specifications; Part 2: Costs. Published by MAFF and the Agricultural Departments in Scotland, Wales and Northern Ireland. Used when claiming government grants on a standard-cost basis.

General Building Cost Information

Books are produced by a number of publishers with annual or more frequent new editions and updates. Examples are *Laxton's Building Price Book, Spon's Architects' and Builders' Price Book,* and *Wessex Comprehensive Building Price Book.* Regularly updated cost information is also given in several professional and trade journals.

I. Constituent Parts

Frame, Roof and Foundations   *per m² floor area*

1. Open-sided timber framed pole barn
   with round pole uprights on concrete
   bases, sawn timber rafters and purlins,
   high-tensile galvanised steel cladding
   to roof and gable ends above eaves,
   hardcore floor, eaves height 4·8 m, 9 m
   span, no side cladding, rainwater drainage
   to soakaways.   £42

2. Open-sided steel portal-framed building
   with fibre-cement or plastic coated steel
   cladding to roof and gables above eaves,
   hardcore floor, eaves height 4·8 m, no
   side cladding, rainwater drainage to
   soakaways.
   9 m span   £89
   13·2 m span   £77
   18 m span   £74

3. Cost breakdown of 2 above
   Materials: portal frame and purlins 26%
          foundations   3%
          roofing   16%
          rainwater and drainage   3%
          hardcore and blinding   2%
          Total Materials   50%
   Erection: portal frame and purlins 19%
          foundations   2%
          roofing   19%
          rainwater and drainage   5%
          hardcore and blinding   5%
          Total Erection   50%

Roof cladding   per m²
1. Natural grey fibre-cement, 146 mm corrugations fixed
   with drive screws
   Materials   £10·90
   Fixing   £10·20
   Total   £21·10
2. Extra for coloured sheet   £3·00
3. Deduct for translucent sheets   £0·10
4. Deduct for PVC-coated steel   £10·00
5. Deduct for high-tensile corrugated galvanised steel
   sheeting   £12·40
6. PVC 150 mm half-round gutter on fascia brackets,
   including stop-ends and outlets   £23·30
7. PVC 100 mm rainwater pipe with fixings, swanneck
   and shoe   £22·50

	per m run
8. Fibre-cement close-fitting ridge	£25·10
9. Fibre-cement ventilating ridge	£27·80

Walls and Cladding   per m²

1. Concrete blockwork, fair faced and pointed both sides

150 mm thick	£25·25
215 mm thick	£36·75
215 mm thick hollow blocks	£40·40
215 mm thick hollow blocks, filled and reinforced	£55·35

2. Extra for rendering or roughcast to blockwork on one side — £11·65

3. Vertical spaced boarding 21 × 145 mm with 19 mm gaps including horizontal rails, all pressure treated — £17·90

4. Fibre-cement vertical cladding, including rails — £30·90

5. Corrugated high-tensile steel side cladding, including rails — £25·40

6. Wall element: 215 mm thick blockwork, including strip foundation (base 750 mm below ground level), 2.5 m height above ground level — £119 per m run

Floors   per m²

1. Concrete floor 100 mm thick, Gen 3 mix, on 150 mm hardcore, including excavation: — £22·00

Breakdown:

(a)	excavate, level and compact	£1·75
(b)	hardcore	£2·60
(c)	blinding	£1·70
(d)	damp-proof membrane	£1·10
(e)	premixed concrete spread and compacted	£14·15
(f)	float finish	£1·80

2. Extra to above for

(a)	150 mm instead of 100 mm	£5·40
(b)	laying concrete to falls	£1·30
(c)	broom or textured finish	£1·80
(d)	Carborundum dust non-slip finish	£2·40
(e)	insulating concrete	£1·90

3. Reinforced concrete slatted floors for cattle

(a)	cattle loading	£46
(b)	tractor loading	£50

4. Reinforced concrete slats for pigs — £37

5. Insulating floor, including excavation and base

| (a) | 27 mm expanded polystyrene, 38 mm screed | £36 |

(b) insulating concrete with lightweight aggregate		£25
(c) as (b) with 20 mm screed		£32
6. Form channel in concrete		£2.70 per m run
7. Excavate for cast 1 m³ in-situ concrete bases for stanchions		£89 each

Services and Fittings

1. Drainage: 100 mm PVC pipe laid in trench, including 750 mm deep excavation and backfill £17.10 per m run
   Breakdown:
   (a) excavate and backfill £8·30
   (b) 100 mm PVC pipe laid £8·80
   Extras:
   (c) add to (a) for 1 m deep £2·60
   (d) add to (b) for 150 mm pipe £7·00
2. Excavate soakaway and fill with stones £84 each
3. Trap and grid top, 100 mm PVC £49·00 each
4. Yard gully with heavy duty road grating 400 × 300 mm £205 each
5. Inspection chamber 900 mm deep, 450 × 600 mm opening and medium duty cast iron cover £340 each
6. Above-ground vitreous enamel slurry tank on concrete base, 1000 m³ £22,500 each
7. Reception pit, 20 m³ £1,350 each
8. Slurry channel beneath (not including) slats, 1·8 m deep, 3 m wide £305 per m run
9. Lighting: 1.5 m 60W single fluorescent unit, including wiring and switch £81 each
   Extras:
   (a) PVC conduit £60
   (b) screwed steel conduit £80
10. Power: 13A switched outlet £62 each
11. Diagonal feed fence, fixed, including posts (painted) £43 per m run
12. Tombstone feed fence, fixed, including posts (painted) £51 per m run
13. Feed bunker £41 per m run
14. Hay rack, wall fixing £34 per m run
15. Cubicle division, galvanised, fixed in place £59 each
16. Fencing: three-rail timber with posts, all pressure treated £15 per m run
17. Gate, 3 m wide, galvanised steel, including posts set in concrete
    (a) medium duty £185 each
    (b) heavy duty £230 each
    Deduct for painted instead of galvanised finish £34

II Complete Buildings

Fully Covered and Enclosed Barn
Portal frame, 18 m span, 6 m bays, 6 m to eaves, 3 m high blockwork walls with sheet cladding above, 6 m sliding doors at either end, 150mm thick concrete floor   £141perm²floorarea

Cows and Cattle Housing
1. Covered strawed yard, enclosed with ventilated cladding, concrete floor, pens only, with 4·0 m² per head floor area   £485 per head
2. Extra to 1 for 4·0 m wide double-sided feeding passage, barrier and troughs   £205 per head
3. Kennel building   £300 per head
4. Portal framed building with cubicles   £540 per head
5. Extra to 4 for feed stance, feeding passage, barriers and troughs   £315 per head
6. Extra to 4 for slatting of cubicle passages   £335 per head
7. Covered collecting yard, 1·1 m² per cow   £155 per head
8. Milking parlour building, example: 5·5 × 11·5 m for 8/16 parlour   £10,800
9. Parlour equipment, herringbone parlours:
   (a) low level, 1 stall per point   £2,085 per point
   (b) pipeline   £1,700 per point
   (c) extra for meter and auto cluster removal   £935 per point
   (d) auto feed dispenser   £415 per stall
10. Dairy building   £170 per m² floor area
11. Bulk tank and washer   £4·90 per litre
12. Loose box, 16 m² floor area laid to falls, rendered walls   £250 per m² floor area
13. Bull pen and open run   £7,600
14. Cattle crush and 20 m race   £3,000
15. Slatted floor cattle building for 120 growing cattle (1·7 m² pen space per head) with drive-through feed passage/troughs   £560 per head

Silage   *per tonne stored*
1. Timber panel clamp on concrete base with effluent tank   £45
2. Precast concrete panel clamp with effluent tank   £42
3. Glass-lined forage tower and unloader   £165

Waste Storage   *per m³ stored*
Lined lagoon with safety fence   £20
Glass-lined steel slurry silo
     small (400 m³)   £33
     medium (1,200 m³)   £24
     large (3,600 m³)   £19

GRP below-ground effluent tank, encased in concrete	per m³ stored
small (12 m³)	£365
large (36 m³)	£290

Sheep Housing
1. Penning, troughs, feed barriers and drinkers installed in suitable existing building   £23 per ewe
2. Purpose-built sheep shed with 1·35 m² per ewe pen space, concentrate troughs, feed passage and barrier for forage feeding   £90 per ewe

    Extras:
    (a) softwood slatted floor panels, materials only   £3·95 per m²
    (b) slatted panels as (a), made up, plus supports   £15·30 per m²

Pig Housing   *per sow and litter*
1. Farrowing and rearing
    (a) Prefabricated farrowing pens with crates, side creep areas, part-slatted floors, including foundations, electrical and plumbing work   £1,510
    (b) Steel-framed farrowing house with insulated blockwork walls, part-slatted pens with side creeps in rooms of eight with off main passage   £2,360

    per weaner
    (c) Flat-deck rearing house 3-6 weeks with fully perforated floors to pens, 0·25 m² per pig pen area   £101
    (d) Prefabricated verandah house including foundations, electrical and plumbing work, 0·3 m² per pig internal lying area   £63

2. Finishing   *per baconer*

    (a) Prefabricated fattening house with part-slatted floors, trough feeding   £136
    (b) Prefabricated fattening house with part-slatted floors, floor fed   £124
    (c) Steel framed building with insulated blockwork walls, part-slatted floors, trough fed   £211
    (d) Automatic feeding systems for items (a), (b) and (c) above:
       dry-feed system with ad-lib hoppers   £5
       dry on-floor feeding   £9
       wet feeding   £12

3. Dry sows and boars   *per sow*
   (a) Yards with floor feeding   £285
   (b) Sow cubicle system   £420
   (c) Yards with electronic feeders   £425
   (d) Yards with individual feeders   £530
   (e) Two-yard system with flat-rate feeding   £545
   (f) Boar pens as part of sow house   £1,785 each

4. Complete pig unit
Building costs calculated on basis of three-week weaning, 23 pigs per sow per year to bacon, excluding external slurry or dung storage, feed storage and handling/weighing facilities:
   (a) Breeding and rearing only   £920 per sow
   (b) Breeding with progeny to bacon   £1,625 per sow

Poultry Housing and Equipment   *per bird*

Battery cages with automatic feeding and egg collection, 5 layers per cage   £11·00-£12·00

Deep litter, 7 layers per m^2 (0·14 m^2 per bird)   £12·50-£16·20

Perchery/barn   £12·50-£16·20

Free Range: maximum stocking rate of 1,000/ha.
(Cost varies with size of unit and degree of automation)   £12·00-£17·00

Broiler breeders, deep litter, 0·167 m^2 per bird   £18·00

Pullets (cage and floor reared)   £7·60

Broilers, deep litter house, 0·05 m^2 per bird   £4·55-£4·80

Turkeys, 20,000 pole barn fattening unit   £12·00-£17·50
(Cost varies with size of unit and degree of automation)

(N.B. Source of Poultry Housing costs: as for poultry, see p.89)

Grain Storage and Drying   *per tonne stored*

1. Intake pit, conveyor, elevator, overhead conveyor and catwalk, storage bins within existing building   £123
   extra for low volume ventilation of bins   £53

2. As 1 in new building   £210

3. Portable grain walling for on-floor storage in existing building   £29

4. On floor grain storage in purpose-built building   £70
   Extras:
   (a) low volume ventilation   £5-£6
   (b) on-floor drying with above-ground main duct and laterals   £86
   (c) add to (b) for below-ground laterals   £9

5. Sealed towers for moist grain, including loading and unloading equipment   £95-£130

Potato Storage	per tonne stored
1. Pallet-box store with recirculation fans	£137
Pallet boxes, 1 tonne	£50
2. Bulk store, building only	£131
Ventilation system: fans, main duct, below-floor lateral ducts	£25

Roads and Fences	per m length
3·2 m wide hardcore road with drainage ditches	
using locally excavated material	£20
using imported hardcore (£6·15/m³)	£32
extra for bitumen macadam surfacing, two coats	£24
Traditional 7-wire stock fence	£2·80
High tensile 7-wire stock fence	£2·60

Construction Equipment Hire	hourly rate, with driver
Excavator	£16-£20
Tipping lorry	£19
10-tonne crane	£22
	weekly rate
Concrete mixer, 100 litre (5/3)	£30
Compressor and heavy breaker	£82

B. Standard Costs

Standard costs are published by MAFF and the Scottish Office and Welsh Office Agriculture Departments on the basis of the cost of farm or casual labour and new materials. They do not include an allowance for overheads and profit: in most cases building contractors would add 15-30% to cover them. Standard costs are therefore usually lower, sometimes by a larger percentage than this, particularly where the labour content of the item is high. The following examples are based on standard costs issued in 1992. Farm buildings costs generally will have risen between 15% and 20% between that year and 1997.

	per m² floor area
Open-sided framed building with cladding to roof and gable peaks only, hardcore floor, rainwater drainage to soakaways:	
9 × 18 m	£32
13·2 × 24m	£30

	per m² wall or roof
Corrugated cladding to roof or walls, *including supports* (purlins or rails):	
fibre cement sheeting	£13·40
extra for coloured sheeting	£0·72
extra for PVC coated steel instead of fibre cement	£0·72
deduct for metallic coated (eg galvanised) steel	£3·85

Spaced boarding	£15·00
Wall element, concrete blockwork 190-324 mm thick with strip foundation (base 750 mm below ground level) and 2·5 mm height above ground level	£73 per m run
Extra for rendering blockwork on one side	£5·00 per m²
Concrete floor, 100 mm thick, including excavation, hardcore and waterproof membrane	£11·32 per m²
Concrete floor, 150 mm thick as above	£14·35 per m²
Reinforced concrete slats for cattle (supports not included)	£39 per m²
Yard gully with heavy grating	£200 each
Drainage pipes, 100 mm, jointed in UPVC, clayware or spun concrete including 900 mm trench and backfill	£8·50 per m run
Drainage pipes 150 mm as above	£15·30 per m run
Tank for water, effluent etc., 20 m³	£2,390 each
Gate, 3 m wide, steel, including posts concreted in: light duty	£86 each
cattle yard type	£114 each
Fully covered enclosed building with concrete floor, and rainwater drainage to soakaways	

	per m² floor area
10 × 18 m	£65
15 × 24 m	£58

C. Storage Requirements

Bulk (cubic metres (feet) per tonne):

Beans	1·2 (43)	Grass silage:	18% DM	1·3 (46)
Wheat, peas	1·3 (46)		30% DM	1·6 (57)
Barley, rye, oilseed rape,		Maize silage		1·3 (46)
linseed, fodder beet	1·4 (50)	Wheat straw		13·0 (464)
Oats	1·9 (68)	Barley straw	small bales	11·5 (411)
Potatoes	1·6 (57)	Hay		7·0 (247)
Dry bulb onions	2·0 (71)	Wheat straw		20·0 (714)
Concentrates: meal	2·0 (71)	Barley straw	big bales	18·0 (643)
cubes	1·6 (57)	Hay		10·0 (353)
		Brewers' grains		0·9 (32)

Boxes (floor area in square metres (feet) per tonne):

Potatoes:	0·5 tonne boxes, 5 boxes high	0·52 (5·6)
	1·0 tonne boxes, 4 boxes high	0·52 (5·6)
	1·0 tonne boxes, 5 boxes high	0·45 (4·8)

Bags (floor area in square metres (feet) per tonne):

Feedingstuffs:	2 bags high	1·6 (17)
Fertilizer:	6 bags high	1·1 (12)
	10 bags high	0·7 (8)

V. CAPITAL, TAXATION AND GRANTS

1. CAPITAL

(i) Tenant's Capital consists of:

(a) *Machinery.* Costs of new machinery are given on pages 114-118. Written-down values in 1998 are likely to be averaging about £550 per hectare (£225 per acre) taking all farm types together—based on current (i.e. replacement) costs (approx. £440/ha (£180/acre) based on historic costs).

(b) *Breeding Livestock.* Over all types of farm the 1998 average is estimated to be about £750 per hectare (£305 per acre), but the figure can vary from zero to over £2,000 (£800) for grazing livestock alone. Approximate average market values (£) of various categories of breeding livestock (of mixed ages in the case of adult stock) are as follows (actual value will vary according to average age and weight, quality and breed):

Holstein Friesian Dairy Cows (inc. dry cows): 700.
Channel Island Dairy Cows (inc. dry cows): 400.
Other Dairy Cows (inc. dry cows): 550.
Beef Cows: 575.

| Other Cattle: | Dairy Followers | | Beef |
	Holstein Friesians	Ayrshires and C.I. Breeds	Cattle
In-calf heifers	675	400	520
Stores over 2 years	500	310	450
Stores 1-2 years	425	250	380
Stores 6-12 months	325	210	325
Calves under 6 months	200	115	210
Ewes: 60. Rams 250.			
Sows and In-pig Gilts: 150. Boars 500.			

(c) *Working Capital.* This is the capital needed to finance the production cycle, the length of which varies considerably between different crop and livestock enterprises and different combinations of these enterprises. Because of this, no generalizations are possible, but it can include the cost of purchased fattening stock, feed, seed, fertilizers, regular labour, machinery running costs, general overhead costs, rent and living expenses. This capital may be only a few pounds per hectare on an all-dairying farm but £500 or more per hectare on an all-cereals farm where the crop is stored until the spring. The average is likely to be about £300 per hectare (£120 per acre) in 1998.

(ii) Return on Capital

(a) *Tenant's capital.* For all lowland farms (excluding intensive pig and poultry units, fruit and glasshouse production), total tenant's capital will average about £1,600 per hectare (approximately £650 per acre) in 1998, with the (written-down) machinery valuations based on current ('replacement') costs £1,500 (610) based on historic costs); (for range, see table on page 156). If the average U.K. management and investment in the mid-to late 1990s were, say, £150 per hectare (£60 per acre), the average return on tenant's capital would be approximately 9·5 per cent. 'Premium' levels (the average of the top 50 per cent of farms) would be likely to be some 50 per cent higher (i.e. around 14 per cent), with the levels achieved for mixed cropping on the very best soils and top dairy farms possibly double the average. Note that no charge has been included for management (but that a rental value for owner-occupied land and the value of the unpaid labour of the farmer and wife have been deducted). The above levels could be difficult to achieve if the price falls of 1997 should prevail.

(b) *Landlord's Capital (i.e.* land, buildings, roads, etc.). With farms in mid-1997 averaging, say, £5,550 per hectare (£2,250 per acre), with vacant possession (assuming no special amenity or house value), an average lowland rent of, say, £150 per hectare (£60 per acre) (see p. 139), and assuming ownership expenses at £60 per hectare (£24 per acre), the (net) return (which is £90 per hectare (£36 per acre)) averages 1·6 per cent. If land is taken at its tenanted value, with a vacant possession premium of say 50 per cent, the return obviously doubles, to 3·2 per cent. If 'tender' rents were paid, at say one-third above the average level for established tenants (i.e. £200/ha (£81/acre)), the return would average about 2·5 per cent with land at the vacant possession price assumed and 5 per cent with land at the tenanted value assumed. Full repairing and insurance leases clearly raise the returns above these levels. Above average quality farms acquire higher rents but also obviously command higher prices than the average levels quoted above.

(c) *Total Owner-Occupier's Capital (i.e.* land plus 'tenant's' capital). The combined (net) return on the above assumptions (£240 per hectare, or £97 per acre) on total capital, (£7,150 per hectare, or £2,895 per acre), with land at its vacant possession value, averages 3·4 per cent. This increases to 5·5 per cent if land is taken at its tenanted value and this is half the vacant possession value. If higher rent levels are assumed (given the same farming return), the overall return remains the same, the distribution simply being reallocated in favour of the land ownership share at the expense of the farming share. 'Premium' farming returns (as defined above), assuming the same capital requirements, raise the returns to 4·4 per cent with land at the vacant possession price and 7·2 per cent with tenanted land values. (To repeat, the above figures all assume that machinery depreciation and valuation are based on its current cost.)

(iii) *Average Tenant's Capital per hectare* (per acre in brackets) for Different Farm Types, as estimated for 1998, are as follows:

154

Farm Type Group	Average No. Hectares	Livestock £	Crops, Cultivns., Stores £	Machinery and Equipment* £	Total Tenant's Capital £ £
Mainly Dairying:					
under 50 ha ...	40	1550	250	850	2650 (1070)
50 to 100 ha ...	75	1350	250	750	2350 (950)
Over 100 ha ...	150	1150	250	650	2050 (830)
Mainly Arable:					
under 100 ha ...	70	150	475	600	1225 (495)
100 to 200 ha ...	150	150	475	550	1175 (475)
over 200 ha ...	350	150	475	550	1175 (475)
Dairy and Arable:					
under 100 ha ...	70	1150	300	725	2175 (880)
100 to 200 ha ...	150	850	375	675	1900 (770)
over 200 ha ...	350	575	325	675	1575 (635)
Mainly Sheep/Cattle:					
under 100 ha ...	65	800	150	400	1350 (545)
over 100 ha ...	170	700	150	300	1150 (465)
Sheep/Cattle and Arable:					
under 100 ha ...	65	750	225	375	1350 (545)
100 to 200 ha ...	150	700	200	350	1250 (505)
over 200 ha ...	240	650	175	325	1150 (465)
Dairy, Sheep/Cattle and Arable: ...	225	650	225	350	1225 (495)
Intensive Arable:					
Fruit	80	0	4250	1050	5300 (2145)
Field Vegetables ...	50	0	2250	2400	4650 (1880)
Mainly Pigs Poultry:					
(per £1000 output)	—	300	35	200	535
Glasshouse:					
(per £1000 output)	—	0	65	775	840

* Based on current *(i.e.* replacement) costs.

Note: The above (deliberately rounded) data are based on Farm Business Survey results compiled annually by University/Colleges centres (as listed on page 133), where actual figures for previous years can be found. None includes the value of milk quota on farms with dairying, even though a case can be made for this on the grounds of opportunity cost; obviously the cost of additional quota must be included when budgeting for, and calculating the return on capital of, introducing or expanding a dairy herd — whether by increasing yield per cow or the number of cows or both.

(iv) *Return on Capital to Individual Enterprises* on a mixed farm is virtually impossible to ascertain, except perhaps for a full-time pig or poultry enterprise, nor would it be of very much use even if it could be determined. It would require the arbitrary allocation both of costs and capital inputs that are common to several, in some cases all, of the enterprises on the farm.

What is relevant and important is the extra (net) return from an enterprise either to be introduced or expanded, as calculated by a partial budget, related to the extra (net) capital needed. The "net" in brackets relates, as regards return, to the addition to gross margins less any addition to (or plus any reduction in) "fixed" costs, bearing in mind that another enterprise may have to be deleted or reduced in size; and, as regards capital, to the fact that deletion or reduction of another enterprise may release capital.

In most cases of "marginal" substitution, it is differences in the value of breeding livestock and differences in variable costs that are particularly relevant, but the timing of both inputs and sales are also obviously very important.

(v) *"Marginal" Capital Requirements for* small changes in crop areas or livestock numbers can be estimated as follows:

Crops: variable costs till sale.
Dairy Cows and Egg Production: value of the cow* or hens, plus one month's food.
Other Breeding Livestock: average value of stock*, plus variable costs to sale of the progeny (e.g. lambs)—or their transfer to another enterprise (e.g. weaners to the pig fattening enterprise).
Rearing Breeding Livestock (e.g. heifers, tegs, gilts, pullets): cost of the calf, lamb, weaner or chick, plus variable costs till they produce their first progeny/eggs.
Fattening Livestock and Production of Stores: cost of stock, plus variable costs till sale.

* Value of breeding stock, including dairy cows: either the average value over their entire breeding or milk producing life (see table on page 153) or their value when they first produce progeny can be taken. The latter will give the lower return on (marginal) capital and is thus the severer test.

Home-reared stock: where stock to be used for milk or egg production, breeding or fattening are home-reared, there are two possibilities:

(i) either they can be valued at variable costs of production when they are transferred from the rearing to the "productive" enterprise; in this case the return on (marginal) capital will be estimated over the combined rearing and "productive" enterprise.

(ii) or they can be valued at market value at point of transfer. This is the procedure if one wishes to work out a return on (marginal) capital for the rearing and the "productive" enterprises separately.

(vi) Return on "Marginal" Capital. This is sometimes expressed as the gross margin less fuel and repair costs of the enterprise expanded as a percentage of the "marginal", or extra, capital. However, two points have to be remembered:

(i) If another enterprise has had to be reduced in size to enable the enterprise under consideration to be expanded, the capital released and the gross margin forfeited by reducing the size of the first enterprise must be brought into the calculation in estimating the net result of the change.

(ii) All the above statements on "marginal" capital refer to small changes. If the change is large enough to cause changes in labour, machinery or building requirements the capital changes brought about may be considerably greater.

(vii) *Return on Investments in Medium-Term and Long-Term Capital. Rate of Return and the Discounted Yield.*

Example: If £5,000 investment results in an annual net return of £500 (after deducting depreciation, but ignoring interest payments):

$$Rate\ of\ Return\ on\ Initial\ Capital = \frac{500}{5,000} \times 100 = 10\%$$

$$Rate\ of\ Return\ on\ Average\ Capital = \frac{500}{2,500} \times 100 = 20\%$$

It is more accurate to calculate the *"Discounted Yield"*, which is the discount rate that brings the present value of the net cash flows (which means ignoring depreciation) to the value of the investment.

The tables on pages 159 and 160 may be used.

"Short-Cut" Estimates of the Discounted Yield on depreciating assets.

The Discounted Yield falls between the simple Rates of Return on Initial and Average Capital. In fact, for investments lasting 5 to 15 years, when the Rate of Return on Initial Capital is 10 per cent and on Average Capital 20 per cent, the Discounted Yield will be almost exactly halfway between, i.e. about 15 per cent. However, this is only so providing the anticipated annual net cash earnings are fairly constant—or fluctuate unpredictably around a fairly constant level.

There are three circumstances when the Discounted Yield will get closer to the Rate of Return on Initial Capital (i.e. the lower per cent return) and further from the Rate of Return on Average Capital:

(a) The longer the life of the investment.
(b) The higher the Rate of Return.
(c) The higher the net cash flow is in the later years of the investment compared with the earlier years.

When the opposite circumstances obtain, the Discounted Yield will be closer to the Rate of Return on Average Capital (i.e. the higher per cent return).

Granted that there are inevitably varying degrees of estimation and uncertainty in calculating future net annual earnings of investments, the following short-cuts might reasonably be used where the annual net cash earnings are expected to be fairly constant—or fluctuate unpredictably (e.g. through weather effects on yields) around a fairly constant level. (W.O. period = write-off period; R.R.I.C. = rate of return on initial capital).

1. Where (i) the W.O. period is 5 years or less,
         (ii) the W.O. period is 6 to 10 years and the R.R.I.C. is
              15 per cent or less,
        (iii) the W.O. period is 11 to 20 years and the R.R.I.C. is
              10 per cent or less,
calculate the Return on Capital as being approximately midway between
the Rates of Return on Initial and Average Capital, i.e. by calculating
the Rate of Return on $^2/_3$ of the original investment.

For example, following the earlier example (page 158):

$$\frac{500}{3,333} \times 100 = 15\%.$$

2. Where (i) the W.O. period is 6 to 10 years and the R.R.I.C.
              exceeds 15 per cent,

         (ii) the W.O. period is 11 to 20 years and the R.R.I.C. is
              between 10 per cent and 25 per cent,

        (iii) the W.O. period exceeds 20 years and the R.R.I.C. is
              10 per cent or less,

calculate the Return on Capital on 80 per cent of the original investment.

For example, again following the earlier example:

$$\frac{500}{4,000} \times 100 = 12\frac{1}{2}\%.$$

3. Where (i) the W.O. period is 11 to 20 years and the R.R.I.C.
             exceeds 25 per cent,

        (ii) the W.O. period exceeds 20 years and the R.R.I.C.
             exceeds 10 per cent,

take the Return on Capital to be the R.R.I.C.

In borderline cases, use method 1 rather than 2, or 2 rather than 3 if
there is a tendency for the cash flow to be higher in the earlier years,
e.g. because of tax allowances on machinery. Take 2 rather than 1, and
3 rather than 2, if the likelihood is that the cash flow will be lower in
earlier years and increase in later years.

However, where the annual cash flow is expected to vary (apart from
unpredictable fluctuations) it is safer to make the full D.C.F. calculation.
This is particularly so where the variation is both up and down and
where further periodic investments are to be made during the life of
the project.

Discounting Table A

Discount Factors for Calculating the Present Value of Future (irregular) Cash Flows.

Year	Percentage																
	3%	4%	5%	6%	7%	8%	9%	10%	11%	12%	13%	14%	15%	16%	18%	20%	25%
1	0·971	0·962	0·952	0·943	0·935	0·926	0·917	0·909	0·901	0·893	0·885	0·877	0·870	0·862	0·847	0·833	0·800
2	0·943	0·925	0·907	0·890	0·873	0·857	0·842	0·826	0·812	0·797	0·783	0·769	0·756	0·743	0·718	0·694	0·640
3	0·915	0·889	0·864	0·840	0·816	0·794	0·772	0·751	0·731	0·712	0·693	0·675	0·658	0·641	0·609	0·579	0·512
4	0·888	0·855	0·823	0·792	0·763	0·735	0·708	0·683	0·659	0·636	0·613	0·592	0·572	0·552	0·516	0·482	0·410
5	0·863	0·822	0·784	0·747	0·713	0·681	0·650	0·621	0·593	0·567	0·543	0·519	0·497	0·476	0·437	0·402	0·328
6	0·837	0·790	0·746	0·705	0·666	0·630	0·596	0·564	0·535	0·507	0·480	0·456	0·432	0·410	0·370	0·335	0·262
7	0·813	0·760	0·711	0·665	0·623	0·583	0·547	0·513	0·482	0·452	0·425	0·400	0·376	0·354	0·314	0·279	0·210
8	0·789	0·731	0·677	0·627	0·582	0·540	0·502	0·467	0·434	0·404	0·376	0·351	0·327	0·305	0·266	0·233	0·168
9	0·766	0·703	0·645	0·592	0·544	0·500	0·460	0·424	0·391	0·361	0·333	0·308	0·284	0·263	0·225	0·194	0·134
10	0·744	0·676	0·614	0·558	0·508	0·463	0·422	0·386	0·352	0·322	0·295	0·270	0·247	0·227	0·191	0·162	0·107
11	0·722	0·650	0·585	0·527	0·475	0·429	0·388	0·350	0·317	0·287	0·261	0·237	0·215	0·195	0·162	0·135	0·086
12	0·701	0·625	0·557	0·497	0·444	0·397	0·356	0·319	0·286	0·257	0·231	0·208	0·187	0·168	0·137	0·112	0·069
13	0·681	0·601	0·530	0·469	0·415	0·368	0·326	0·290	0·258	0·229	0·204	0·182	0·163	0·145	0·116	0·093	0·055
14	0·661	0·577	0·505	0·442	0·388	0·340	0·299	0·263	0·232	0·205	0·181	0·160	0·141	0·125	0·098	0·078	0·044
15	0·642	0·555	0·481	0·417	0·362	0·315	0·275	0·239	0·209	0·183	0·160	0·140	0·123	0·108	0·084	0·065	0·035
20	0·554	0·456	0·377	0·312	0·258	0·215	0·178	0·149	0·124	0·104	0·087	0·073	0·061	0·051	0·037	0·026	0·012
25	0·478	0·375	0·295	0·233	0·184	0·146	0·116	0·092	0·074	0·059	0·047	0·038	0·030	0·024	0·016	0·010	0·004
30	0·412	0·308	0·231	0·174	0·131	0·099	0·075	0·057	0·044	0·033	0·026	0·020	0·015	0·012	0·007	0·004	0·001

Example: The Present Value of £500 received 10 years from now, at 12 per cent discount rate of interest = 500 × 0·322 = £161. Conversely, £161 invested now, at 12 per cent compound interest, will be worth £500 in 10 years' time.

Discounting Table B
Discount Factors for Calculating the Present Value of Future Annuity (i.e. Constant Annual Cash Flow) Receivable in Years 1 to n inclusive.

Percentage

Year	3%	4%	5%	6%	7%	8%	9%	10%	11%	12%	13%	14%	15%	16%	18%	20%	25%
1	0.971	0.962	0.952	0.943	0.935	0.926	0.917	0.909	0.901	0.893	0.885	0.877	0.870	0.862	0.847	0.833	0.800
2	1.913	1.886	1.859	1.833	1.808	1.783	1.759	1.736	1.713	1.690	1.668	1.647	1.626	1.605	1.566	1.528	1.440
3	2.829	2.775	2.723	2.673	2.624	2.577	2.531	2.487	2.444	2.402	2.361	2.322	2.283	2.246	2.174	2.106	1.952
4	3.717	3.630	3.546	3.465	3.387	3.312	3.240	3.170	3.102	3.037	2.974	2.914	2.855	2.798	2.690	2.589	2.362
5	4.580	4.452	4.329	4.212	4.100	3.993	3.890	3.791	3.696	3.605	3.517	3.433	3.352	3.274	3.127	2.991	2.689
6	5.417	5.242	5.076	4.917	4.767	4.623	4.486	4.355	4.231	4.111	3.998	3.889	3.784	3.685	3.498	3.326	2.951
7	6.230	6.002	5.786	5.582	5.389	5.206	5.033	4.868	4.712	4.564	4.423	4.288	4.160	4.039	3.812	3.605	3.161
8	7.020	6.733	6.463	6.210	5.971	5.747	5.535	5.335	5.146	4.968	4.799	4.639	4.487	4.344	4.078	3.837	3.329
9	7.786	7.435	7.108	6.802	6.515	6.247	5.995	5.759	5.537	5.328	5.132	4.946	4.772	4.607	4.303	4.031	3.463
10	8.530	8.111	7.722	7.360	7.024	6.710	6.418	6.145	5.889	5.650	5.426	5.216	5.019	4.833	4.494	4.192	3.570
11	9.253	8.760	8.306	7.887	7.499	7.139	6.805	6.495	6.207	5.938	5.687	5.453	5.234	5.029	4.656	4.327	3.656
12	9.954	9.385	8.863	8.384	7.943	7.536	7.161	6.814	6.492	6.194	5.918	5.660	5.421	5.197	4.793	4.439	3.725
13	10.635	9.986	9.394	8.853	8.358	7.904	7.487	7.103	6.750	6.424	6.122	5.842	5.583	5.342	4.910	4.533	3.780
14	11.296	10.563	9.899	9.295	8.745	8.244	7.786	7.367	6.982	6.628	6.302	6.002	5.724	5.468	5.008	4.611	3.824
15	11.938	11.118	10.380	9.712	9.108	8.559	8.061	7.606	7.191	6.811	6.462	6.142	5.847	5.575	5.092	4.675	3.859
20	14.877	13.590	12.462	11.470	10.594	9.818	9.129	8.514	7.963	7.469	7.025	6.623	6.259	5.929	5.353	4.870	3.954
25	17.413	15.662	14.094	12.783	11.654	10.675	9.823	9.077	8.422	7.843	7.330	6.873	6.464	6.097	5.467	4.948	3.985
30	19.600	17.292	15.372	13.765	12.409	11.258	10.274	9.427	8.694	8.055	7.496	7.003	6.566	6.177	5.517	4.979	3.995

Example: The Present Value of £500 a year for the next 10 years, at 12 per cent discount rate of interest = 500 × 5.650 = £2,825. This is the same answer that would be obtained by multiplying 500 by each discount factor (at 12 per cent) in Table A for each year from 1 to 10, and adding together the ten resulting figures.

To obtain the Discounted Yield of a constant annual net cash flow, divide this into the original investment and look up the resulting figure in the table above, against the number of years. *Example:* an investment of £1,000 is estimated to produce £80 a year additional profit over 10 years (before charging interest). Add £100 depreciation a year = £180 annual net cash flow. 1000 ÷ 180 = 5.56. This equals just over 12 per cent (the 10 years/12 per cent figure being 5.650).

160

Compounding Table A

The Future Money Value of £1 after n Years.

Rate of Interest

Year	3%	4%	5%	6%	7%	8%	9%	10%	11%	12%	13%	14%	15%	16%	18%	20%	25%
1	1·03	1·04	1·05	1·06	1·07	1·08	1·09	1·10	1·11	1·12	1·13	1·14	1·15	1·16	1·18	1·20	1·25
2	1·06	1·08	1·10	1·12	1·14	1·17	1·19	1·21	1·23	1·25	1·28	1·30	1·32	1·35	1·39	1·44	1·56
3	1·09	1·12	1·16	1·19	1·23	1·26	1·30	1·33	1·37	1·40	1·44	1·48	1·52	1·56	1·64	1·73	1·95
4	1·13	1·17	1·22	1·26	1·31	1·36	1·41	1·46	1·52	1·57	1·63	1·69	1·75	1·81	1·94	2·07	2·44
5	1·16	1·22	1·28	1·34	1·40	1·47	1·54	1·61	1·69	1·76	1·84	1·93	2·01	2·10	2·29	2·49	3·05
6	1·19	1·27	1·34	1·42	1·50	1·59	1·68	1·77	1·87	1·97	2·08	2·19	2·31	2·44	2·70	2·99	3·81
7	1·23	1·32	1·41	1·50	1·61	1·71	1·83	1·95	2·08	2·21	2·35	2·50	2·66	2·83	3·19	3·58	4·77
8	1·27	1·37	1·48	1·59	1·72	1·85	1·99	2·14	2·30	2·48	2·66	2·85	3·06	3·28	3·76	4·30	5·96
9	1·30	1·42	1·55	1·69	1·84	2·00	2·17	2·36	2·56	2·77	3·00	3·25	3·52	3·80	4·44	5·16	7·45
10	1·34	1·48	1·63	1·79	1·97	2·16	2·37	2·59	2·84	3·11	3·39	3·71	4·05	4·41	5·23	6·19	9·31
11	1·38	1·54	1·71	1·90	2·10	2·33	2·58	2·85	3·15	3·48	3·84	4·23	4·65	5·12	6·18	7·43	11·64
12	1·43	1·60	1·80	2·01	2·25	2·52	2·81	3·14	3·50	3·90	4·33	4·82	5·35	5·94	7·29	8·92	14·55
13	1·47	1·67	1·89	2·13	2·41	2·72	3·07	3·45	3·88	4·36	4·90	5·49	6·15	6·89	8·60	10·70	18·19
14	1·51	1·73	1·98	2·26	2·58	2·94	3·34	3·80	4·31	4·89	5·53	6·26	7·08	7·99	10·15	12·84	22·74
15	1·56	1·80	2·08	2·40	2·76	3·17	3·64	4·18	4·78	5·47	6·25	7·14	8·14	9·27	11·97	15·41	28·42
20	1·81	2·19	2·65	3·21	3·87	4·66	5·60	6·73	8·06	9·65	11·52	13·74	16·37	19·46	27·39	38·34	86·74
25	2·09	2·67	3·39	4·29	5·43	5·85	8·62	10·83	13·59	17·00	21·23	26·46	32·92	40·87	62·67	95·40	264·7
30	2·43	3·24	4·32	5·74	7·61	10·06	13·27	17·45	22·89	29·96	39·12	50·95	66·21	85·85	143·4	237·4	807·8

Compounding Table B

The Future Money Value of £1 per annum after n Years *

Rate of Interest

Year	3%	4%	5%	6%	7%	8%	9%	10%	11%	12%	13%	14%	15%	16%	18%	20%	25%
1	1·03	1·04	1·05	1·06	1·07	1·08	1·09	1·10	1·11	1·12	1·13	1·14	1·15	1·16	1·18	1·20	1·25
2	2·09	2·12	2·15	2·18	2·21	2·25	2·28	2·31	2·34	2·37	2·41	2·44	2·47	2·51	2·57	2·64	2·81
3	3·18	3·25	3·31	3·37	3·44	3·51	3·57	3·64	3·71	3·78	3·85	3·92	3·99	4·07	4·22	4·37	4·77
4	4·31	4·42	4·53	4·64	4·75	4·87	4·98	5·11	5·23	5·35	5·48	5·61	5·74	5·88	6·15	6·44	7·21
5	5·47	5·63	5·80	5·98	6·15	6·34	6·52	6·72	6·91	7·12	7·32	7·54	7·75	7·98	8·44	8·93	10·26
6	6·66	6·90	7·14	7·39	7·65	7·92	8·20	8·49	8·78	9·09	9·40	9·73	10·07	10·41	11·14	11·92	14·07
7	7·89	8·21	8·55	8·90	9·26	9·64	10·03	10·44	10·86	11·30	11·76	12·23	12·73	13·24	14·33	15·50	18·84
8	9·16	9·58	10·03	10·49	10·98	11·49	12·02	12·58	13·16	13·78	14·42	15·09	15·79	16·52	18·09	19·80	24·80
9	10·46	11·01	11·58	12·18	12·82	13·49	14·19	14·94	15·72	16·55	17·42	18·34	19·30	20·32	22·52	24·96	32·25
10	11·81	12·49	13·21	13·97	14·78	15·65	16·56	17·53	18·56	19·65	20·81	22·04	23·35	24·73	27·76	31·15	41·57
11	13·19	14·03	14·92	15·87	16·89	17·98	19·14	20·38	21·71	23·13	24·65	26·27	28·00	29·85	33·93	38·58	53·21
12	14·62	15·63	16·71	17·88	19·14	20·50	21·95	23·52	25·21	27·03	28·98	31·09	33·35	35·79	41·22	47·50	67·76
13	16·09	17·29	18·60	20·02	21·55	23·21	25·02	26·97	29·09	31·39	33·88	36·58	39·50	42·67	49·82	58·20	85·95
14	17·60	19·02	20·58	22·28	24·13	26·15	28·36	30·77	33·41	36·28	39·42	42·84	46·58	50·66	59·97	71·04	108·7
15	19·16	20·82	22·66	24·67	26·89	29·32	32·00	34·95	38·19	41·75	45·67	49·98	54·72	59·93	71·94	86·44	137·1
20	27·68	30·97	34·72	38·99	43·87	49·42	55·76	63·00	71·27	80·70	91·47	103·8	117·8	133·8	173·0	224·0	428·7
25	37·55	43·31	50·11	58·16	67·68	78·95	92·32	108·2	127·0	149·3	175·8	207·3	244·7	289·1	404·3	566·4	1318
30	49·00	58·33	69·76	83·80	101·1	122·3	148·6	180·9	220·9	270·3	331·3	406·7	500·0	615·2	933·3	1418	4034

* Payments made at the beginning of each year.

Amortisation Table
Annual Charge to write off £1,000

Write-off Period (Years)	Rate of Interest															
	3	4	5	6	7	8	9	10	11	12	13	14	15	16	18	20
5	218	225	231	237	244	250	257	264	271	277	284	291	298	305	320	334
6	185	191	197	203	210	216	223	230	236	243	250	257	264	271	286	301
7	161	167	173	179	186	192	199	205	212	219	226	233	240	248	262	277
8	142	149	155	161	167	174	181	187	194	201	208	216	223	230	245	261
9	128	134	141	147	153	160	167	174	181	188	195	202	210	217	232	248
10	117	123	130	136	142	149	156	163	170	177	184	192	199	207	223	239
11	108	114	120	127	133	140	147	154	161	168	176	183	191	199	215	231
12	100	107	113	119	125	133	140	147	154	161	169	177	184	192	209	225
13	94	100	106	113	120	127	134	141	148	156	163	171	179	187	204	221
14	89	95	101	108	114	121	128	136	143	151	159	167	175	183	200	217
15	84	90	96	103	110	117	124	131	139	147	155	163	171	179	196	214
16	80	86	92	99	106	113	120	128	136	143	151	160	168	176	194	211
17	76	82	89	95	102	110	117	125	132	140	149	157	165	174	191	209
18	73	79	86	92	99	107	114	122	130	138	146	155	163	172	190	208
19	70	76	83	90	97	104	112	120	128	136	144	153	161	170	188	206
20	67	74	80	87	94	102	110	117	126	134	142	151	160	169	187	205
25	57	64	71	78	86	94	102	110	119	127	136	145	155	164	183	202
30	51	58	65	73	81	89	97	106	115	124	133	143	152	162	181	201
40	43	51	58	66	75	84	93	102	112	122	131	141	151	160	180	200

Example: £3,000 is borrowed to erect a building. The annual charge to service interest and capital repayment on the £3,000, repayable over 10 years at 12%, is 3 × £177 = £531. Where the write-off period of the building (10 years) is equal to the repayment period of the loan, then the average annual depreciation and interest will also equal £531.

The proportion of the total annual charge representing the average amount of capital repaid per annum can be readily determined by dividing the sum borrowed by the number of years of the loan: (in the above example this is £3,000 ÷ 10 = £300/year). The remainder is clearly the average amount of interest paid per annum: (in the above example, £531 — £300 = £231/year). The year to year variations between the two items (i.e. capital repaid and interest) are shown in the tables on pages 166 to 168, which demonstrate the way in which the capital repayment part increases and the interest part decreases over time.

Sinking Fund Table

The annual sum required to be set aside at the end of each year to accumulate to £1,000 at the end of the period

No. of Years	Rate of Interest															
	3	4	5	6	7	8	9	10	11	12	13	14	15	16	18	20
5	188	185	181	177	174	170	167	164	161	157	154	151	148	145	140	134
6	155	151	147	143	140	136	133	130	126	123	120	117	114	111	106	101
7	131	127	123	119	116	112	109	105	102	99	96	93	90	88	82	77
8	112	109	105	101	97	94	91	87	84	81	78	76	73	70	65	61
9	98	94	91	87	83	80	77	74	71	68	65	62	60	57	52	48
10	87	83	80	76	72	69	66	63	60	57	54	52	49	47	43	39
11	78	74	70	67	63	60	57	54	51	48	46	43	41	39	35	31
12	70	67	63	59	56	53	50	47	44	41	39	37	34	32	29	25
13	64	60	56	53	50	47	44	41	38	36	33	31	29	27	24	21
14	59	55	51	48	44	41	38	36	33	31	29	27	25	23	20	17
15	54	50	46	43	40	37	34	31	29	27	25	23	21	19	16	14
16	50	46	42	39	36	33	30	28	26	23	21	20	18	16	14	11
17	46	42	39	35	32	30	27	25	22	20	19	17	15	14	11	9
18	43	39	36	32	29	27	24	22	20	18	16	15	13	12	10	8
19	40	36	33	30	27	24	22	20	18	16	14	13	11	10	8	6
20	37	34	30	27	24	22	20	17	16	14	12	11	10	9	7	5
25	27	24	21	18	16	14	12	10	9	7	6	5	5	4	3	2
30	21	18	15	13	11	9	7	6	5	4	3	3	2	2	1	1
40	13	11	8	6	5	4	3	2	2	1	1	1	1	1	—	—

MORTGAGE REPAYMENT DATA

Items per £1,000 invested where I = Interest, P = Principal repaid, L = Loan outstanding

Loan through 5 years	6%			8%			10%			12%			14%			16%		
	I	P	L	I	P	L	I	P	L	I	P	L	I	P	L	I	P	L
1	60	177	823	80	170	830	100	164	836	120	157	834	140	151	849	160	145	855
2	49	188	635	66	184	645	84	180	656	101	175	670	119	172	677	137	169	686
3	38	199	435	52	199	447	66	198	458	80	197	469	92	196	481	110	196	490
4	26	211	224	36	215	232	46	218	240	56	221	248	57	224	257	78	227	263
5	13	224	0	19	232	0	24	240	0	30	248	0	32	257	0	42	263	0
10 years																		
1	60	76	924	80	69	931	100	63	939	120	57	934	140	52	948	160	47	953
2	55	80	844	75	75	856	94	69	868	113	64	879	133	59	889	152	54	899
3	51	85	758	69	81	776	87	76	792	106	71	808	124	68	821	144	63	836
4	46	90	668	62	87	689	79	84	709	97	80	728	115	77	744	134	73	762
5	40	96	572	55	94	595	71	92	617	87	90	638	104	88	656	122	85	677
6	34	102	471	48	101	494	62	101	516	77	100	538	92	100	556	108	99	579
7	28	108	363	39	110	384	52	111	405	65	112	425	78	114	442	93	114	465
8	22	114	249	31	118	266	40	122	282	51	126	299	52	130	312	74	133	332
9	15	121	128	21	128	138	28	134	148	36	141	158	44	148	164	53	154	178
10	8	128	0	11	138	0	15	148	0	19	158	0	23	164	0	29	178	0

MORTGAGE REPAYMENT DATA (continued)

Loan through 20 years	6%			8%			10 %			12%			14 %			16 %		
	I	P	L	I	P	L	I	P	L	I	P	L	I	P	L	I	P	L
1	60	27	973	80	22	978	100	17	983	120	14	986	140	11	989	160	9	991
5	53	34	847	72	30	872	92	26	893	112	22	912	132	19	927	153	16	940
10	41	46	642	58	44	683	76	41	722	95	38	756	115	36	788	136	33	815
15	26	61	367	38	64	407	51	66	445	66	68	483	82	69	518	99	69	552
20	5	82	0	8	94	0	11	107	0	14	120	0	19	132	0	23	145	0
30 years																		
1	60	13	987	80	9	991	100	6	994	120	4	996	140	3	997	160	2	998
5	57	16	929	77	12	948	97	9	963	118	7	974	138	5	986	158	3	987
10	51	21	833	71	18	872	92	14	903	113	11	927	134	9	951	155	7	960
15	44	29	706	63	26	760	83	23	807	104	20	846	126	17	890	147	15	903
20	34	38	535	51	38	596	69	37	652	88	36	701	108	35	751	130	32	782
25	21	51	306	33	56	355	46	60	402	61	63	488	83	60	494	95	66	530
30	4	69	0	7	82	0	10	96	0	13	111	0	16	127	0	22	140	0

MORTGAGE REPAYMENT DATA *(continued)*

Loan through 40 years	6%			8%			10%			12%			14%			16%		
	I	P	L	I	P	L	I	P	L	I	P	L	I	P	L	I	P	L
1	60	6	994	80	4	995	100	2	998	120	1	999	140	1	999	160	0	1000
5	58	8	964	79	5	977	99	3	986	119	2	992	139	2	995	160	1	997
10	56	11	915	76	8	944	97	5	964	118	4	977	138	3	989	159	2	991
15	52	15	850	73	11	895	94	9	928	115	6	951	136	5	973	157	3	978
20	47	20	762	67	17	823	88	14	871	110	11	906	130	11	942	153	7	951
25	40	26	645	59	24	713	80	22	778	102	20	826	123	18	874	145	15	894
30	31	35	489	48	36	563	66	36	628	86	35	685	109	32	742	129	31	775
35	20	47	280	31	53	335	45	58	388	60	61	437	85	56	487	95	66	525
40	4	63	0	6	78	0	9	93	0	13	108	0	18	123	0	22	138	0

Note—All figures rounded to nearest £.

Rates of Interest: Further Points

(i) *Rate of Interest on Bank Loans.* Typically 2·25% to 2·5% above Base Rate. Main range is 1·5% above to 3·5% above. Extremes are likely to be 1% above (minimum) and 5% above (maximum).

(ii) *Annual Percentage Rate (APR).* This is the effective rate of interest calculated on an annual basis and should be used when seeking to make a true comparison between interest charges on money borrowed from different sources. The *APR* allows for the fact that when interest is applied to accounts at half yearly, quarterly or monthly intervals an element of compounding will arise. For example, £100 borrowed for one year at a quoted annual *nominal* interest rate of 12% (*e.g.* 2% over base rate of 10%) with interest charged quarterly, will lead to an accumulated interest charge of £12·55 (*i.e.,* giving an APR of just under 12·6%). The higher the annual nominal interest rate and the more frequently the interest charges are applied to the account, the more pronounced the compounding element becomes. For example, an annual nominal interest rate of 20% produces an APR of 21% with half yearly charging, 21·6% with quarterly charging and 21·9% with monthly charging.

In the case of some loans and hire purchase agreements, interest charges may be quoted as a *flat rate* on the original amount borrowed. The APR will be considerably greater than the flat rate if the loan is repaid by equal periodic instalments, comprising part capital and part interest, so that the borrowing is completely repaid by the end of the agreed term. For example, the APR for a loan at a flat rate of interest of 8% repaid by monthly instalments over 5 years will be 15%. The shorter the repayment period, and the more frequent the payments, the higher is the APR compared with the flat rate.

(iii) *The Real Rate of Interest.* When preparing simple profit and loss budgets to estimate the worthwhileness of an investment in a fixed asset (machinery, buildings, land), it is usual to price inputs and outputs at present-day values even when most costs and returns are expected to rise due to inflation over the life of the investment. Where this *real terms* approach is adopted a more realistic estimate of the effect on profitability can be gained by basing charges for capital on the *real rate of interest* rather than the APR. The real rate of interest is the APR adjusted for the annual rate at which prices relevant to the investment are expected to increase. A crude estimate of the real rate of interest can be obtained by simply subtracting the expected rate of price increase from the APR; for example, if the APR were 11% and the expected rate of inflation 6%, the real rate of interest would be $11 - 6 = 5\%$.

Financial Ratios

1. Common Ratios

The following ratios are often quoted as rough guidelines:

		% of Gross Output
Variable Costs		30-35%
Labour	15-17½%	} 35-40%
Machinery	15-17½%	
Sundry Fixed Costs	5%	
Rent & Interest		15%
Margin*		15%

* to cover drawings, tax, capital repayments, reinvestments

It has to be borne in mind, however, that these are indeed only rough guidelines and need to be considered with great care. Values vary, for example, with type of farming and size of farm. Furthermore, it is often unclear how certain items are being measured, especially whether unpaid manual labour of the farmer and family has been included or whether a rental value has been allowed for owner-occupied land.

2. Farm Survey Ratios

The following are rounded averages over recent years on a large sample of *all types of farm*. It is to be noted that Total Output includes the market value of any production retained for use/consumption on the farm (e.g. cereals for feed or seed), Rent includes the rental value of owner-occupied land and Interest charges are not included in the costs. Casual labour and all Contract work are included in fixed costs.

	% Total Output	% Total Gross Margin	% Total Fixed Costs
Variable Costs (excl. casual labour and contract work)	35		
Fixed Costs:			
Labour: Paid (inc. casuals)	10 } 20	15 } 30	18·5 } 37
Labour: Unpaid	10	15	18·5
Power & Machinery (inc. contract work)	17·5	25	33
Labour & Machinery	37·5	55	70
Rent/Rental Value	8	14	17
Occupier's Repairs	2	3	3
Sundry Fixed Costs	5	8	10
Total Fixed Costs	52·5	80	100
Margin	12·5	20	—

Total Gross Margin = 65% of Total Output

3. *Lending Criteria*

Another set of standards widely used by lending and leasing institutions is as follows:

Finance Charges

(rent, interest, leasing charges, etc.)

% of Gross Output	*% of Gross Margin*	*Lending Criteria*
0-10%	0-15%	Normally very safe
11-15%	16-22·5%	Common range, should be safe
16-20%	23-29%	Care required
20% plus	30% plus	Potentially dangerous

As lenders will be well aware, however, these ratios too must be regarded with caution and in conjunction with the farm's level of net worth (% equity) and its trend in recent years, recent trends in its profitability and the potential borrower's record of expenditure both on and off the farm, together with his or her character and potential. Also, of course, some enterprises / types of farming are more risky than others.

2. TAXATION

1. *Income Tax*

Husbands and wives have been taxed independently since April 1990.

(a) *Rates of Tax (1997-98)*

Slice of taxable income £	Rate per cent	Cumulative Tax (at top of slice) £
0-4,100	20	820
4,100-26,100	23	5,880
Over 26,100	40	—

(b) *Allowances and Reliefs (1997-98)*

   (i) Personal Allowance: £4,045.

   (ii) Married Couple's Allowance: £1,830.

Couples are able to choose to allocate this allowance either all to the husband or all to the wife or to share it equally between them. Action is required before the start of the tax year from which election is to have effect. For the 1997-98 tax year this allowance will be at the reduced rate of 15%.

   (iii) Personal Pension Plans. Subject to a maximum income rule of £84,000 a year, full relief is obtainable for premiums which fall within the following limits:

Age at start of tax year	Max. % of earnings
35 or less	17 5
36-45	20·0
46-50	25·0
51-55	30·0
56-60	35·0
61-74	40·0

Different percentages apply for continuing Retirement Annuity Premiums.

2. *Private Company Taxation*

   (i) Profits are chargeable to Corporation Tax at 31 per cent (1997-1998) except where profits are less than £300,000 and where there are no associated companies, when the rate is reduced to 21 per cent. There is also marginal relief between £300,000 and £1·5 million: within this band the marginal rate is 33·5%, the rate on the first £300,000 being 21%.

   (ii) Capital Gains of companies are charged at the appropriate rate of Corporation Tax.

(iii) Distributions, e.g. dividends are not deductible in arriving at the amount of Corporation Tax profit. An Advanced Payment of Corporation Tax is required at the rate of ¼ of distributions made between April 1997 and April 1998. The recipient of distributions will be credited with a tax payment of one-quarter of distributions received, which will be deemed to discharge the liability of basic rate (23%) taxpayers; however, higher rate taxpayers will have to pay additional tax of 20% of the grossed up value of the dividend; dividends are treated as the top slice of income.

(iv) Losses. Restricted carry back to one year (previously 3 years) with effect from 2 July 1997.

3. *Agricultural Businesses: Other Items.*

(a) *Assessing Self-Employed Profits*

From 1997-98 self-employed people will be assessed for tax in any tax year on the basis of the profits recorded in the annual accounts which end in that tax year, i.e. on a 'current year basis' rather than the existing 'preceding year basis'. For existing businesses 1996-97 will be a transitional year and effectively two years' profits will be summed and tax will be paid on half this amount in one tax year. For new businesses starting after 6th April 1994 the current year basis comes into effect immediately.

(b) *Livestock*

Dairy cows or breeding livestock may be treated on the herd basis or on a trading stock basis.

Herd basis: valuation changes are not included in the trading account, nor are additions to the herd, but sales from the herd and replacements are. On the sale of all or a substantial proportion (normally taken as 20% or more) of the herd, no tax is paid on any profit over the original cost price, nor is there any relief for loss.

Trading stock basis: purchases, sales and valuation changes are all included in the trading account.

(c) *Stock Valuations: Crops*

The deemed cost method allows 75% of market value to be used, but market value must include a proportion of the relevant area aid payment (including set-aside).

(d) *Allowances for Capital Expenditure*

Machinery and Plant (whether new or second hand). For machinery purchased after 30 October 1993 a 25 per cent annual writing down allowance is available on a reducing balance basis. As a temporary measure small and medium-sized businesses will be eligible to claim a 50 per cent allowance for the first year for machinery and plant purchased in the year ending 1 July 1998. The writing down allowances will normally be calculated on a "pool" basis. However, where it is expected that a machine will be sold within five years of acquisition and realise less than its written-down value for tax it will be possible for the taxpayer to elect to have allowances calculated separately for each machine. Although the annual writing down allowance will still be 25 per cent this system will enable balancing allowances to be claimed when a machine is sold for less than its written-down value. If at the end of five years the machine has not been sold its tax written-down value will be transferred to the main machinery pool. Motor cars are included in a separate "pool" in the year of purchase, on which a 25 per cent writing down allowance is available. The allowance is restricted to a maximum of £3,000 for motor cars with a written-down value of more than £12,000. Special rules apply where a motor car is only partly used for business purposes.

Machinery Leasing. Tax allowances for rental payments on new financial leases entered into after 11th April 1991 will be spread to reflect the commercial depreciation of the asset. This may mean that full tax relief for rental payments may no longer be gained in the years in which the payments are made.

Buildings. From 1st April, 1986, farm buildings, fencing, drainage and other improvements (including up to one-third of farmhouses) qualify for a writing-down allowance of 4 per cent annually, given equally over 25 years. These annual allowances are normally available to succeeding owners during the 25 year period. Balancing allowances can now be claimed where buildings are demolished and also on the transfer of the land, but only with the new owner's consent.

(e) *Losses*

Losses can normally be set off against other income in the year in which they are incurred and in the subsequent year. If other income is insufficient in the year when the loss occurs and in the subsequent year, any unrelieved losses can be carried forward and set off against future profits from farming. Special rules apply to prevent abuse of loss relief provisions by "hobby" farmers who are not running their farms on a commercial basis with a view to producing a profit: normally losses are disallowed against other income after 5 consecutive years of loss.

With effect from 5 April 1991 trading losses may be set against capital gains.

(f) *Profit Averaging*

This relief is to enable farmers, other than companies, to average their taxable profits over two consecutive years. Where the difference between the profits of two consecutive years is 30 per cent or more of the higher profits, the total profits for the two years are equally divided between the two years. Marginal relief is available where the difference is less than 30 per cent but more than 25 per cent of the higher profits. Profit for the purposes of tax averaging calculations used to be before the deduction of capital allowances. Under the new current year basis profit will be after the deduction of capital allowances. There is a two year limit in which to make the claim.

4. *Capital Gains Tax*

Applies to capital gains by an individual. Capital gains accruing to companies are chargeable to Corporation Tax. A capital gain is the difference between the acquisition value and the sale price. In the case of agricultural property, allowance would be made for any capital expenditure undertaken to improve the property, even though the expenditure may have obtained a buildings allowance referred to at 3 (d) above. For assets owned on 31st March, 1982 and disposed of subsequently, providing an appropriate election is made (within two years), only the gain attributable to the period after that date is taxable, i.e. the chargeable gain is the gain from a valuation at 31st March, 1982 to the date of disposal. Capital Gains Tax is designed to tax that part of the gain which exceeds the rise in the Retail Price Index. Capital Gains Tax is chargeable only on the disposal (including gifts) of assets.

The first £6,500 of capital gains realised by an individual in a year are free of tax. Capital gains in excess of £6,500 are chargeable at rates equivalent to the rates of income tax that would apply if the gains were treated as the top slice of income.

Capital Gains Tax is not payable on death. For persons of 50 or over, the first £250,000 of gain and half the gains between £250,000 and £1 million may be exempt (subject to claimants meeting certain conditions) where they accrue from the disposal by sale or gift of a family business or shares or securities in the family trading company; this exemption also applies to individuals who have to retire before reaching 50 because of ill-health; full relief only applies where the business or the interest in the business has been owned at least ten years and the person has been either the proprietor, a partner, or a full-time working director in a family company. Capital Gains Tax retirement relief is also available in part for those over the age of 50 who have held the assets for more than one year, increasing to full relief after ten years.

Exempt assets include a principal private residence (e.g. farm house, if non-exclusive business occupation applies) if occupied as such, normal life assurance policies, animals and tangible movable property (i.e. chattels) disposed of for £6,000 or less.

Payment of tax may be deferred on gains accruing from the sale of business assets (including land and buildings occupied and used for trade purposes, fixed plant and machinery, milk, ewe and suckler cow quotas, and from the sale of shares in a family business) if part or all of the proceeds are spent on acquiring new assets liable to the tax. The tax is deferred by deducting the gain from the acquisition price of the new asset. Normally it can only be done if the new asset is acquired within 12 months before and 3 years after the disposal of the old assets. Disposal and acquisition dates for Capital Gains purposes are almost always contract, not completion, dates.

Payment of tax may be deferred by investing the gains in unquoted trading companies, including farming companies.

Payments of tax may be deferred where disposal is by gift. This relief only applies to gifts of business assets, land which qualifies for agricultural property relief at either the 100 per cent or 50 per cent rate under Inheritance Tax (see next section) and gifts which lead to an immediate charge to Inheritance Tax (e.g. gifts into a discretionary trust). The amount of the chargeable gain which would normally have accrued to the donor will be held over; the value at which the donee is deemed to acquire the asset will be its market value reduced by the amount of the donor's chargeable gain held over. The held over gain is netted down by any time apportionment, indexation allowance or retirement relief available to the donor. Where deferral is not available payment of tax by interest bearing annual instalments over 10 years will be allowed for gifts of land, controlling share holdings and minority share holdings in unquoted companies.

Should a transaction produce a loss, this may be set against any long term chargeable gains arising in the same year or, if these are insufficient, those accruing in subsequent years. Losses brought forward will be used only to the extent necessary to reduce gains for the year to £6,500. For disposals after 30th November 1993 indexation allowances (for inflation) may not be utilised to create or increase a capital loss.

After 5th April 1991, where a trading loss can be set off against other income in the same or following year, for income tax purposes, any unused loss can be set against capital gains for those years.

Payment of Capital Gains Tax is due on the 1st December in the tax year following disposal up to and including 1995/96. From 1996/97 the tax will be payable on 31st January following the tax year of disposal on the new self-assessment return.

5. Inheritance Tax

This tax, which replaced Capital Transfer Tax, is charged on lifetime gifts and transfers on death.

Slice of Chargeable Transfer	Rate per cent
£0- 215,000	0
Over 215,000	40

Outright gifts to individuals, accumulation and maintenance trusts and interest in possession trusts will be exempt from tax at the time of the gift. All other gifts will be taxed at half the above rates at the time of the transfer. Tax will be charged on the value of an individual's estate at death plus the value of all gifts made within seven years of death. Allowance is made for any tax paid on lifetime gifts included in the value of the estate on death. Relief is given for outright gifts made more than three years before death according to the following scale:

Years between gift and death	Percentage of the full charge to tax
0-3	100
3-4	80
4-5	60
5-6	40
6-7	20

Exemptions include: transfers between husband and wife; the first £3,000 of gift made by a donor in the income tax year and separately up to £250 per year to any number of persons; gifts made out of income which form part of normal expenditure; marriage gifts within limits of £5,000 for a parent, £2,500 for a lineal ancestor and £1,000 for other donors.

Relief may be available for agricultural land. Subject to a general rule that the agricultural land must have been occupied by the transferor (or by his controlled company) for two years, or owned by the transferor for 7 years and occupied for agricultural purposes by someone else before any relief is granted, the relief is at two different rates. If the basis of valuation is vacant possession, the taxable value of the land is reduced by 100%. If the basis of valuation is tenanted value, the taxable value of the land is reduced by 50% of that tenanted value. Ownership and occupation periods normally include prior periods of ownership or occupation by husbands and wives. From 1st September 1995 100% relief will apply to new lettings of agricultural land as farm business tenancies.

Relief is also available in respect to "business property" transferred during lifetime or on death. The relief extends to the business assets of a proprietor and the interest of a partner or controlling shareholder of a company in the business capital. The value of such property, providing certain tests are satisfied (e.g. it has been owned by the transferor for two years preceding transfer), is reduced by 100 per cent. Where a partner or controlling shareholder owns assets (e.g. land) that the business uses the value will be reduced by 50 per cent. Shareholdings in unquoted companies are eligible for a 100 per cent reduction in market value.

Lifetime gifts of property eligible for Agricultural and Business Property Relief have to be retained (or replaced by similar property) until the death of the donor (or earlier death of the donee) if those reliefs are to be available when the tax (or additional tax) becomes payable subsequent to the donor's death.

In the case of the transfer of property eligible for Agricultural Relief and Business Property Relief the tax can be paid by annual instalments over ten years free of interest.

6. *Stamp Duty*

Stamp Duty arises when the title to property changes hands. In the case of land the duty will usually be paid by the purchaser; the rate payable is 1 per cent on the full value where the consideration (purchase price) or value is over £60,000 and less than £250,000, 1·5 per cent if the consideration is more than £250,000 and less than £500,000, and 2 per cent if the consideration is more than £500,000. However, the 1 per cent ad valorem duty does not apply on lifetime voluntary gifts. Such gifts are only liable to a 50p fixed duty. Stamp duty on share purchases and sales is at the rate of 0·5 per cent.

7. *Value Added Tax*

Agricultural businesses with a turnover of taxable goods and services in excess of £48,000 per annum (£49,000 from 1 December 1997) are required to register for VAT. Businesses with a turnover below this limit may apply for voluntary registration. The standard rate of VAT is 17·5 per cent. Most agricultural products are zero rated for VAT purposes. VAT has to be paid on certain inputs. Registered businesses are eligible to reclaim the tax paid where the goods or services purchased have been used in the production of zero-rated supplies.

A flat rate scheme is available to farmers as an alternative to registering for VAT. Farmers under the flat rate scheme do not have to submit tax returns and consequently cannot reclaim tax.

They can, however, charge (and keep) a flat rate addition of 4 per cent when they sell to VAT registered customers goods and services which qualify. This addition is not VAT but acts as compensation for losing input tax on purchases. The local VAT office may refuse to issue a certificate to participate in the flat rate scheme if this would mean the farmer would recover substantially (£3,000) more than through the normal system.

8. *National Insurance Contributions (1997/98)*

Class 1.

Employee's weekly earnings	Employee	Employer
Not contracted out		
£62·00 to £109·99	10%*	3·0%
£110·00 to £154·99	10%*	5·0%
£155·00 to £209·99	10%*	7·0%
£210·00 to £465·00	10%*	10·0%
Over £465·00	no additional liability	10·0%

*2% on first £62·00

Contracted out	Employee		Employer	
	on first £61·00	on remainder	on first £61·00	on remainder
£62·00 to £109·99	2%	8·4%	3·0%	nil
£110·00 to £154·99	2%	8·4%	5·0%	2·0%
£155·00 to £209·99	2%	8·4%	7·0%	4·0%
£210·00 to £465·00	2%	8·4%	10·0%	7·0%
Over £465·00	no additional liability		£34·59	plus 10·0% on excess over £465

Class 2.

Self-employed flat rate (no liability if earnings below £3,480 a year)	£6·15 a week

Class 3.

Non-employed (voluntary) flat rate	£6·05 a week

Class 4.

Self-employed. On profits or gains between £7,010 a year and £24,180 a year)	6% (max. £1,032·20 a year)

3. GRANTS

1. *GRANTS FOR PROCESSING AND MARKETING AGRICULTURAL PRODUCTS*

A. MARKETING DEVELOPMENT SCHEME

This scheme was withdrawn in England from 5 November 1996 but continues to operate in Scotland, Wales and Northern Ireland. It is administered by MAFF and provides grant aid to individual farmers and growers or groups of producers, food processors or manufacturers and trade associations or industry bodies, towards the non-capital costs of projects designed to improve the efficiency of the food marketing chain. Assistance is given at the rate of 50 per cent of approved expenditure on:

— Feasibility studies and market research.

— Costs of establishment, expansion and merger of producer groups including legal and accountancy costs, redundancy costs of key staff and the costs of recruiting new members.

— Salaries of key staff of a project including recruitment costs.

— Production and dissemination of suitable promotional material intended to encourage the take-up of industry-wide projects.

— Promotional events to demonstrate marketing innovation or excellence of marketing practice.

— Training of directors and key staff members.

— Expenses of outside directors.

The maximum grant payable for a project is £150,000.

Sector Challenge. From October 1996 businesses have been able to apply for Sector Challenge grants, the first round of which took place in autumn 1996. Under this scheme grant aid of up to 50 per cent can be available on a wide range of non-capital expenditure. The scheme is competitive and is currently subject to review. No decision has yet been taken as to the date of second round applications.

B. PROCESSING AND MARKETING GRANT

Under EU Regulation 866/90 the UK Government and the European Agricultural Guidance Fund jointly fund grant aid towards the cost of investment aimed at the improvement, rationalisation of the treatment, processing and marketing of agricultural produce. Grants at the rate of 30% will be available for projects costing a minimum of £70,000. The maximum grant will be £1·2 million in most cases. As funds for this scheme are limited it is likely that there will be stiff competition for these grants. The scheme was withdrawn in England from 31st March 1996 but continues to operate in Scotland, Wales and Northern Ireland.

C. FRESH FRUIT AND VEGETABLE PRODUCER ORGANISATIONS

Producer organisations recognised under European Commission Directive 2200/96 may apply for a contribution towards an operating fund which the organisation has set up to finance a planned programme to improve performance in marketing, produce quality and environmental considerations. The contribution from the European Commission will be a minimum of 2 per cent and a maximum of 4 per cent (increasing to 2·5 and 4·5 per cent respectively from 1999) of the producer organisation's turnover and may be no more than 50 per cent of eligible expenditure under the planned programme.

2. OBJECTIVE 5B FUNDING

Areas designated under the European Union Objective 5b (rural development) programme may benefit from EAGGF (European Agricultural Guidance Fund) assistance towards the cost of projects which provide new opportunities for developing and diversifying the rural economy. Projects should have the potential to generate business opportunities which sustain rural development and employment and, where appropriate, conserve and enhance the environment. They could include farm diversification, the development of speciality products, promoting rural tourism, and environmental initiatives.

Funding is limited and projects will be considered on a competitive basis. Projects serving the needs of individual businesses may be submitted but those which benefit groups of farms are more likely to be successful. EAGGF funding should be matched by an equivalent level of UK public money. Application forms can be obtained from MAFF Regional Service Centres.

3. GRANTS FOR ENVIRONMENTAL IMPROVEMENT

A. ENVIRONMENTALLY SENSITIVE AREAS (ESAs)

The first ESAs were designated in 1987. Currently there are 22 in England alone, covering a total area of 1,150,000 hectares, some 10% of its agricultural land. Within these areas farmers are offered annual payments if they enter into 10 year agreements to manage their land, buildings, walls and other features in ways which will conserve the traditional environment. The levels of annual payments vary between ESAs and between different tiers within ESAs depending upon the severity of the restrictions imposed upon farming activities and any extra costs associated with additional work which farmers are required to undertake. They can be substantial, e.g. £415 per ha under tier 3 of the Somerset Levels and Moors ESA, where the requirement is to create wet winter and spring conditions. Farmers may submit a Conservation Plan which is aimed at enhancing the environment, e.g. by planting new hedgerows, which, if accepted, will entitle them to grant aid towards the cost of undertaking the work. Farmers in ESAs can enter a voluntary public access option and will be paid £274 per mile (£170 per km) of access route plus grants of up to 80% of relevant capital work.

Arable land which is subject to an ESA agreement will qualify for area payments or set-aside if it is used to grow eligible arable crops. Arable land reverted to grassland or heathland under an ESA agreement is not eligible for area payments.

B. GRANTS FOR LANDSCAPE CONSERVATION

See pages 184-5

C. COUNTRYSIDE STEWARDSHIP SCHEME

This scheme offers capital and annual payments for conserving, managing and re-creating valued landscapes. The following landscapes have been targeted: chalk and limestone grassland, lowland heath, waterside landscapes, coastal areas, historic landscapes (such as deer parks), old orchards, meadows and pastures, Community Forests, countryside around towns, and uplands. Participants must enter a 10 year agreement. Annual payments range from £15 to £70 per hectare for regenerating suppressed heather moor up to £275 per hectare for recreating lowland heath and £280 per hectare for recreating grassland on cultivated land. They are reviewed on a fixed three-year cycle. An additional payment of £35 per hectare is available for allowing public access, with further supplements for linear access strips for walking, horse riding, cycling and the disabled. The scheme also offers grant aid towards the cost of restoring hedgerows and field boundaries which are either long-established features of the landscape, important wildlife habitats or of high amenity value. The scheme is administered by MAFF and is available throughout England, except in ESAs. Priority is given to proposals offering the best potential for environmental improvement and public benefit.

D. NITRATE SENSITIVE AREAS (NSAs)

In 1990 ten pilot NSAs were set up in England to reduce nitrate levels in water supplies to below the EC-permitted levels of 50 mg/litre. A further 22 new NSAs were established in 1994, adding a further 35,000 ha to the 10,500 ha of the pilot NSAs. The ten pilot schemes are to be continued and incorporated within the scheme for the 22 new NSAs.

Under the scheme, farmers who change their farming practices to reduce nitrate leaching receive payments of between £65 and £590 per hectare.

Entry into the scheme will be voluntary. Farmers will have to enter whole fields, or, in the case of the arable conversion option, parts of fields of at least 4 hectares in area. Agreements will be for five years' duration. Farmers will have three main options available to them:

(i) Arable conversion—which requires the conversion of arable land to extensive grassland. Sub-options include:

a.	Grassland with no fertilizer and no grazing	£450-£550/ha
b.	As A but with native grass species	£490-£590/ha
c.	As A but with limited grazing	£420-£520/ha
d.	Reversion to grassland with limited fertilizer and grazing	£340-£440/ha

Alternatively, arable land which is planted to a MAFF approved mix of native grass species and maintained as unfertilized, ungrazed grassland for 5 years will count towards set-aside obligations. Payment will be at the annual set-aside rate (£338 per ha in 1997) plus an additional environmental payment of £50 per ha.

(ii) Low nitrogen grassland—which requires a change from intensive to extensive grassland management. Payment is £250/ha.

(iii) Low nitrogen arable—where the level of nitrogen applied is restricted. Two sub-options include:

a. Nitrogen usage restricted to 150 kg/ha for all 5 years of the scheme and no potatoes or vegetable brassicas   £80-£105/ha

b. Nitrogen usage restricted to 200 kg/ha in 1 out of 5 years and to 150 kg/ha in remaining 4 years. No restrictions on cropping.   £65/ha

E. FARM WASTE GRANT SCHEME

This scheme provides grant aid to farmers in Nitrate Vulnerable Zones who undertake investment in farm waste handling facilities in order to comply with restrictions on the spreading of livestock manures. Grant is available at 25 per cent of eligible expenditure up to an investment ceiling of £85,000. Eligible expenditure includes manure, slurry and silage effluent stores, and ancillary items and costs including landscaping and professional fees.

F. HABITAT SCHEME

Introduced in 1994, this scheme is designed to encourage farmers to take land out of production for 20 years to create important wildlife habitats. A number of options are available. The annual payments are intended to reflect the cost of entering land into the scheme.

	Annual Payment (£ per Ha)	
	Land currently in arable/temporary grass	Land currently in permanent grass
Creation of intertidal habitats, particularly salt marshes for birds	525 (448*)	250
Establish/enhance water fringe habitats in designated pilot areas by:		
— creating buffer strips with no agricultural production	485 (405*)	240
— extensive grazing	435	125

(*where the land is counted as set-aside)

A supplement of £40/ha may be paid where measures are then taken to raise the water level

Management of valuable habitats established under the Five Year Set-aside Scheme	290

G. MOORLAND SCHEME

Introduced in 1995, this scheme is designed to encourage the conservation and enhancement of heather and other shrubby moorland vegetation in those parts of the Less Favoured Areas which are not part of Environmentally Sensitive Areas. Sheep farmers who adopt a more extensive system of production will receive an annual payment for each ewe eligible for Hill Livestock Compensatory Allowances by which their flock is reduced. Applicants must enter at least 20 hectares of moorland containing at least 25% heather and the flock must be reduced by at least 10 animals. Compensation is at the rate of £30 per ewe removed.

4. *OTHER GRANTS/SCHEMES*

WOODLAND GRANT SCHEME and FARM WOODLAND
PREMIUM SCHEME (See pages 41-43)

COUNTRYSIDE ACCESS SCHEME (See page 46)

ORGANIC AID SCHEME (See page 34)

BEEF and SHEEP (including HILL LIVESTOCK) (See page 72)

V. MISCELLANEOUS DATA

1. CONSERVATION COSTS

(N.B. *Abbreviations.* CC: Countryside Commission; FC: Forestry Commission; EN: English Nature; BTCV: British Trust for Conservation Volunteers; CPRE: Council for Preservation of Rural England; ATB: Agricultural Training Board).

Hedge Trimming (flail). Contract labour, £13 to £15/hour. 3 miles a day (maximum; much less if overgrown or difficult). Aug.-Feb. *(not* April-July). Every 2 or 3 years; *(possibly* annually).

Hedge Laying. Contract labour, £3-£5 a metre, or £5 per hour. Contractor, 15 metres/day; BTCV, 5 metres/day per person. Nov./March. Every 8 to 20 years. Grant aid: CC, MAFF, EN. ATB quote £1·50 a metre plus 60p a metre for stakers and pleachers, 40 metres a day.

Hedge Planting. Transplants av. £25/100; netlon guards av. 25p; canes av. 10p; fencing (labour and materials): stock proof £2/metre, stock and rabbit proof up to £3/metre. Overall, £1·80/metre unguarded and unfenced, £6·50/metre guarded and fenced. Contract labour: planting up to £2/metre, fencing up to £2·50/metre. Contractor 100-150 metres/day; BTCV 20 metres/day. Pref Oct./March. Above includes repair. Grant aid: CC, MAFF, EN.

Hedge Coppicing. By hand: 2 men and a chain saw, 100 metres/day, £2/metre. Contractor: tractor mounted saw, driver and 2 men, 13 metres/hour, £27/hour. Grant aid: CC, MAFF.

Dry Stone Walling. £12.50/square metre with skilled contract labour. Cornish Hedging: £25-£40/metre length depending upon type of stone. Grant aid: MAFF, CC.

Amenity Tree Planting; (half acre block or less). Transplants av. 75p; shelter plus stake and tie av. £1; stake av. 50p; whip av. 70p. (50p-£1); rabbit spiral guard 30p; netlon guard av. 50p (but 15p in a 50 m roll); cane av. 10p. Trees per man day: farmer 200, contractor 400; (large-scale, 33 man days/ha). Nov.-April. Grant aid: CC, MAFF, CLA, CPRE (occasionally).

Shelter Belts. Per 100 metre length: 100 large species (oak, lime, etc.) £35; 66 medium species (cherry, birch, etc.) £25; 100 shrubs, £30; 166 tree stakes, shelters and ties, £250; total £340; (site preparation, weed control, labour and fencing extra). MAFF standard costs £637·50/ha; windbreaks £33·85/ha. Grant aid: CC, MAFF.

Woodland Establishment. Conifers £150/1000. To supply and plant oak or beech transplants in tubes £2 each. Rabbit fencing £2·80/metre. Contract labour: conifers at 2m (inc. trees) £580/ha; broadleaves at 3m (inc. trees) £800/ha; forest transplants (not inc. trees) £70/1000. 12·5 days/ha (contractor). Nov.-April. (Above not inc. maintenance). Grant aid: FC, CC, MAFF.

Forestry: General. Contract labour: chain sawing £8/hr., brush cutting £7·15/hr., extracting timber/pulp £4-£10/tonne, chemical spot weeding 5p-7p/tree, rhodedendron control £600-£800/acre.

Pond Construction. Butyl lining (0·75mm) £5/m^2; other lining £2·5/m^2. Contract labour: Hymac £12·50/hr., 150 Komatsu £16/hr.; bulldozer D6C £16·50/hr. Autumn (dry ground conditions). Grant aid: MAFF, CC (discretionary), EN (possibly).

Pond Maintenance. Hymac £15/hr.; Backhoe £12·50/hr. 5m^2/day (BTCV); 100 m^2/day (contractor). Timing: probably winter; time depends on ground condition and species whose life cycles may be disturbed. Every 5 to 50 years. Grant aid: CC, EN.

Ditch Maintenance. Backhoe excavator £12·50/hr. Preferably in winter. Every 3 to 7 years on rotation. Grant aid: MAFF (improvement plan), EN (conservation interest).

Pollarding and Tree Surgery. Pollard: £40-£60/stool; surgery: £150/tree. Pollarding: 2 or 3 trees/day. Surgery: 2 days/tree. Winter. Pollard every 20-40 years. Grant aid: CC (discretionary).

Grassland Establishment. Grass seed/wild flower mixes: £400-£1800/ha. Grasses only mix, low seed rate, £200-£350/ha. 11 ha/day. Pref. Aug.-Oct. Grant aid: possibly CC for small areas as part of whole farm plan.

Reducing Pesticide Drift. Use of appropriate spray nozzles: tilt jets £22-£25 for 6; lo-drift nozzles £15 for 6.

Permanent Grass Margins at Field Edges. To provide wildlife benefits and help control pernicious weeds, reducing herbicides at the field edge. A sterile strip provides virtually no wildlife benefit and the initial establishment costs may be offset by savings in maintenance costs in future years. Establishment costs (2m wide) per 100m run, approx. £3, with maintenance (mowing) 50p. Subsequent years, mowing only.

Fertilizer Losses at Field Boundaries. For a 12m spread pattern, at 150 kg/ha, loss is approx. 30p per 100m per application, or £3 for a 6 ha field (450 × 150m). Loss avoided by driving further away from the field boundary/using a tilting hopper mechanism/using an appropriate border disc or deflector, costing £90.

GRANT AID. For a summary of "Grants for Landscape Conservation" available from the CC, FC, MAFF and EN: apply for leaflet from Countryside Commission, Publications Despatch Dept., 19/23 Albert Road, Manchester, M19 2EQ. Countryside Commission grants are usually available through local authorities.

Acknowledgement. Above information supplied by Farming and Wildlife Advisory Group (FWAG). Sources: County FWAG personnel, BTCV, Local authorities.

2. FERTILIZER PRICES

A. *Compounds*

N	P_2O_5	K_2O	£
	Analysis		Price per tonne
0	24	24	107·50-125
0	18	36	112·50-127·50
0	20	30	110-125
0	30	15	112·50-125
0	30	20	112·50-127·50
5	24	24	117·50-130
8	24	24	125-140
10	24	24	132·50-145
10	10	30	130-145
12	15	20	125-137·50
13	13	20	122·50-135
15	15	20	127·50-140
15	15	19	125-137·50
17	17	17	135-147·50
20	4	14	117·50-130
20	10	10	117·50-130
20	8	12	122·50-135
22	11	11	127·50-137·50
24	4	4	110-125
25	5	5	112·50-132·50
25	0	16	107·50-120

B. *Straights*

Type	Price per tonne
	£
Ammonium Nitrate: UK (34·5% N.)	100-125
Imported (34·5% N.)	85-112·50
Sulphate of Ammonia (21% N.)	100-115
Urea (46% N.): granular/ prills	120-155/105-140
Liquid Nitrogen	82·50-105
Triple Superphosphate (47% P_2O_5)	130-145
Muriate of Potash (Granular) (60% K_2O)	107·50-117·50

Average price (p) per kg: N : 32·5 (29-36) (UK AN)
P_2O_5 : 29 (triple supers).
K_2O : 19 (muriate).

The fertilizer prices are the main ranges in mid-1997; (the price of AN fell sharply in June). Prices also vary according to area and bargaining power. They are prices delivered to the farm in bags; delivery in bulk averages £7/tonne less. Discounts for cash payment approx. £2·50/tonne. Where separate prices are quoted for granular and blended the former are generally between £2 and £5/tonne more. They assume delivery in 20 tonne lots; add approximately £2 for 10 tonne lots, £4 for 6-9 tonne lots, £6 for 4-5 tonne lots.

3. MANURIAL VALUE OF SLURRY AND FARMYARD MANURE

1. Composition (% by weight)

	N	P_2O_5	K_2O
Undiluted Slurry (faeces plus urine, or droppings):			
Cow	0·5	0·2	0·5
Pig	0·6	0·2	0·2
Poultry	1·7	1·4	0·7
Farmyard Manure:			
Cattle	0·5	0·4	0·6
Pig	0·6	0·6	0·4
Poultry	1·8	1·8	1·2

2. Available Nutrients (kg)

	N	P_2O_5	K_2O
Undiluted Slurry (per 10m³*):			
Cow	35	11	58
Pig	42	11	23
Poultry	118	82	82

(* = 10 tonnes; 10,000 litres)

	N	P_2O_5	K_2O
Farmyard Manure (per 10 tonnes):			
Cattle	17	20	46
Pig	20	31	31
Poultry	110	92	92

3. Amount per head

(faeces plus urine, or droppings)	litres per day	kg per year (1)		
		N	P_2O_5	K_2O
1 dairy cow	40	51	16	84
1 pig (dry meal fed)	4·5	6·8	1·8	3·7
100 laying hens	13	55	39	39

(1) assuming housed all year and no losses.

4. AGROCHEMICAL COSTS (1997)

Only the names of the active ingredients are given below, with their principal use. These materials should only be applied in accordance with the manufacturers' recommendations. Application rates can vary and there are differences between the prices of various proprietary brands. The list is not intended to be exhaustive and there is no implied criticism of materials omitted.

Crop	Function	Material	Approx. Cost £ per ha per application
Cereals	Herbicides: General	MCPA	3·00- 7·50
		Mecoprop	8·75-10·50
		Dicamba+Mecoprop+MCPA	21·00
		Ioxynil+Bromoxynil	12·00-24·00
		Ioxynil+Bromoxynil+ Mecoprop	25·00-36·00
		Metsulfuron-methyl	17·00-19·00
	Undersown	MCPA+MCPB	28·00-30·00
	Crops	Benazolin+2, 4-DB+MCPA	42·00
	Blackgrass	Chlortoluron	18·00-22·00
		Isoproturon	16·00-26·00
		Isoproturon+Diflufenican	30·00-35·00
		Isoproturon+Trifluralin	25·00-38·00
	Cleavers	Fluroxypyr	19·00-25.00
	Wild Oats	Difenzoquat	30·00-40·00
		Tri-allate	30·00
		Diclofop-methyl	26·00-52·00
	Growth Regulator	Chlormequat	3·50- 4·50
		Chlormequat + Choline Chloride	4·00- 5·00
		2-chloroethylphosphonic acid + Mepiquat Chloride	10·00-20·00
	Fungicides	Benomyl	13·50
		Carbendazim	2·50- 3·00
		Fenpropimorph	23·00-30·00
		Prochloraz	14·00-18·00
		Propiconazole	22·00
		Triadimefon	23·50
	Seed Dressing	Ethirimol + Flutriafol + Thiabendazole	12·00-18·50
		Fuberidazole + Triadimenol	11·00-16·00
	Aphicide	Cypermethrin	2·00- 2·50
		Deltamethrin	4·50- 5·50
		Pirimicarb	13·00-15·00
	Slug Killer	Metaldehyde	12·00-13·00
		Methiocarb	37·00-40·00
Oilseed Rape	Herbicides	Propyzamide	30·00-42·00
		Trifluralin	5·50- 6·50
	Insecticide	Deltamethrin	5·00- 6·00
		Pirimicarb	17·00-25·00
		Alphacypermethrin	4·00- 8·00
	Fungicide	Iprodione	38·00-57·00
		Prochloraz + Carbendazim + Xylene	30·00-32·00

Crop	Function	Material	Approx. Cost £ per ha per application
Potatoes	Herbicides: Pre-emergence	Monolinuron	34·00-50·00
	Pre-and post-	Metribuzin	32·00-64·00
	emergence	Terbutryne + Terbuthylazine	35·00-51·00
	Blight Control	Fentin Acetate + Maneb	16·50
		Oxadixyl+Cymoxanil+Mancozeb	28·00
		Mancozeb	6·75
	Haulm Dessicant	Diquat	50·00
	Sprouting Suppressant	Tecnazene	£5·20/tonne
Sugar Beet	Herbicides: Pre-emergence	Chloridazon:	
		overall	32·00-97·00
		band spray	11·00-32·00
		Metamitron:	
		low dose	32·00-34·00
		band spray	29·00-39·00
	Post-emergence	Phenmedipham:	
		low dose	11·00
		band spray	7·00-10·00
	Insecticide	Aldicarb	50·00-52·00
		Pirimicarb	17.50
Beans	Herbicide	Simazine	4·50- 6·00
	Fungicide	Carbendazim	4.50
Peas	Herbicide	Terbutryne + Terbuthylazine	35·00-51·00
Beans and Peas	Insecticide	Triazophos	12·00
		Deltamethrin	5·50- 6·50
Maize	Herbicide	Atrazine	10·50 14·00
Brassicas	Herbicides	Desmetryne	57·00-89·00
		Propachlor	48·00-69·00
		Trifluralin	6·00- 7·00
Broadleaved Crops	Grass weeds and volunteer cereals	Fluazifop-P-butyl	30·00-60·00
Grassland	Herbicides	MCPA	6·50-10·50
		MCPA + MCPB	29·00
		2,4-D+ Dicamba + Triclopyr	36·00-54·00
General	Weed and Grass Killer General	Paraquat	8·00-22·00
	Prior to Direct Drilling	Paraquat	16·00-38·00
	Couch Grass Control	Glyphosate	15·00-20·00
	WoodyWeed Control	Triclopyr	107·00

Note. The above prices are based largely on retail prices paid by farmers (spring 1997) and reflect the discounts available where there are competing products from several manufacturers.

5. FEEDINGSTUFF PRICES

			£ per tonne
1. Cattle	Dairy:	High Energy	140-175
		Medium Energy	130-150
		Low Energy	120-140
		Concentrate	230-290
	Beef:	Pellets	115-150
		Concentrate	220-245
	Calf:	Milk Substitute	1,225-1,275
		High Fat (bags)	915-950
		Calf Weaner Pellets	155-170
		Calf Rearer Nuts	145-160
2. Sheep	Lamb Pellets	140-155
	Sheep/lamb cake	120-135
	Ewe cake	130-145
3. Horses	Horse and Pony Pencils	205-225
4. Goats	Goat Nuts	195-215
5. Pigs	Piglet Weaner	210-230
	Sow Nuts	130-160
	Early Grower Pellets	175-210
	Grower/Finisher Pellets	145-170
	Sow Concentrate	275-290
	Grower Concentrate	260-275
6. Poultry	Chick and Rearer Feeds	215-240
	Layers Feeds	195-210
	Broiler Feeds	205-235
	Turkey Feeds	205-230
8. Straight Feeds	Fish Meal (English; 66/72%)	380-450
	Soya Bean Meal (45/48%)	175-250
	Rapeseed Meal (35/36%)	90-140
	Palm Kernel Meal/Cake (17%CP)	65-115
	Linseed Cake	135-170
	Sunflower Seed Pellets (29/33%)	80-125
	Citrus Pulp Nuts	65-115
	Rice Bran Pellets	65-105
	Grass Cubes (16%)	110-130
	Wheatfeed	60-115
	Maize Germ Meal	75-140
	Maize Gluten (20-23%)	75-125
	Molasses	95-130
	Sugar Beet Pulp Nuts/Pellets	82-120
	Molassed Sugar Beet Feed	80-120
	Pressed Sugar Beet Pulp	25-30
	Wet Brewers' Grains	15-30
	Citrus pulp	17-22
	Supergrains	35-37
	Fodder Beet	22-27

The straight feed prices are approximate ranges for 1996-97 (including delivery). The other prices are approximate ranges of purchased compounds in mid-1997.

They are (mainly) delivered prices on the farm *in bulk* in 15-20 tonne loads, and exclude any credit charges. The additional cost for *bags* is generally £18 to £24 a tonne. Delivery in bags is assumed for horse and pony pencils, goat nuts, chick and rearer feeds.

ME requirements for Friesian cows (590kg LW) (see page 192)

Liveweight Change		Milk yield (kg/day)			
(kg/day)	Maintenance	20	25	30	35
−0·5		147	172	196	221
0	62	161	186	210	235
+0·5		178	203	227	252

Source: Broster, W.H. and Alderman, G., Livestock Production Science, 4 (1977).

6. FEEDINGSTUFFS: NUTRITIVE VALUES

Type of Feed	Dry Matter Content g/kg	Metabolizable Energy MJ/k DM	Digestible Crude Protein g/kg DM
Pasture, rotational close grazed (monthly)	200	11·2	130
Ryegrass, perennial post flowering	250	8·4	72
Hay—moderate digestibility grass	850	8·8	39
Silage—moderate digestibility grass	200	8·8	102
Pea Haulm and Pods (Canning) Silage	210	8·7	95
Barley (spring) Straw	860	7·3	9
Oat (spring) Straw	860	6·7	11
Threshed Ryegrass Hay (approximate)	850	7·0	38
Kale (marrow stem)	140	11·0	114
Mangels	100	12·4	80
Swede	105	13·9	64
Turnips	100	12·7	70
Fodder Beet	180	12·5	50
Sugar Beet Tops	160	9·9	88
Rape	140	9·5	144
Potatoes	205	13·3	80
Brewers' Grains (barley)—fresh	280	10·4	154
Barley	860	12·9	82
Oats	860	12·0	84
Maize	860	13·8	69
Wheat	860	13·5	105
Flaked Maize	900	15·0	106
Maize Gluten Feed	900	12·5	195
Maize Gluten Meal	900	17·2	736
Pressed Sugar Beet Pulp	180	12·3	60
Dried Molassed Sugar Beet Pulp	860	12·5	80
Beans, field spring	860	12·8	248
Cassava	880	12·8	18
Dec. Groundnut Cake	900	12·3	449
Dec. Cotton Cake	900	12·3	393

Source: M.A.F.F. (1984) Reference Book 433, Energy Allowances and Feeding Systems for Ruminants.

For relative value of different feeds see page 80.

7. STANDARD OUTPUTS, STANDARD GROSS MARGINS AND STANDARD MAN-DAYS (1)

Crops (per hectare)

	S.O.	S.G.M.	S.M.D.
Winter Wheat	915	660	
Spring Wheat	790	585	
Winter Barley	765	550	1·25/2 (2)
Spring Barley	685	510	
Winter Oats	820	645	
Spring Oats	735	580	
Winter Oilseed Rape ...	875	650	1·25
Spring Oilseed Rape ...	740	580	1·25
Linseed	690	530	1·25
Field Beans	720	570	1·25
Dried Peas	770	555	1·5
Vining Peas	1080	870	3·0
Potatoes	3155	1285	12/22 (3)
Sugar Beet	1810	1220	3·5
Herbage Seeds... ...	1200	825	1·5
Hops	6750	5100	7·5
Mangolds (carted) ...	—	—	25
Turnips/Swedes:			
folded	—	—	4
lifted	—	—	10
Kale: cut and carted ...	—	—	10
Kale: grazed	—	—	1·5
Hay/Silage: 1 cut ...	—	—	2·5
Hay/Silage: 2 cuts ...	—	—	4
Grazing only	—	—	0·5
Hay for sale	450	350	2·25
Keep let	220	190	0·75
Bare Fallow	—	—	1·25
Set-aside	—	—	0·25
Rough grazing	—	—	0·2

Livestock (per head) (4, 5)

	S.O.	S.G.M.	S.M.D.
Dairy Cows	1235	820	5
Bulls	—	—	3·5
Beef Cows			
(S.S. inc. Calf):			
Lowland	340	205	1·4
Upland	460	305	1·7

Livestock (per head) (4, 5)

	S.O.	S.G.M.	S.M.D.
Cereal Beef			
(0-12 months) ...	390	70	2·0
18 month Beef (6) ...	460	215	1·5
Grass Silage Beef (6)...	385	140	
Other Cattle over			
2 years	170	75	1·4
Other Cattle			
1-2 years	170	75	1·0
Other Cattle			
½-1 year	85	40	1·0
Calves, M.S.-to			
6 months (add			
to S.S.)	120	75	0·75
Calves, Others, to			
6 months (6):			
steers	180	55	1·25
heifers	150	45	1·25
Ewes: lowland ...	63	37	0·5
upland ...	60	40	0·45
hill ...	56	44	0·4
Rams	—	—	0·5
Other Sheep over			
6 months	34	21	0·3
Sows	710	250	3
Boars	—	—	2
Other Pigs over			
1 month	135	30	0·3
Laying Birds			
(Intensive)	9·1	1·8	0·025
Pullets reared (6) ...	1·9	0·4	·005
Broilers (6)	1·1	0·24	0·002
Turkeys (6):			
Heavy	15	6·2	
Lt./Med.: Christmas	11/13	6/6·7	
All year ...	7·8/9·7	3·2	
Capons (6)	10	6·3	
Ducks (6)	5	2·2	
Geese (6)	18	13	

1. *Author's estimates for 1998 for average performance under average conditions. Wide variations can occur from farm to farm. Some of the S.M.D. estimates are based on only limited data — though all that is available; these are subject to substantial variations with scale.*

2. 1·25 if straw ploughed in; 2 if straw harvested.

3. Automatic planter and mechanical harvester/hand-fed planter and hand harvesting. Including casual labour.

4. In calculating the Standard Outputs and Standard Gross Margins for livestock, herd depreciation or livestock (e.g. calf) purchases or the value of transfers in have been deducted.

5. Note that for grazing livestock, the S.M.D. per head exclude field work, e.g. grass production and silage making, i.e. the labour for these has to be added to give the *total* labour for these enterprises.

6. For these livestock, S.O., S.G.M. and S.M.D. per annum should be based on numbers produced (sold) during the year. *For all other livestock, average numbers during the year should be used* (i.e. average of numbers at end of each month).
For number of Standard Man-Days per worker per year, see page 93.

8. FARM RECORDS

The following records should be kept for management purposes:

1. *Basic Whole Farm Financial Position*
   1. Cash Analysis Book, fully detailed.
   2. Petty Cash Book.
   3. Annual Valuation, including physical quantities, with crops in store and livestock at (near) market value, less any variable costs yet to be borne. Fertilizers, seeds, sprays, casual labour or contract work applied to growing crops should be recorded, but "cultivations" and manurial residues can be ignored for management purposes.
   4. Debtors and creditors at the end of the financial year.

2. *Other Financial and Physical Records*
   1. Output (quantities and value) of each Crop and Livestock Enterprise for the "Harvest Year" (or Production Cycle). It may be possible to get information of Sales from a fully detailed cash analysis book (although, for crops, the financial year figures will then have to be allocated between crops from the current harvest and those from the harvest in the previous financial year, in order to check on the accuracy of the opening valuation of crops in store; this is particularly a problem with Michaelmas ending accounts). The following records of Internal Transfers and Consumption will also be required:
      (a) Numbers and Market Value of livestock transferred from one livestock category to another, e.g. dairy calves to Dairy Followers or Beef Enterprise, or dairy heifers to Dairy Enterprise.
      (b) Quantity and Market Value of Cereals fed on farm and used for seed.
      (c) Quantity and Market Value of Milk and other produce consumed by the farmer or his employees, used on the farm (e.g. milk fed to calves), or sold direct.
   2. A Monthly record of Livestock Numbers; preferably reconciled with the previous month according to births, purchases, deaths, sales and transfers.
   3. Costs and Quantities of Concentrate Feed to each category of livestock, including Home-Grown Cereals fed on the farm.

4. Allocation of costs of seed, fertilizer, sprays, casual labour and contract work specific to an enterprise. This is in order to calculate gross margins, where required. It is less essential than the other records listed.

5. Breeding record for cows, including bulling dates, date(s) served, type of bull used, pregnancy testing, estimated calving date, actual calving date, and date when dried off.

6. For each crop, total output and yield per hectare, in both quantity and value. Include each field where the crop has been grown and its approximate yield, where this can be satisfactorily obtained.

7. For each field, keep one page to cover a period of say, ten years. Record on this, each year, crop grown, variety sown, fertilizer used, sprays used, date sown, date(s) harvested, approximate yield (if obtainable), and any other special notes that you feel may have significance for the future.

8. A rotation record. On a single page, if possible, list each field down the side and say, ten years along the top. Colour each field-year space according to the crop grown, e.g. barley yellow, potatoes red, etc.

9. DEFINITIONS OF FARM MANAGEMENT TERMS

Mainly abstracted from "Terms and Definitions used in Farm and Horticulture Management", M.A.F.F., 1970.

1. Valuations and Capital

Valuations. Valuation is essentially a process of estimation. Thus alternative bases are sometimes possible, according to the purpose intended. The basis should be consistent throughout the period of any series of figures.

(i) *Saleable crops in store.* At estimated market value less costs still to be incurred, e.g. for storage and marketing. Both may be estimated either at the expected date of sale or at the date of valuation.

(ii) *Growing crops.* Preferably at variable costs to the date of valuation, although estimated total cost can alternatively be used.

(iii) *Saleable crops ready for harvesting* but still in the ground. Preferably valued as (i), less estimated harvesting costs, although they can alternatively be treated as (ii).

(iv) *Fodder stocks (home-grown).* Preferably at variable costs when calculating gross margins. Alternatively at estimated market value (based on hay-equivalent value according to quality). Fodder crops still in the ground, e.g. kale, treated as (ii).

(v) *Stocks of purchased materials (including fodder).* At cost net of discounts (where known) and subsidies.

(vi) *Machinery and equipment.* Original cost net of investment grants, less accumulated depreciation to date of valuation.

(vii) *Livestock.* At current market value, less cost of marketing. Fluctuations in market value expected to be temporary should be ignored.

Tenant's Capital. The estimated total value of capital on the farm, other than land and fixed equipment. There is no easy way of determining this sum precisely and estimates are made in several ways depending on the information available and the purpose for which the estimate is required. One method is to take the average of the opening and closing valuations (at either market value or cost) of livestock, crops, machinery and stores (feed, seed, fertilizers). See also pages 154-7.

Landlord's Capital. Value of the land and fixed equipment (including buildings).

2. Output Terms

Revenue (or Income). Receipts adjusted for debtors at the beginning and end of the accounting period. Items such as subsidies, grants, contract receipts and wayleaves are included.

Returns. Revenue adjusted for valuation changes (add closing, deduct opening, valuation).

Gross Output. Returns plus the value of produce consumed in the farmhouse or supplied to workers for which no payment is made, less purchases of livestock, livestock products and other produce bought for resale.

Enterprise Output. The total value of an enterprise, whether sold or retained on the farm. It therefore equals Gross Output of the enterprise plus the market value of any of the products kept on the farm (transfers out). Products transferred from another enterprise to be used in the production of the enterprise whose output is being calculated are deducted at market value (transfers in). Instead of the accounting year the "harvest year" can be used for crops; valuations are then not relevant.

(Enterprise) Output from Forage. Primarily the sum of the enterprise outputs of grazing livestock, but includes keep let and occasional sales, e.g. of surplus hay, together with an adjustment for changes in the valuation of stocks of home-grown fodder. However, fortuitous changes in stocks caused by yield variations due to the weather, the severity or length of the winter, or minor changes in livestock numbers or forage area can be either ignored (if small in relation to total annual usage) or included in miscellaneous output.

Adjusted Forage (Enterprise) Output is Output from Forage less rented keep and purchases of bulk fodder.

Net Output. Gross Output less the cost of purchased feed, livestock keep, seed, bulbs and plants.

Standard Output. The average enterprise output per hectare of a crop or per head of livestock calculated from either national or local average price and average yield data.

3. Input Terms

Expenditure. Payments adjusted for creditors at the beginning and end of the accounting period. Capital expenditure is not included.

Costs. Expenditure adjusted for valuation changes (add opening, deduct closing, valuation), with the following adjustments. Add:

depreciation on capital expenditure including machinery, any loss made on machinery sales (add to depreciation) and the value of payments in kind to workers if not already included in their earnings. Deduct: purchases of livestock, livestock products and other produce bought for resale, any profit made on machinery (deduct from depreciation), allowance for private use of farm vehicles (deduct from machinery costs), the value of purchased stores used in the farmhouse (e.g. electricity) or sold off the farm (deduct from the relevant item).

Inputs. Costs with the following adjustments, made in order to put all farms on a similar basis for comparative purposes. Add: the value of unpaid family labour, including the manual labour of the farmer and his wife, and, in the case of owner-occupiers, an estimated rental value (based on average rents of similar farms in the area), less any cottage rents received. Deduct: any mortgage payments and other expenses of owner-occupation, interest payments and the cost of paid management. A proportion of the rental value of the farmhouse may also be deducted.

Fixed Costs. See pages 1-2, 133.

Variable Costs. See page 1.

4. Margin Terms

Management and Investment Income. Gross Output less Inputs. It represents the reward to management and the return on tenant's capital invested in the farm, whether borrowed or not. It is mainly used for comparative purposes, all farms having been put on a similar financial basis by the adjustments made to costs in calculating Inputs.

Net Farm Income. Management and Investment Income, less paid management, plus the value of the manual labour of the farmer and his wife.

Profit (or Loss). Gross Output less Costs. This represents the surplus or deficit before imputing any notional charges such as rental value or unpaid labour. In the accounts of owner-occupiers it includes any profit accruing from the ownership of land.

Gross Margin. See page 1.

Net Margin. A term sometimes used to denote Gross Margin less direct labour and machinery costs charged to an individual enterprise. This is not, however, nationally accepted terminology.

5. Area Terms

Total Hectares. All hectares comprising the farm.

Hectares. Total hectares less the area of woods, waste land, roads, buildings, etc.

Adjusted Hectares. Hectares reduced by the conversion of rough grazings into the equivalent hectares of average quality grassland. This is the figure often used for lowland farms when calculating "per hectare" results.

Forage Hectares. Total hectares of forage crops grown, less any hectares exclusively used by pigs or poultry and the area equivalent of any home-grown fodder fed to barley beef. Usually, too, the area of rough grazings is converted to its grassland equivalent (see Adjusted Hectares). Forage crops are all crops, grass and rough grazings grown specifically for grazing livestock, other than catch crops and crops harvested as grain and pulses.

Adjusted Forage Hectares. Forage hectares adjusted as follows. Add area equivalent of keep rented, deduct area equivalent of keep let; deduct the area equivalent of occasional sales of fodder, e.g. surplus hay, and seed cuts (note: hay and seed grown regularly for sale should be regarded as cash crops, not forage crops); add or deduct the area equivalent of planned changes in the valuation of stocks of home-grown fodder (fortuitous changes in stocks resulting from weather conditions may be ignored); convert rough grazings into their grassland equivalent if not already done. The following adjustments also may be made: add the area equivalent of catch crops and of grazing from cash crops of hay or seed: add the area equivalent of purchased fodder.

In calculations such as *Gross Margins per Forage Hectare,* Adjusted Forage Hectares are usually used. If the area equivalent of purchased fodder has been added the cost of purchased fodder must not be charged as a variable cost: this is probably the best calculation for comparative purposes. Alternatively, when considering all the grazing enterprises taken together, purchased fodder can be deducted as a variable cost and no addition made for its area equivalent.

10. AGRISTATS
Some basic agricultural statistics relating to U.K. agriculture.
(All figures are for the U.K. in 1996 unless otherwise stated.)

A. Structure

1. Agriculture's contribution to Gross Domestic   £8,888 million
   Product (provisional):   1·4%

2. (a) Agriculture's proportion of total workforce in
       employment: 2·0%
   (b) Numbers of Persons Engaged in Agriculture (June):

			1991	1996
A.	Employed:			
	(i) Regular Whole-time:			
		Hired: male	80,400	68,800
		female	11,200	9,700
		Family: male	24,200	20,200
		female	3,700	2,800
		Total male	(104,600)	(89,000)
		Total female	(14,900)	(12,500)
		Total	119,500	101,500
	(ii) Regular Part-time:			
		Hired: male	18,300	19,400
		female	20,500	16,800
		Family: male	12,900	13,700
		female	7,100	6,800
		Total male	(31,200)	(33,100)
		Total female	(27,600)	(23,600)
		Total	58,800	56,700
	(iii) Seasonal or Casual:			
		Total male	53,800	55,800
		Total female	32,800	25,900
		Total	86,600	81,700
	(iv) Salaried managers*		7,900	7,800
	Total Employed		272,800	247,700
B.	Employers (farmers, partners, directors):**			
	Whole-time		178,250	***166,400
	Part-time		100,350	***114,400
	Total employers**		278,600	280,800
	Wives/husbands of farmers, partners and directors doing farm work		76,500	74,600
Overall Total			627,900	603,100

* Great Britain only.
** Doing farm work. Excludes wives/husbands of farmers, partners and directors, even if themselves partners or directors.
*** 132,400 whole-time and 87,700 part-time are principal farmers and partners. Other partners and directors are for Great Britain only, those for Northern Ireland being included with principal partners and directors.

3. Crop Areas (in June)

	Area ('000 ha) 1991	Area ('000 ha) 1996	% Total Area 1996	%Crops and Grass (excl. R.G.) 1996
Wheat	1,981	1,976	10·7	17·3
Barley (% winter in brackets) ...	1,393 (60)	1,267 (59)	6·9	11·1
Oats	103	96	0·5	0·8
Other Grain (excl. maize)	23	18	0·1	0·2
Total Cereals	3,500	3,357	18·2	29·4
Potatoes	177	177	1·0	1·5
Sugar Beet	196	199	1·1	1·7
Oilseed Rape (non-SA) ...	440	356	1·9	3·1
Peas harvested dry	131	78	0·4	0·7
Field Beans	72	100	0·5	0·9
Linseed (non-SA)	92	29	0·2	0·3
Horticulture	208	189	1·0	1·7
Maize	NA	111	0·6	1·0
Other Crops (non-SA) and Fallow	204	160	0·9	1·4
Total Tillage	5,020	4,756	25·8	41·6
Temporary Grass (under 5 years old)	1,581	1,376	7·5	12·0
Total Arable	6,601	6,132	33·3	53·7
Permanent Grass (5 years old and over)	5,267	5,289	28·7	46·3
(Total Grass (excluding R.G.)) ...	(6,848)	(6,665)	(36·2)	(58·3)
Total Crops and Grass (excl. R.G.)	11,868	11,421	62·1	100·0
Rough Grazing (R.G.)	5,907	5,726 *	31·1	
Other Land (inc. Set-Aside) ...	712	1,255 **	6·8	
Total Agricultural Area*** ...	18,487	18,401	100·0	

(non-SA) = excluding crops grown on set-aside land
 * Including an estimated 1,237,000 ha of common grazing.
** All other land on agric. holdings, inc. woodland (458,000 ha) and set-aside (509,000 ha).
*** Urban land and forest each approx. 2·0 million ha; other non-agricultural land approx. 1·5 million ha; total U.K. land area including inland waters: 24·1 million.

4. Livestock Numbers (in June; '000 head):

		1991	1996
Total Cattle and Calves		11,866	11,913
of which:	Dairy herd (inc. heifers in milk)	2,770	2,587
	Beef herd (inc. heifers in milk)	1,666	1,829
	Heifers in calf (first calf)	733	813
Total Sheep and Lambs		43,621	41,530
of which:	Female sheep used or to be used for breeding	N/A	20,277
	Rams and ram lambs	N/A	494
Total Pigs		7,596	7,496
of which:	Breeding herd (sows and gilts in pig)	786	744
Total Fowls (excl. turkeys, guinea fowl, ducks and geese)		127,228	125,981*
of which:	Table chicken	75,701	76,621*
	Laying flock	33,273	31,692*
	Growing pullets	11,016	10,098*
Ducks and Geese		N/A	2,648*
Deer (farmed)		N/A	34
Goats		N/A	81

* = 1995

5. Size Structure
Number ('000) and Size distribution of holdings, 1996

Area (ha)	Total land area			Tillage and grass area		
	No.	%	% area	No.	%	% area
0·1 to 19·9	96·6	41·2	4·8	95·7	43·1	7·0
20 to 49·9	56·3	24·0	11·0	56·5	25·4	16·6
50 to 99·9	40·9	17·5	17·1	39·8	17·9	24·9
100 and over	40·4	17·2	67·1	30·2	13·6	51·5
Total	234·3	100·0	100·0	222·2	100·0	100·0

Average area (ha/(acres)) per holding: 72·6 (179); tillage and grass 50·7 (125).

Size of business (ESU)	No. of holdings ('000)	% of holdings	% of total ESU
Under 8	103·1	44·0	2·9
8 to under 40	67·4	28·8	16·0
40 to under 100	41·9	17·9	30·7
100 to under 200	16·0	6·8	24·9
200 and over	6·0	2·6	25·7
Total	234·3	100·0	100·0

Average size of holdings over 8 ESU (which is judged to be the minimum for full-time holdings) = 64·7 ESU, 111·5 ha (275 acres). ESU = European Size Unit (the number provides a measure of the financial potential of the holding, based on standardised gross margins).

Number and Size distribution of holdings in England and Wales, 1995

Size Groups (ha)	By Total Area				By Crops and Grass Area			
	Holdings		Hectares		Holdings		Hectares	
	'000	%	'000,000	%	'000	%	'000,000	%
Under 10	45·4	26.0	0·22	2·0	53.3(1)	30.6	0·21	2·4
10- 30	44·0	25.2	0·80	7·4	42.7	24.5	0·79	9·1
30- 50	24.4	14.0	0·95	8.8	24.7	14.2	0·97	11·1
50-100	30.8	17·7	2·19	20·4	30.1	17.3	2·13	24.5
100-200	19.3	11.1	2·66	24·8	16·6	9.5	2·27	26·1
200-300	5·3	3.0	1·29	12.0	3·9	2.2	0·94	10·8
300-500	3·4	2.0	1·27	11·8	2·1	1.2	0·80	9.2
500-700	0·9	0·5	0·54	5.0	0·5	0·3	0·28	3·2
700 and over	0·8	0·5	0·82	7.6	0·3	0·2	0·31	3·6
Total	174.2	100·0	10.74	100·0	174.2	100·0	8·68	100·0

1. Including 8.1 with nil crops and grass.

6. Average Size of Enterprises

	1991	1996		1991	1996
	hectares			no.	
Crops and Grass	51·6	50·7	Dairy cows	63	69
Cereals	44·8	46·1	Beef cows	22	26
Oilseed Rape	26·7	24·5	Breeding sheep	223	240
Potatoes	6·7	9·0	Breeding pigs	63	80
Sugar Beet	18·9	20·8	Fattening pigs	365	469
			Laying fowls	985	1,134*
			Broilers	27,185	33,869*

* = 1995

7. Tenure

The following figures are for England and Wales, 1995; the areas are '000 hectares (percentages in brackets).

	No. of holdings	Area owned	Area rented
Wholly owned	114,163 (65·5)	5,056 (47.1)	—
Mainly owned	20,859 (12.0)	1,743 (16·2)	430 (4·0)
Wholly rented	25,459 (14.6)	—	2,075 (19·3)
Mainly rented	13,707 (7·9)	329 (3·1)	1,109 (10·3)
Total	174,188 (100)	7,128 (66.4)	3,615 (33·6)*

N.B. Mixed tenure holdings: mainly owned = over 50% owned;
mainly rented = over 50% rented.
Wholly or mainly owned, 77·3% of holdings; wholly or mainly rented, 22·7%

*N.B. As the above figures for rented land include family arrangements (e.g. farmers, or family farming companies, renting from other members of the family, or family shareholders) the percentage of "truly" rented land is almost certainly a few percentage points less than the figures given above.

B. Finance

1. *Inputs and Outputs* (1996 provisional, £ million).

Inputs			Outputs		%
Feeding stuffs		3116	Wheat	2064	(11·4)
Seeds		334	Barley	898	(5·0)
Fertilizers and lime		823	Oats and other cereals ...	71	(0·4)
Pesticides		459	Oilseed rape	419	(2·3)
Livestock (imptd. & inter-fm.)		178	Linseed	39	(0·2)
Vet. and med.		317	Potatoes	564	(3·1)
Labour:			Sugar beet	360	(2·0)
Hired	1711		Peas/Beans for stockfeed ...	140	(0·8)
Fam., partns., direcs.	1036		Vegetables	1147	(6·4)
		2747	Fruit	260	(1·4)
Power and Machinery:			Ornamentals	675	(3·7)
Depreciation... ...	1266		Cattle and calves	2534	(14·0)
Repairs	772		Finished sheep and lambs ...	1391	(7·7)
Fuel, oil, electricity...	610		Finished pigs...	1316	(7·3)
		2648	Poultry	1497	(8·3)
Farm maintenance		404	Milk and milk products ...	3514	(19·5)
Deprec on buildings			Eggs	460	(2·5)
and works		682	Miscellaneous	538	(3·0)
Net rent		151	Set-aside	163	(0·9)
			TOTAL GROSS OUTPUT	18050	(100)
Interest		548			
Miscellaneous		1790	Total Crops	4673	(25·9)
			Total Horticulture	2090	(11·6)
TOTAL INPUTS		14197	Total Livestock	6884	(38·1)
FARMING INCOME		3853	Total Livestock Products ...	4044	(22·4)
			Other	359	(2·0)
		18050			
			TOTAL GROSS OUTPUT ...	18050	(100)

2. U.K. Farming Income

Index of UK Farming Income* in Real Terms
(average 1940-69 = 100)

1940-49	101	1982	77
1950-59	100	1983	57
1960-69	99	1984	86
1970	95	1985	37
1971	96	1986	46
1972	110	1987	50
1973	138	1988	34
1974	103	1989	45
1975	98	1990	43
1976	113	1991	41
1977	98	1992	56
1978	89	1993	79
1979	73	1994	77
1980	56	1995	96
1981	66	1996 (forecast)	87

*The return to farmers and spouses for their labour, management, own land and own capital, after providing for depreciation.

Indices of UK Farming Income and Total Income from Farming*
in Real Terms (1975 = 100)

	FI	TIFF		FI	TIFF
1975	100	100	1986	47	59
1976	115	112	1987	51	62
1977	100	98	1988	35	50
1978	91	90	1989	46	57
1979	74	77	1990	44	55
1980	57	65	1991	42	53
1981	67	73	1992	56	66
1982	79	82	1993	79	84
1983	58	67	1994	77	82
1984	88	89	1995	96	97
1985	38	51	1996 (forecast)	87	90

*Farming income with the estimated value of the labour of family workers, non-principal partners and directors (and their spouses) added back.

3. Indices of Net Farm Income per Farm in Real Terms by main Types of Farming, UK: 6-year average 1977/8-1982/3 = 100.

	Dairy	LFA Cattle and Sheep	Lowland Cattle and Sheep	Specialist Cereals	Other Cropping	Pigs and Poultry
6-year average 1977/8-1982/3* ...	100	100	100	100	100	100
1983/84	69	94	63	134	137	50
1984/85	64	99	41	160	108	119
1985/86	70	80	18	16	23	82
1986/87	72	61	10	62	104	65
1987/88	94	100	22	10	43	47
1988/89	113	115	21	11	28	21
1989/90	98	77	10	24	128	91
1990/91	68	57	6	30	100	71
1991/92	71	67	8	29	82	43
1992/93	91	86	12	40	87	49
1993/94	98	98	14	38	107	15
1994/95	81	71	10	50	184	30
1995/96	96	98	10	77	209	62
1996/97 (forecast)	81	87	8	65	128	90

*i.e. 1980 is the centre year.

4. *Balance Sheet of UK Agriculture* (1995 provisional, £ mills.), *and Ratios*

Assets		£	£
Fixed:	Land and buildings	47,400	
	Plant, machinery and vehicles	8,000	
	Breeding livestock	4,850	
	Total Fixed Assets		60,250
Current:	Trading livestock	3,430	
	Crops and stores	3,400	
	Debtors, cash deposits	3,700	
	Total Current Assets		10,500
	Total Assets		70,750

Liabilities
Long and medium-term:

		£	£
	Bank loans	1,600	
	Other	1,800	
	Total long & medium-term assets		3,400
Short-term:	Bank Overdraft	2,500	
	Other	2,300	
	Total short-term assets		4,850
	Total Liabilities		8,250
	Net Worth		£62,500

% Equity (Net Worth as % of Total Assets):

1980: 90·2	1984-6: 86·9	1990: 81·5	1995: 88·3

Net Worth as % of Total Assets, England, 1995/96, owner-occupied and tenanted land:
    owned: 88·9   tenanted: 78·1

Farming Income and Total Income from Farming as % of Net Worth and Total Assets:

1993-95	% Net Worth	% Total Assets
Farming Income...	6·1	5·4
Total Income from Farming	7·9	6·9

5. *Bank Lending, Interest Payments and Investment*

Bank Lending to Agriculture (£ mills. approx.):

1980: 2,900	1986: 6,000	1992: 6,925	1996: 6,625	1997: 6,850

Interest payments per annum (£ mills.):

	1979-81	1984-86	1991-92	1996 provis.
Actual	417	718	785	548
At 1996 prices (approx.) ...	965	1170	880	548

Interest as % of Farming Income before interest deducted:

	25%	30%	43%	12%

Gross capital formation per annum (£ mills.):

				1995
Actual	1217	1380	1356	1890
At 1996 prices (approx.)	2810	2245	1520	1935
As % 1979-81 (in real terms) ...	100	80	54	69

C. Miscellaneous

1. Crop Yields and Prices, 1992-96

Estimated Average Yields (tonnes/ha) (harvest years)

	1992	1993	1994	1995	1996	Average 1992/6
Wheat	6·82	7·33	7·35	7·70	8·15	7·47
Barley (all)	5·68	5·19	5·37	5·73	6·14	5·62
Winter	6·08	5·70	5·68	6·09	6·61	6·03
Spring	4·58	4·50	4·61	4·83	5·46	4·80
Oats (England and Wales)	5·21	5·73	5·83	5·84	6·14	5·75
Oilseed Rape	2·88	2·60	2·53	2·81	3·39	2·84
Linseed	1·56	1·23	2·50	1·30	1·61	1·39
Field Beans (for stockfeed)	3·45	3·75	3·04	2·69	3·17	3·22
Dried Peas (for stockfeed)	3·30	4·10	3·91	3·77	3·84	3·78
Potatoes (all)	43·3	41·4	39·9	36·9	39·2	40·1
Early	26·0	26·0	21·4	22·1	23·5	23·8
Maincrop	45·0	43·2	41·9	39·1	41·0	42·0
Sugar Beet (adj. [16% SC] tonnes)	51·5	49·1	44·7	43·0	48·0	47·3

Average Realised/Producer Prices per tonne (calendar years)
(approx. return per tonne inc. area payments in brackets)

	1993	1994	1995	1996
Wheat	124 (142)	108 (133)	117 (150)	113 (144)
Barley	122 (145)	114 (146)	120 (164)	112 (153)
Oats	129 (152)	106 (138)	101 (146)	106 (146)
Oilseed Rape	157 (324)	175 (327)	174 (318)	182 (314)
Linseed	123 (NA)	131 (505)	150 (415)	169 (490)
Field Beans (for stockfeed)	114 (226)	108 (225)	127 (271)	156 (276)
Dried Peas (for stockfeed)	106 (207)	106 (195)	120 (221)	121 (217)
Potatoes (all)	62	125	184	101
Early	94	188	156	97
Maincrop	61	118	186	96
Sugar Beet (less transport)	32·8	35·2	38·3	37 7

2. Self Sufficiency (1996 provisional)

(a) Total Food and Feed:

all food and feed	53·4
indigenous type food and feed	69·4

(b) Individual Products:

(Production as % of total new supply for use in the UK)

	1991	1996		1991	1996
Wheat	130	121	Beef and veal	95	86
Barley	130	122	Mutton and lamb	97	99
Oats	102	129	Pork	103	98
Rye/Mixed Corn/Trit.	93	100	Bacon and ham	41	44
Total Cereals	119	113	Poultry meat	95	95
Oilseed rape	101	101	Butter	67	67
Linseed	144	80	Cheese	68	69
Potatoes	90	90	Cream	117	138
Sugar	54	60			
Hops	80	89	Hen eggs	96	96
Apples	42	36	Wool	60	54
Pears	29	27			
Cauliflowers	90	74			
Tomatoes	34	28			

3. Food Consumption and Trends

Expenditure on food and drink as % of total consumers' expenditure (excluding meals out) (1995): household food, 10·9%; alcoholic drinks, 5·9%. (Meals out 8·5%).

Estimated Average Household Food Consumption (kg per person per year):

	1986	1991	1996
Milk and cream (equivalent pints) ...	216	195	193
Cheese	6·14	6·08	5·77
Fats	15·44	12·90	11·80
Eggs (number)	157	117	97
Meat and meat products	54·65	50·02	49·04
Fish	7·59	7·23	8·01
Fresh potatoes	57·20	49·87	41·86
Fresh green vegetables	16·38	13·47	12·12
Other fresh vegetables	24·80	23·97	25·43
Processed vegetables	28·86	28·34	30·73
Fresh fruit	29·95	31·72	35·67
Processed fruit and nuts	15·44	17·73	17·52
Sugar and preserves	14·77	11·34	9·62
Bread	45·40	39·10	39·10
Cakes and biscuits	13·31	13·73	14·77
Flour and other cereals or cereal products	22·26	22·78	27·30
Beverages	4·06	3·69	3·33

Average expenditure, per person, per week, 1996	£
on household food	14·51
on food eaten out	4·35
total food	18·86
on household alcoholic drinks	1·14
on alcoholic drinks consumed outside household	1·70
total alcoholic drinks	2·84
on household soft drinks and confectionery	0·81
on soft drinks and confectionery consumed outside household	0·48
total soft drinks and confectionery	1·29
overall total	22·99

Total household £16·46; total outside household £6·53.

---

4. Percentage of Total Household Expenditure on Food and Drink, 1995:

Meat/meat products (inc. bacon)	23·1	Cheese	3·1
Cereals (inc. bread, cakes, etc.)	15·6	Soft drinks	3·1
Vegetables (inc. potatoes)	13·8	Beverages	2·9
Milk and cream	9·1	Fats and oils (inc. butter, marg.)	2·3
Fruit	7·0	Confectionery	1·7
Alcoholic drinks	6·9	Eggs	1·1
Fish	4·7	Sugar and preserves	1·1
		Other	4·5

Sources: Agriculture in the UK: 1996 (MAFF). All items except for the following:
A5 (part), A7: Other MAFF Statistics.
B4, Bank Lending: Bank of England, Financial Statistics Division.
C3 and C4: National Food Survey, 1995, MAFF.

11. RATE OF INFLATION; PRICE AND COST INDICES

1. *Retail Price Index* (all items)

	% increase on year earlier	Index* (1970 = 100)	Index (1980 = 100)
1970	—	100	
1971	9·5	109·5	
1972	7	117	
1973	9	128	
1974	16	148·5	
1975	24	184·5	
1976	16·5	215	
1977	16	249	
1978	8·3	270	
1979	13·4	306	
1980	18	361	100
1981	11·9	404	112
1982	8·6	439	122
1983	4·6	459	127
1984	5·0	482	133
1985	6·1	511	142
1986	3·4	528	146
1987	4·2	551	153
1988	4·9	578	160
1989	7·8	623	173
1990	9·5	682	189
1991	5·9	722	200
1992	3·7	749	207
1993	1·6	761	210
1994	2·4	779	215
1995	3·5	806	223
1996	2·4	825	228
1997 (estimated)	2·9	849	235
1998 (forecast)	3·5	879	243

*Index in 1965: 80.
„ „ 1962: 70.
Source: Economic Trends.

2. *Price and Cost Indices 1996 (1990 = 100)*

(N.B. Retail Price Index: 121; RPI for Food only: 118·5)

(a) *Producer Prices*

Breadmaking Wheat	109	Dessert Apples	113
Other Milling Wheat	104	All Fresh Fruit	108
Feed Wheat	102	*All Crop Products*	105
Malting Barley	111	Calves	94
Feed Barley	101	Cattle	98
Milling Oats	100	Cows and Bulls	107
Feed Oats	101	Sheep	163
All Cereals	105	Wool	117
Early Potatoes	139	Pigs	122
Maincrop Potatoes	94	Poultry	108
Sugar Beet	123	Milk	134
Seeds	123	Eggs	108
Fresh Vegetables	108	*All Animals/Animal Products*	122
Flowers and Plants	115	*All Products*	115

(b) *Input Prices*

General Expenses	127	Animal Feedingstuffs	118
Seeds	147	Energy and Lubricants	117
Fertilisers	113	Maintce./Repair of Plant	139
Plant Protection Products	123	Machinery & Other Equipt.	122
Animals for Rearing/Prodn.	139	Farm Buildings	124

Source: MAFF Statistics.

12. METRIC CONVERSION FACTORS

	Metric to Imperial		*Imperial to Metric*
Area			
1 hectare	2·471 acres	1 acre	0·405 ha
1 square km	0·386 sq. mile	1 square mile	2·590 sq. km
1 square m	1·196 sq. yard	1 square yard	0·836 sq. m
1 square m	10·764 sq. feet	1 square foot	0·093 sq. m
	(m = metre, km = kilometre)		

Length			
1 mm	0·04 inch	1 inch	25·4 mm
1 cm	0·39 inch	1 inch	2·54 cm
1 m	3·279 feet	1 foot	0·305 m
1 m	1·094 yard	1 yard	0·914 m
1 km	0·6214 mile	1 mile	1·609 km
	(mm = millimetre, cm = centimetre)		

Volume			
1 litre	35·2 fluid oz	1 fluid oz	0·028 litre
1 litre	1·76 pints	1 pint	0·568 litre
1 litre	0·22 gallon	1 gallon	4·546 litres
	(1 litre of milk = 1·03 kg; 1 kg milk = 1·712 pints, 0·214 gallon)		
1 cubic m	35·31 cu feet	1 cubic foot	0·028 cu m
1 cubic m	1·307 cu yard	1 cubic yard	0·765 cu m
1 cubic m	220 gallons	1 gallon	0·005 cu m

Weight			
1 gram	0·0353 oz	1oz	28·35 gm
1 kg	2·205 lb	1 lb	0·454 kg
1 tonne (1000 kg)	19·68 cwt	1 cwt	50·80 kg
1 tonne	0·984 ton	1 ton	1·016 tonne

Rates of Use			
1 tonne/ha	0·398 ton/acre	1 ton/acre	2·511 tonnes/ha
1 tonne/ha	7·95 cwt/acre	1 cwt/acre	0·125 tonne/ha
1 gram/ha	0·014 oz/acre	1 oz/acre	70·053 g/ha
1 kg/ha	0·892 lb/acre	1 lb/acre	1·121 g/ha
1 kg/ha	0·008 cwt/acre	1 cwt/acre	125·5 g/ha
1 kg/ha (fert.)	0·80 unit/acre	1 unit/acre	1·255 kg/ha
1 litre/ha	0·712 pint/acre	1 pint/acre	1·404 litre/ha
1 litre/ha	0·089 gal/acre	1 gal/acre	11·24 litres/ha

Power, Pressure, Temperature			
1 kW	1·341 hp	1 hp	0·746 kW
1 kilojoule	0·948 Btu	1 Btu	1·055 kilojoule
1 therm	10000 Btu	1 Btu	0·0001 therm
1 lb f ft	1·356 Nm	1 Nm	0·738 lb f ft
1 bar	14·705 psi	1 psi	0·068 bar
°C to °F	×1·8, +32	°F to °C	−32, ÷1·8

13. USEFUL ADDRESSES AND TELEPHONE NUMBERS*

1. GENERAL

ADAS (Agricultural Development and Advisory Service)
Headquarters: Oxford Spires Business Park, The Boulevard, Langford Lane,
Kidlington, Oxford OX5 1NZ   01865 842742

Agricultural Central Trading Ltd.
90 The Broadway, Chesham, Bucks. HP5 1EG   01494 784931

Agricultural Economics Unit
Queen Elizabeth House, 21 St. Giles, Oxford OX1 3LA   01865 273600

Agricultural Engineers' Association
Samuelson House, Paxton Road, Orton Centre, Peterborough,
Cambs. PE2 5LT   01733 371381

Agricultural Mortgage Corporation PLC
AMC House, Chantry Street, Andover, Hants. SP10 1DD   01264 334344

Agricultural Wages Board
Nobel House, Room 320D, 17 Smith Square, London SW1P 3JR   0171-238 6540

Association of Independent Crop Consultants
Agriculture House, Station Road, Liss, Hampshire GU33 7AR   01730 895354

ATB — Landbase
National Agricultural Centre, Kenilworth, Coventry CV8 2LG   01203 696996

BBC Farming etc., Radio
Pebble Mill Road, Birmingham B5 7QQ   0121 414 8888

British Agricultural and Garden Machinery Association
14-16 Church Street, Rickmansworth, Herts. WD3 1RQ   01923 720241

British Agrochemicals Association Ltd.
4 Lincoln Court, Lincoln Road, Peterborough, Cambs. PE1 2RP   01733 349225

British Cereal Exports
HGCA, Hamlyn House, Highgate Hill, London N19 5PR   0171-263 3391

British Crop Protection Council
49 Downing Street, Farnham, Surrey GU9 7PH   01252 733072

British Deer Society
Burgate Manor, Fordingbridge, Hampshire SP6 1EF   01425 655434

British Grassland Society
University of Reading, 1 Earley Gate, Berks. RG6 2AT   01734 318189

British Institute of Agricultural Consultants
The Estate Office, Torry Hill, Milstead, Sittingbourne, Kent ME9 0SP   01795 830100

British MilkSheep Society
The Row, Roweltown, Carlisle, Cumbria CA6 6LX   01697 748217

British Pig Association
7 Rickmansworth Road, Watford, Herts. WD1 7HE   01923 234377

British Potato Council
Broadfield House, 4 Between Towns Road, Cowley, Oxford OX4 3NA   01865 714455

British Poultry Meat Federation
7th Floor, Imperial House, 15/19 Kingsway, London WC2B 6UA   0171-240 9889

---

*For a 600-page current directory of names, addresses and telephone numbers of agricultural firms and associations, with over 40,000 listings covering 70 categories and in 11 regions see **Green Pages,** 7th edition, available from 192 Acton Lane, London W4 5DL (tel. 0181-747 8028; fax. 0181-747 8054); price £16.*

British Sheep Dairying Association
Wield Wood, Upper Wield, Alresford, Hampshire SO24 9RU   01420 563151

British Society of Plant Breeders
Woolpack Chambers, Market Street, Ely, Cambs. CB7 4ND   01353 664211

British Sugar plc
Oundle Road, Peterborough, Cambs. PE2 9QU   01733 63171

British Veterinary Association
7 Mansfield Street, London W1M 0AT   0171-636 6544

British Wool Marketing Board
Oak Mills, Station Road, Clayton, Bradford
West Yorkshire BD14 6JD   01274 882091

CAB International
Wallingford, Oxon OX10 8DE   01491 832111

Central Association of Agricultural Valuers
1st Floor, 4 Lord's Hill, Coleford, Gloucestershire GL16 8BD   01594 832979

Centre for Agricultural Strategy
University of Reading, P.O. Box 236, Earley Gate, Reading,
Berks. RG6 6AT   0118 931 8150

Council for the Protection of Rural England
Warwick House, 25 Buckingham Palace Road, London SW1W 0PP   0171-976 6433

Country Landowners Association
16 Belgrave Square, London SW1X 8PQ   0171-235 0511

Countryside Commission
John Dower House, Crescent Place, Cheltenham
Gloucestershire, GL50 3RA   01242 521381

Dairy Industry Federation
19 Cornwall Terrace, London NW1 4QP   0171-486 7244

Department of Agriculture, N. Ireland
Dundonald House, Upper Newtownards Road, Belfast BT4 3SB   01232 520100

English Heritage
23 Savile Row, London W1X 1AB   0171-973 3000

English Nature
Northminster House, Northminster, Peterborough PE1 1UA   01733 455000

English Tourist Board
Thames Tower, Blacks Road, London W6 9EL   0181-846 9000

Environment Agency
Rio House, Waterside Drive, Aztec West, Almonsbury, Bristol
BS12 4UD   01454-624400

European Commission
London Office, Jean Monnet House, 8 Storey's Gate, London
SW1P 3AT   0171-973 1992

Family Farmers' Association
Osborne Newton, Aveton Gifford, Kingsbridge, Devon TQ12 4PE   01548 852794

Farmers Club
3 Whitehall Court, London SW1A 2EL   0171-930 3751

Farmers Union of Wales
Llys Amaeth, Queens Square, Aberystwyth, Ceredigion SY23 2EA   01970 612755

Farming and Agricultural Finance Limited
New Agriculture House, Barnett Way, Barnwood, Gloucester GL4 3RT   01452 376000

Farming and Wildlife Advisory Group (FWAG)
National Agricultural Centre, Stoneleigh, Kenilworth, Warks. CV8 2RX   01203 696699

Federation of Agricultural Co-operatives (UK) Ltd.
164 Shaftesbury Avenue, London WC2H 8HL   0171-331 7216

The Fertilizer Manufacturers' Association Ltd.
Greenhill House, Thorpe Road, Peterborough PE3 6GF   01733 331303

Food and Farming Information Service
National Agricultural Centre, Stoneleigh, Kenilworth, Warks. CV8 2LZ   01203 696969

Food from Britain
123 Buckingham Palace Road, London SW1W 9SA   0171-233 5111

Food and Drink Federation
6 Catherine Street, London WC2B 5JJ   0171-836 2460

Forestry Commission
231 Corstorphine Road, Edinburgh EH12 7AT   0131-334 0303

Grain and Feed Trade Association (GAFTA)
GAFTA House, 6 Chapel Place, Rivington Street, London EC2A 3DQ 0171-814 9666

Health and Safety Executive
Information Centre, Broad Lane, Sheffield S3 7HQ   0541 545500

Her Majesty's Stationery Office
Publications Centre, PO Box 276, London SW8 5DT   0171-873 0011

Home Grown Cereals Authority
Hamlyn House, Highgate Hill, London N19 5PR   0171-263 3391
Price Information Service   0171-263 3494

Horticultural Development Council
Bradbourne House, Stable Block, East Malling, Kent ME19 6DZ   01732 848383

Institution of Agricultural Engineers
West End Road, Silsoe, Bedford MK45 4DU   01525 861096

Institute of Agricultural Management
Farm Management Unit, University of Reading, PO Box 236,
Reading RG6 6AT   0118 935 1458

Institute of Agricultural Secretaries and Administrators
National Agricultural Centre, Stoneleigh, Kenilworth, Warks. CV8 2LZ 01203 696592

Institute of Chartered Foresters
7a St. Colme Street, Edinburgh EH3 6AA   0131 225 2705

International Grains Council
1 Canada Square, Canary Wharf, London E14 5AE   0171-513 1122

Intervention Board Executive Agency
Kings House, 33 Kings Road, Reading RG1 3BU   0118 958 3626

Land Drainage Contractors Association
National Agricultural Centre, Stoneleigh, Kenilworth, Warks. CV8 2LG 01327 263264

Lands Improvement Holdings plc
1 Buckingham Place, London SW1E 6HR   0171-222 5331

Life Commodity Products
1 Commodity Quay, St. Katherine Dock, London E1 9AX   0171-481 2080

Meat and Livestock Commission
PO Box 44, Winterhill House, Snowdon Drive, Milton Keynes
MK6 1AX   01908 677577

Milk Development Council
5-7 John Princes Street, London W1M 0AP   0171-629 7262

Ministry of Agriculture, Fisheries and Food
3 Whitehall Place, London SW1A 2HH   0171-270 3000

National Agricultural Centre
Stoneleigh, Kenilworth, Warks. CV8 2LZ   01203 696969

National Association of Agricultural Contractors
Huts Corner, Tilford Road, Hindhead, Surrey GU26 6SF   01428 605360

National Association of British & Irish Millers (NABIM)
21 Arlington Street, London SW1A 1RN   0171-493 2521

National Cattle Association
60 Kenilworth Road, Leamington Spa, Warks. CV32 6JX   01926 337378

National Dairy Council
5-7 John Princes Street, London W1M OAP   0171-499 7822

National Farmers' Union
Agriculture House, 164 Shaftesbury Avenue, London WC2H 8HL   0171-331 7200

National Farmers Union of Scotland
Rural Centre, West Mains, Ingliston, Newbridge, Midlothian
EH28 8LT   0131-335 3111

National Federation of Young Farmers Clubs
YFC Centre, National Agricultural Centre, Stoneleigh, Kenilworth,
Warks. CV8 2LG   01203 696544

National Sheep Association
The Sheep Centre, Malvern, Worcs. WR13 6PH   01684 892661

Residuary Milk Marketing Board
Thames Ditton, Surrey KT7 0EL   0181-398 4101

Royal Agricultural Benevolent Institution
Shaw House, 27 West Way, Oxford OX2 0QH   01865 724931

Royal Agricultural Society of England
National Agricultural Centre, Stoneleigh, Kenilworth, Warks. CV8 2LZ 01203 696 969

Royal Association of British Dairy Farmers
Dairy House, 60 Kenilworth Road, Leamington Spa, Warwicks
CV32 6JX   01926 887477

Royal Forestry Society
102 High Street, Tring, Herts. HP23 4AF   01442 822028

Royal Highland and Agricultural Society of Scotland
Ingliston, Edinburgh EH28 8NF   0131-333 2444

Royal Horticultural Society
80 Vincent Square, London SW1P 2PE   0171-834 4333

Royal Institution of Chartered Surveyors
12 Great George Street, Parliament Square, London SW1P 3AD   0171-222 7000

Royal Welsh Agricultural Society
Llanelwedd, Builth Wells, Powys LD2 3SY   01982 553683

Rural, Agricultural and Allied Workers Trade Group (TGWU)
Transport House, 16 Palace Street, Victoria, London SW1E 5JD   0171-828 7788

Rural Development Commission
Dacre House, 19 Dacre Street, London SW1H 0DH   0171-340 2906

Scottish Office: Agriculture and Fisheries Department
Pentland House, 47 Robb's Loan, Edinburgh EH14 1TY   0131-556 8400

Tenant Farmers' Association
7 Brewery Court, Theale, Reading, Berks. RG7 5AJ   01734 306130

Ulster Farmers Union
475 Antrim Road, Belfast BT15 3DA   01232 370222

UK Agricultural Supply Trade Association (UKASTA)
3 Whitehall Court, London SW1A 2EQ   0171-930 3611

UK Register of Organic Food Standards
Nobel House, Room 320c, 17 Smith Square, London SW1P 3JR   0171-238 5915

Welsh Office Agriculture Department
Crown Buildings, Cathays Park, Cardiff CF1 3NQ   01222 825111

Women's Farming Union
National Agricultural Centre, Stoneleigh, Kenilworth, Warks. CV8 2LZ 01203 693171

2. UNIVERSITY AGRICULTURAL ECONOMISTS
(Farm Business Survey work)

ENGLAND AND WALES

Northern:	Department of Agricultural Economics and Food Marketing, University of Newcastle-upon-Tyne, Newcastle-upon-Tyne NE1 7RU	0191 222 6900

North Eastern: Rural Business Research Unit, Askham Bryan College, Askham Bryan, York YO2 3PR   01904 772233

North Western: Farm Business Unit, School of Economic Studies, The University of Manchester, Dover Street Building, Oxford Road, Manchester M13 9PL   0161 275 4793

East Midland: Rural Business Research Unit, University of Nottingham, Sutton Bonington Campus, Loughborough LE12 5RD   0115 9516070

Eastern: Agricultural Economics Unit, Department of Land Economy, University of Cambridge 19 Silver Street, Cambridge CB3 9EP   01223 337147

South Eastern: Farm Business Unit, Department of Agricultural Economics and Business Management, Wye College (University of London), Ashford, Kent TN25 5AH   01233 812401

Southern: Department of Agricultural and Food Economics University of Reading, 4 Earley Gate, Whiteknights Road, PO Box 237, Reading RG6 6AR   0118 987 4035

South Western: Agricultural Economics Unit, University of Exeter, Lafrowda House, St. German's Road, Exeter EX4 6TL   01392 263839

Wales: Welsh Institute of Rural Studies, Llanbadarn Campus, Aberystwyth, Ceredigion SY23 3AL   01970 624411

SCOTLAND (Advisory Services also)
Scottish Agricultural College
Rural Resource Management Department, Kings Buildings,
West Mains Road, Edinburgh EH9 3JG   0131-667 1041

Regional Offices:
North: SAC Aberdeen, Craigstone, Bucksburn, Aberdeen AB9 1UD   01224 480291
East: SAC Edinburgh, West Mains Road, Edinburgh EH9 3JG   0131-667 1041
West: SAC Auchincruive, Ayr KA6 5HW   01292 520331

NORTHERN IRELAND (Advisory Services also)
Economics & Statistics Division, Department of Agriculture, Dundonald House,
Upper Newtownards Road, Belfast BT4 3SB   01232 524655

3. ADAS

Headquarters: see page 210. Consultancy Centres are located at:

Bury St Edmunds	Lincoln	Ruthin
Cardiff	Maidstone	Starcross
Guildford	Newcastle	Taunton
Huntingdon	Oxford	Wolverhampton
Leeds	Preston	Worcester

4. COMMERCIAL BANKS: AGRICULTURAL DEPARTMENTS

Barclays Bank PLC
Agricultural Services Dept., St. Swithin's House, 11/12 St. Swithin's
Lane, London EC4N 8AS   0171-929 4080

Clydesdale Bank PLC
Business Banking Centre, 10 Fleet Place, London EC4M 7RB   0171-395 5662

Lloyds Bank PLC
Agricultural Finance Unit, UK Retail Financial Services, PO Box 112,
Canons Way, Bristol BS99 7LB   0117 9433433

Midland Bank PLC
Midland Agriculture, 27 Poultry, London EC2P 2BX   0171-260 6760

National Westminster Bank PLC
Agricultural Office, Ground Floor, National Westminster House,
73a Commercial Road, Swindon SN1 5NX   01793 422891

The Royal Bank of Scotland PLC
Agricultural Services, PO Box 31, 42 St. Andrew Square, Edinburgh
EH2 2YE   0131-523 2227

TSB Bank plc
Agricultural Office, 5 St. Helen's Square, York YO1 2QW   01904 671180

5. RESEARCH ORGANISATIONS

Biotechnology and Biological Sciences Research Council
Polaris House, North Star Avenue, Swindon, Wilts. SN2 IUH   01793 413253

Arable Research Centres
Manor Farm, Daglingworth, Cirencester, Glos. GL7 7AH   01285 652184

Babraham Institute
Babraham, Cambridge CB2 4AT   01223 832312

Broom's Barn (IACR)
Higham, Bury St. Edmunds, Suffolk IP28 6NP   01284 812200

CEDAR (Centre for Dairy Research)
Arborfield Hall Farm, Reading Road, Arborfield, Reading, RG2 9HX   01734 760964

Hannah Research Institute
Ayr, Scotland KA6 5HL   01292 476013

Institute for Animal Health
Compton, Newbury, Berks. RG20 7NN   01635 578411

Institute of Food Research
Norwich Research Park, Colney, Norwich NR4 7UA   01603 255000
Earley Gate, Whiteknights Road, Reading RG6 3EF   0118 935 7000

Institute of Grassland and Environmental Research
Aberystwyth Research Centre, Plas Gogerddan, Aberystwyth,
Ceredigion SY23 3EB 01970 828255

North Wyke Research Station, Okehampton, Devon EX20 2SB 01837 82558

Kingshay Farming Trust
Henley Manor, Crewkerne, Somerset TA18 8PH 01460 72977

Long Ashton Research Station (IACR)
Long Ashton, Bristol BS18 9AF 01275 392181

Macauley Land Use Research Institute
Craigiebuckler, Aberdeen AB15 8QH 01224 318611

Morley Research Centre
Morley St. Botolph, Wymondham, Norfolk NR18 9DB 01953 605511

National Institute of Agricultural Botany
Huntingdon Road, Cambridge CB3 OLE 01223 276381

Roslin Institute
Roslin, Midlothian EH25 9PS 0131 527 4200

IACR – Rothamsted
Harpenden, Hertfordshire AL5 2JQ 01582 763133

Rowett Research Institute
Buckshurn, Aberdeen AB21 9SB 01224 712751

Scottish Crop Research Institute
Invergowrie, Dundee DD2 5DA 01382 562731

Silsoe Research Institute
Wrest Park, Silsoe, Bedford MK45 4HS 01525 860000

6. NATIONAL AGRICULTURAL COLLEGES

Cranfield University, Silsoe Campus
Silsoe, Bedford MK45 4DT 01525 863000

Harper Adams Agricultural College
Edgmond, Newport, Shropshire TF10 8NB 01952 820280

Royal Agricultural College
Stroud Road, Cirencester, Glos. GL7 6JS 01285 652531

Seale-Hayne Faculty (University of Plymouth)
Newton Abbot, Devon TQ12 6NQ 01626 325800

Shuttleworth College
Old Warden Park, Biggleswade, Beds. SG18 9DX 01525 863100

Welsh Institute of Rural Studies
Llanbadarn, Aberystwyth, Ceredigion SY23 3AL 01970 624471

Writtle College
Lordship Road, Writtle, Chelmsford, Essex CM1 3RR 01245 420705

N.B. The Scottish Agricultural College and its regional offices are listed on page 214.

INDEX

OTHER PUBLICATIONS

Other Department of Agricultural Economics publications include:

Farm Management Pocketbook, 27th edition (1997). John Nix. £8.00

Farm Business Statistics for South East England: Supplement for 1997. Nigel Williams. £5.50

Costs and Benefits of Pesticide Usage in Wheat and Apples in the UK. Paul Webster et al. 1996. £20.00

The Eradication of Bovine Brucellosis in Great Britain — An Evaluation of Current Policies and Future Options. FBU Occasional Paper No. 25. S. R. Goss, N. T. Williams and A. H. Andrews. 1995. £25.00

The Dutch Glasshouse Industry: An Economic History. Julian Nicholson with Roger Folley. 1995. £10.00

Field Scale Vegetables. Special Studies in Agricultural Economics Report No. 26. Nigel Williams. 1994. £15.00

Bovine Somatotropin (bST) — The French Perspective. FBU Occasional Paper No. 24. M. J. M. Bent et al. 1994. £10.00

The Effects of the Reform of the Common Agricultural Policy on Arable Farms in South East England. FBU Occasional Paper No. 23. A. Donaldson, P. Hutley-Bull, J. P. G. Webster. 1994. £10.00

Socio-Economic Evaluation of the Capital Grant Element of the Farm Diversification Scheme. FBU Occasional Paper No. 22. A. M. Edwards, R. M. Gasson, J. E. Haynes and G. P. Hill. 1994. £10.00

Changes in Cropping & Stocking, Kent & England, 1939 to 1992. (With special reference to 1982-92). FBU Occasional Paper No. 21. Angela Edwards and John Nix. 1994. £6.00

Agricultural Business Management in a Changing World
Inaugural Lecture. J. P. G. Webster. 1993. £0.50

The Socio-Economic Effects of Bovine Somatropin (bST)—
A European Review. FBU Occasional Paper No. 20.
M. J. M. Bent and A. E. Buckwell.1993. £10.00

A Socio-Economic Evaluation of the One Year Set-aside Scheme
in England. FBU Occasional Paper No. 19. N. Young and
N. T. Williams. 1993. £15.00

An Evaluation of the Beef and Sheep Pilot Extensification Schemes
in the UK. FBU Occasional Paper No. 18. N. Young and
N. T. Williams. 1993. £15.00

Available from Wye College Press, Wye College, Ashford, Kent, TN25 5AH.
(From which a full list of the Department's publications is available).
(Telephone: 01233 812401, ext. 285; Fax: 01233 813320).

Please send cheque or postal order (made out to Wye College) with order.
All prices post free UK.